Concise Maths 1

George Humphrey

Gill & Macmillan

Gill & Macmillan Ltd
Hume Avenue
Park West
Dublin 12
with associated companies throughout the world
www.gillmacmillan.ie

© George Humphrey
0 7171 2813 X
Print origination by Mathematical Composition Setters Ltd, Salisbury, Wiltshire

The paper used in this book is made from the wood pulp of managed forests. For every tree felled, at least one tree is planted, thereby renewing natural resources.

I would like to dedicate this book to my wife, Aideen O'Connell

CONTENTS

PREFACE

New Concise Mathematics 1 covers in one volume the complete course for Junior Certificate mathematics, Ordinary level. *New Concise Mathematics 2* will complete the Higher level course.

The author strongly sympathises with the main aims and objectives of the new syllabus and the new examination. In particular, it is crucial for pupils to be presented with mathematics at a level that is appropriate to their abilities. This book has been written to take account of these aims and objectives. For instance, the use of the calculator is actively encouraged throughout the text. The book begins with a chapter on the order of operations, to provide a link between primary and secondary mathematics.

The emphasis is on a clear and practical presentation of the material. Simple and concise language is used throughout, instead of technical terms, which are not required in the exam. Long explanations are avoided, which are best left to the teacher. A comprehensive range of worked examples, with helpful comments highlighted in colour, is included. The author has very carefully graded the exercises through testing them in class; this allows the widest range of abilities to be catered for and should be of benefit to teachers who teach mixed-ability classes. Great effort is made throughout the book to ensure that the answers to the problems work out evenly. Each chapter is broken down into short, manageable sections and ends with a chapter test containing plenty of questions of the type encountered in the Junior Certificate exam.

A numbered, step-by-step approach, highlighted in colour, is used throughout the book to help with problem-solving. Key terms are defined simply, and also highlighted in colour. This has been found to reduce valuable class time spent in copying notes from the board. Concepts are built up in a logical manner. In many places the early questions are included in tables, which are intended to provide plenty of routine and practice in newly acquired skills before pupils are brought to exam-standard questions.

I would like to thank Mr Michael Dunne, Principal of Maryfield College, Dublin, who read the entire manuscript and made many invaluable suggestions that are included in the final text. Thanks must also go to Geraldine Finucane, fifth-year pupil, Holy Faith School, Clontarf, Dublin, who took on the task of checking my answers as well as reading the entire manuscript and also making many constructive suggestions.

I also wish to express my thanks to the staff of Gill & Macmillan, and special thanks to Séamas Ó Brógáin, for their advice, guidance and untiring assistance in the preparation and presentation of the text.

George Humphrey
St Andrew's College
Dublin

ORDER OF OPERATIONS

Notation

Multiplication:
There are three ways to denote multiplication. 5 multiplied by 4 can be written:

(i) 5×4 **(ii)** $5(4)$ **(iii)** $(5)(4)$

Division:
There are three ways to denote division. 6 divided by 3 can be written:

(i) $6 \div 3$ **(ii)** $\dfrac{6}{3}$ **(iii)** $6/3$

Powers:
Powers can be thought of as repeated multiplication. The power simply tells you how many times a number is multiplied by itself.

$$2 \text{ to the power of 5 is written } 2^5. \quad 2^5 = \underbrace{2 \times 2 \times 2 \times 2 \times 2}_{5 \text{ times}} = 32$$

The **power key** on your calculator can also be used.

Press: 2 $\boxed{y^x}$ 5 $\boxed{=}$.

Square roots:
The '**square root**' of a number is a number that when multiplied by itself gives the number.

3 is the square root of 9, because $3 \times 3 = 9$.

The symbol $\sqrt{}$ is used to denote 'square root', so that $\sqrt{9} = 3$.

The easiest way to find the square root of a number is to use the $\boxed{\sqrt{}}$ button on your calculator.

For example, to find $\sqrt{9}$, key in 9 $\boxed{\sqrt{}}$

If you are using a DAL calculator, key in $\boxed{\sqrt{}}$ 9 $\boxed{=}$.

Order of operations

The order in which calculations are carried out is as follows:

1.	B	Brackets	Do calculations in brackets first
2.	E	Exponents	Powers or roots next
3.	M	Multiplication	Multiplication and division next
	D	Division	(working from left to right)
4.	A	Addition	Addition and subtraction last
	S	Subtraction	

This order of operations is called 'algebraic logic'.
A very useful memory aid is: BEMDAS.
Your scientific calculator uses algebraic logic.

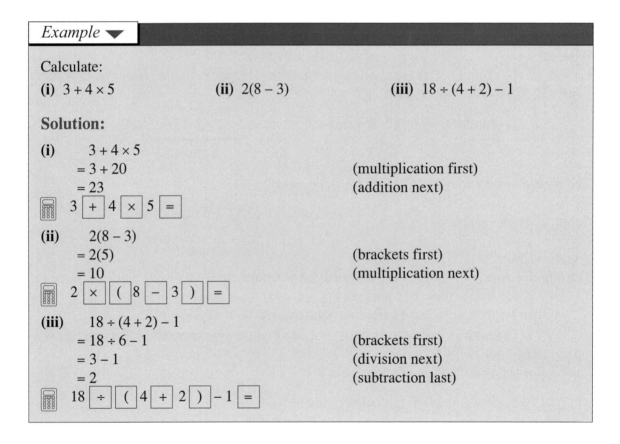

Example ▼

Calculate:

(i) $3 + 4 \times 5$ **(ii)** $2(8 - 3)$ **(iii)** $18 \div (4 + 2) - 1$

Solution:

(i) $3 + 4 \times 5$
      $= 3 + 20$ (multiplication first)
      $= 23$ (addition next)

$3 \boxed{+} 4 \boxed{\times} 5 \boxed{=}$

(ii) $2(8 - 3)$
      $= 2(5)$ (brackets first)
      $= 10$ (multiplication next)

$2 \boxed{\times} \boxed{(} 8 \boxed{-} 3 \boxed{)} \boxed{=}$

(iii) $18 \div (4 + 2) - 1$
      $= 18 \div 6 - 1$ (brackets first)
      $= 3 - 1$ (division next)
      $= 2$ (subtraction last)

$18 \boxed{\div} \boxed{(} 4 \boxed{+} 2 \boxed{)} - 1 \boxed{=}$

Calculate each of the following:

1.	$3 \times 5 + 2$	**2.**	$3 \times 6 + 4$	**3.**	$6 \times 2 + 3$
4.	$5 + 4 \times 3$	**5.**	$20 \div 4 + 3$	**6.**	$3 + 12 \div 6$
7.	$24 \div 8 + 1$	**8.**	$5 + 10 \div 5$	**9.**	$2(5) + 4$
10.	$11 + 3(2)$	**11.**	$5(3 + 1)$	**12.**	$2(2 + 3)$
13.	$5(100 \div 20)$	**14.**	$3(8 - 6)$	**15.**	$4 \times 5 - 12$
16.	$15 \div 5 - 3$	**17.**	$2 \times 5 + 24 \div 8 + 2$	**18.**	$36 \div 9 - 1$
19.	$5 \times 2 + 15 \div 3 + 4$	**20.**	$20 \div 4 + 3 \times 2$	**21.**	$5 + 2 \times 3 + 12 \div 4$
22.	$32 \div 8 + 2 + 5 \times 4$	**23.**	$8 + 20 \div 4$	**24.**	$4 - 18 \div 6$
25.	$(48 \div 6) \div (12 \div 3)$	**26.**	$18 \div (7 + 2)$	**27.**	$30 \div (6 - 1) + 2$
28.	$(40 \div 10) \div (12 \div 3)$	**29.**	$9 - 10 \div 2 + 3$	**30.**	$(8 - 2) \div (5 - 2)$

Example ▼

Calculate:

(i) $2(3 + 2)^2 + 3\sqrt{4}$ **(ii)** $\dfrac{6 + 5 \times 3}{11 - 4}$

Solution:

(i) $2(3 + 2)^2 + 3\sqrt{4}$

$= 2(5)^2 + 3\sqrt{4}$ (brackets first)
$= 2(25) + 3(2)$ (powers and square roots next)
$= 50 + 6$ (multiplication next)
$= 56$ (addition last)

(ii) $\dfrac{6 + 5 \times 3}{11 - 4}$ The line acts like a bracket.
                Calculate the top and bottom first separately.

$\dfrac{\text{Top}}{\text{Bottom}}$

$= \dfrac{21}{7}$

$= 3$

Top
$= 6 + 5 \times 3$
$= 6 + 15$
$= 21$

Bottom
$= 11 - 4$
$= 7$

Calculate each of the following:

1. 2^3

2. $5^2 + 3^2$

3. $(8-5)^2$

4. $(12 \div 3)^2$

5. $4^2 + 3^2$

6. $1^5 + 2^2$

7. $(6+1)^2 + (5-2)^2$

8. $3(3-1)^2$

9. $2(7-3)^2 + 4$

10. $36 \div (2+1)^2$

11. $10 \times 8 \div 4$

12. $8^2 \div 16$

13. $(3+1)^2 \div (10-2)$

14. $(30 \div 10 + 1)^2$

15. $4^3 + 3^3$

16. $3(2)^2 + 5(2) + 2$

17. $4(3)^2 + 2(3) + 5$

18. $2(4)^3 + 3(4)^2$

19. $\sqrt{9} + \sqrt{16}$

20. $\sqrt{100} - \sqrt{81}$

21. $5\sqrt{36}$

22. $3\sqrt{4} + 2$

23. $5\sqrt{49} - 2\sqrt{64}$

24. $3(5-1)^2$

25. $6^2 - 5^2$

26. $\sqrt{144} \div (8-2)$

27. $3(5 \times 2 - 7)^2$

28. $4(2)^2 + 3(2) + 5(2)$

29. $3(4)^2 + 5(3) + 6$

30. $2(5)^2 + 3(5) + 2$

31. $\dfrac{20}{2+3}$

32. $\dfrac{45-3}{21}$

33. $\dfrac{20+10}{8-2}$

34. $\dfrac{3 \times 5 + 3}{4+2}$

35. $\dfrac{4 + 8 \times 3}{9-2}$

36. $\dfrac{\sqrt{81} + 1}{5}$

37. $\sqrt{5+4}$

38. $\sqrt{5 \times 7 + 1}$

39. $\sqrt{3^2 + 4^2}$

40. $\dfrac{(5+3)^2}{5 \times 2 + 6}$

41. $\dfrac{9 + \sqrt{121}}{\sqrt{16}}$

42. $\dfrac{\sqrt{144} + 4}{2 \times 9 - 2}$

43. $\dfrac{20 + 12 \div 6}{3^2 + 2}$

44. $\dfrac{\sqrt{225} + 3}{\sqrt{36}}$

45. $\dfrac{3\sqrt{64} - 4}{3 \times 7 - 1}$

NATURAL NUMBERS

Natural numbers

The whole numbers 0, 1, 2, 3, 4, 5 … are called the counting numbers and are denoted by **N**. The natural numbers can be shown on the number line:

Natural numbers can be classified in many different ways; here are some:

Natural numbers: 0, 1, 2, 3, 4, 5 …
Even numbers: 0, 2, 4, 6, 8, 10 …
Odd numbers: 1, 3, 5, 7, 9, 11 …
Square numbers: 0, 1, 4, 9, 16 25 …
Cube numbers: 0, 1, 8, 27, 64, 125 …

Note: The dots indicate that the number patterns are infinite (go on for ever).

Factors (divisors)

> The factors (divisors) of any whole number are the whole numbers that divide exactly into the given number.

For example,
4 is a factor of 12, because 4 divides into 12.
6 is also a factor of 12, because 6 divides into 12.

> 1 is a factor of every number.
> Every number is a factor of itself.

To find all the factors of a number, we write out all the pairs of factors that make up the number and then write down every number that occurs. Always start off with 1 and the number itself. Then try 2, then try 3, then try 4, and so on in pairs, and stop when the pairs of factors begin to repeat.

Note: A calculator can help you to find all the factors by putting the number in memory, which you can keep recalling to do the divisions. Write down all the numbers that divide exactly, and show your work.

Find the factors of   **(i)** 30   **(ii)** 36

Solution:

Write down all the pairs of factors.

(i) $\dfrac{30}{}$

1×30 Thus, the factors of 30 are:
2×15 1, 2, 3, 5, 6, 10, 15, 30
3×10
5×6

(As the next pair of factors is 6×5, we have all the factors.)

(ii) $\dfrac{36}{}$

1×36 Thus, the factors of 36 are:
2×18 1, 2, 3, 4, 6, 9, 12, 18, 36
3×12 (Notice that 6 is only written once.)
4×9
6×6

(As the next pair of factors is 9×4, we have all the factors.)

Exercise 2.1 ▼

Find the factors of each of the following numbers:

1. 6	**2.** 8	**3.** 10	**4.** 12	**5.** 15	**6.** 18
7. 20	**8.** 24	**9.** 28	**10.** 32	**11.** 40	**12.** 48
13. 60	**14.** 80	**15.** 90	**16.** 120	**17.** 4	**18.** 9
19. 16	**20.** 25	**21.** 64	**22.** 100		

Prime numbers

> A '**prime number**' is a whole number greater than 1 that
> has only two factors, 1 and itself.

For example, 7 is a prime number, as it has only two factors (divisors), 1 and 7.
The first fifteen prime numbers are:

2, 3, 5, 7, 11, 13, 17, 19, 23, 29, 31, 37, 41, 43, 47

Notes: 1 is not considered a prime number, as it has only one factor, i.e. 1.
2 is the first prime number, and it is the only even prime number; all other prime
numbers are odd.

There is an infinite number of prime numbers.
Numbers, such as 8, that have **more** than two factors are called '**composite numbers**'.

Prime factors of a number are factors (divisors) that are also prime numbers.
The factors of 12 are: 1,②,③, 4, 6, 12. Therefore 2 and 3 are prime factors of 12.

We can find the prime factors of a composite number by successively dividing the number by the prime numbers in increasing order. Start with the smallest prime number that divides exactly, repeat if necessary, try the next prime number in the same way, and stop when you are left with 1. You can do the divisions with a calculator, but show your work step by step.

Example ▼

Express: **(i)** 36   **(ii)** 150   **(iii)** 315   as the product of its prime factors.

Solution:

2	36
2	18
3	9
3	3
	1

2	150
3	75
5	25
5	5
	1

3	315
3	105
5	35
7	7
	1

(i) $36 = 2 \times 2 \times 3 \times 3$ **(ii)** $150 = 2 \times 3 \times 5 \times 5$ **(iii)** $315 = 3 \times 3 \times 5 \times 7$

Exercise 2.2 ▼

Write down the prime factors of each of the following numbers:

1. 6   **2.** 8   **3.** 9   **4.** 15   **5.** 20   **6.** 24
7. 40   **8.** 39

Express each of these numbers as the product of its prime factors:

9. 12   **10.** 18   **11.** 28   **12.** 45   **13.** 56   **14.** 84
15. 90   **16.** 105   **17.** 108   **18.** 120   **19.** 150   **20.** 180
21. 175   **22.** 192   **23.** 252   **24.** 350

Highest common factor (HCF)

> The '**highest common factor**' of two or more numbers is the largest factor that is common to each of the given numbers.

In other words, the highest common factor of two or more numbers is the **largest** number that will divide exactly into each number.

For example, the highest common factor of 6 and 8 is 2, as 2 is the largest number that divides exactly into 6 and 8.

The highest common factor of two or more numbers is found with the following steps:

Method 1:
1. Write down the factors of each number.
2. Write down the common factors of each number and select the largest.

Method 2:
1. Write each number as a product of its prime factors in full.
2. Write down the prime factors that are common to all the numbers, and multiply them together.

Note: If the numbers are small, the highest common factor can be written down from inspection. For example, the highest common factor of 10 and 15 is 5.

Example ▼

Find the highest common factor of 36, 60, and 84.

Solution:
Method 1: Write out the factors of each number.
Factors of 36: 1, 2, 3, 4, 6, 9, 12, 18, 36
Factors of 60: 1, 2, 3, 4, 5, 6, 10, 12, 15, 20, 30, 60
Factors of 84: 1, 2, 3, 4, 6, 7, 12, 14, 21, 28, 42, 84
The common factors are 1, 2, 3, 4, 6, 12.
Therefore the highest common factor of 36, 60 and 84 is 12.

Method 2: Write each number as a product of its prime factors.

2	36
2	18
3	9
3	3
	1

2	60
2	30
3	15
5	5
	1

2	84
2	42
3	21
7	7
	1

$36 = 2 \times 2 \times 3 \times 3$ $60 = 2 \times 2 \times 3 \times 5$ $84 = 2 \times 2 \times 3 \times 7$

The common prime factors that appear in each number are 2, 2, and 3.
(Notice that 2 occurs twice in each.)
$2 \times 2 \times 3 = 12$
Therefore the highest common factor of 36, 60 and 84 is 12.

Find the highest common factor of each of the following:

1.	6, 10	**2.** 16, 36	**3.** 24, 40	**4.** 14, 35
5.	10, 40	**6.** 18, 45	**7.** 24, 54	**8.** 11, 55, 99
9.	8, 12, 20	**10.** 15, 25, 30	**11.** 27, 36, 63	**12.** 48, 80, 120
13.	40, 60, 120	**14.** 24, 40, 104	**15.** 45, 75, 105	**16.** 100, 150, 400

Multiples and the lowest common multiple (LCM)

> The multiples of a number are found by multiplying the number by
> 1, 2, 3 … and so on.

The multiples of 3 are: 3, 6, 9, 12, 15, 18, 21 …
The multiples of 5 are: 5, 10, 15, 20, 25, 30, 35 …

> The '**lowest common multiple**' of two or more numbers is the **smallest**
> **multiple** that is common to each of the numbers.

In other words, the lowest common multiple is the **smallest** number into which each of the numbers will divide exactly.

For example, the lowest common multiple of 2, 4 and 5 is 20, as 20 is the smallest number into which 2, 4 and 5 will divide exactly.

The lowest common multiple of two or more numbers is found with the following steps:

Method 1:
1. Write down the multiples of each number.
2. The lowest common multiple is the smallest (first) multiple they have in common.

Method 2:
1. Write each number as a product of its prime factors in full.
2. Write down the **highest** number of times that **every** factor occurs, and multiply them together.

Note: If the numbers are small, the lowest common multiple can be written down from inspection. For example, the lowest common multiple of 2, 3 and 4 is 12.

Find the lowest common multiple of 10, 15, and 18.

Solution:

Method 1: Write out all the multiples:
Multiples of 10: 10, 20, 30, 40, 50, 60, 70, 80, ⑨⓪, 100 …
Multiples of 15: 15, 30, 45, 60, 75, ⑨⓪, 105 …
Multiples of 18: 18, 36, 54, 72, ⑨⓪, 108 …

90 is the first number common to all three multiples.
Therefore the lowest common multiple of 10, 15 and 18 is 90.

Method 2: Write each number as a product of its prime factors:

2	10
5	5
	1

3	15
5	5
	1

2	18
3	9
3	3
	1

$10 = 2 \times 5$ $\qquad\qquad$ $15 = 3 \times 5$ $\qquad\qquad$ $18 = 2 \times 3 \times 3$

The factors that occur are 2, 3, and 5, and 3 occurs twice.

$$2 \times 3 \times 3 \times 5 = 90$$

Therefore the lowest common multiple of 10, 15 and 18 is 90.

Alternatively, the working can be set out as follows:

	10	15	18
2	10	15	18
3	5	15	9
3	5	5	3
5	5	5	1
	1	1	1

$2 \times 3 \times 3 \times 5 = 90$
Therefore the lowest common multiple of 10, 15 and 18 is 90.

Find the lowest common multiple of each of the following:

1. 4, 8	**2.** 2, 3	**3.** 3, 4	**4.** 4, 5
5. 6, 8	**6.** 8, 12	**7.** 2, 3, 6	**8.** 3, 4, 6
9. 6, 9	**10.** 3, 5, 10	**11.** 2, 3, 5	**12.** 2, 3, 8
13. 3, 5, 6	**14.** 5, 8, 10	**15.** 6, 12, 15	**16.** 8, 12, 16
17. 4, 5, 6	**18.** 8, 12, 18	**19.** 5, 6, 8	**20.** 3, 4, 5, 6

Chapter test

Write down the factors of each of the following numbers:

1. 14   **2.** 27   **3.** 35   **4.** 54

5. 90   **6.** 49

Find the highest common factor of each of the following:

7. 6, 8   **8.** 6, 15   **9.** 8, 12, 20   **10.** 18, 24, 30

11. 10, 15, 20   **12.** 16, 40, 48   **13.** 18, 36, 45   **14.** 24, 36, 108

Find the lowest common multiple of each of the following:

15. 2, 3   **16.** 3, 5   **17.** 4, 6   **18.** 6, 9

19. 5, 8   **20.** 4, 7   **21.** 2, 3, 4   **22.** 5, 6, 10

23. 4, 5, 8   **24.** 8, 12, 18

25. Divide the lowest common multiple of 6, 9 and 12 by their highest common factor.

INTEGERS

Integers

The integers are all the positive and negative whole numbers, including zero, i.e.

$$\ldots -5, -4, -3, -2, -1, 0, 1, 2, 3, 4, 5 \ldots$$

The integers are denoted by the letter **Z**.

Integers can be represented on a number line:

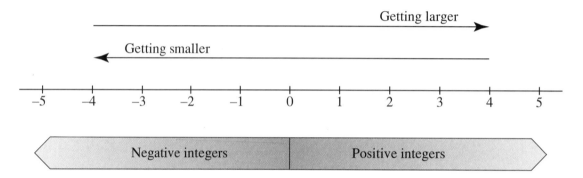

Integers to the right of 0 are called **positive integers**, and integers to the left of 0 are called **negative integers**. 0 is neither positive nor negative.

Note: Plus 3 is written as 3. Minus 2 is written as −2 (never leave out the minus sign).

Addition and subtraction

The integers can be added or subtracted using two methods:

> **Method 1:**
> Find the starting position on the number line, then move right (adding) or move left (subtracting) to find the finished position.
>
> **Method 2:**
> Use one of the two rules:
> 1. When the signs are the same, add the numbers and keep their sign.
> 2. When the signs are different, take the smaller number from the bigger number and keep the sign of the bigger number.

Calculate: **(i)** $3 + 4$ **(ii)** $-1 - 5$ **(iii)** $-2 + 7$ **(iv)** $-6 + 4$

Solution:

Method 1:

(i) $3 + 4$

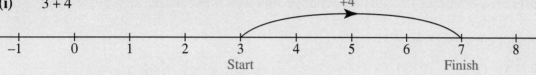

Start at 3 and move four units to the right to finish at 7.

Therefore $3 + 4 = 7$

(ii) $-1 - 5$

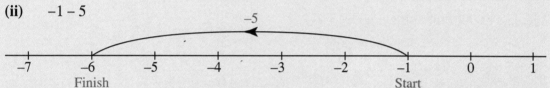

Start at −1 and move five units to the left to finish at −6.

Therefore $-1 - 5 = -6$

(iii) $-2 + 7$

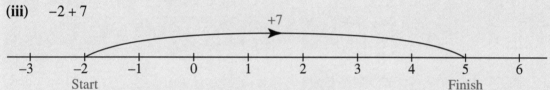

Start at −2 and move seven units to the right to finish at 5.

Therefore $-2 + 7 = 5$

(iv) $-6 + 4$

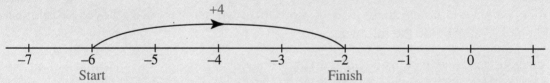

Start at −6 and move four units to the right to finish at −2.

Therefore $-6 + 4 = -2$

Method 2:

(i) $3 + 4 = 7$ (same sign, both +; add the numbers and keep the +)

(ii) $-1 - 5 = -6$ (same sign, both −; add the numbers and keep the −)

(iii) $-2 + 7 = 5$ (different signs; subtract the smaller number, 2, from the larger number, 7, and keep the sign of the larger number, +)

(iv) $-6 + 4 = -2$ (different signs; subtract the smaller number, 4, from the larger number, 6, and keep the sign of the larger number, −).

It is often a good idea to think of positive numbers as having money in a bank and negative numbers as owing money to the bank.

Thus, $-2 - 5 = -7$: if you owe 2 and you owe 5 then you owe 7,
and $-4 + 7 = 3$: if you owe 4 and you have 7, then you have 3,
and $-6 + 1 = -5$: if you owe 6 and you have 1, then you owe 5.

Note: Pressing the key $\boxed{+/-}$, the '**change sign key**', changes the sign of the number on the display.

Thus, to enter -6 press: $6 \boxed{+/-}$

To calculate $-4 + 7$ press: $4 \boxed{+/-} \boxed{+} 7 \boxed{=}$.

Exercise 3.1 ▼

Calculate each of the following:

1. $5 + 3$	**2.** $8 - 6$	**3.** $6 - 3$	**4.** $6 - 2$
5. $3 - 3$	**6.** $9 - 4$	**7.** $10 - 7$	**8.** $12 - 4$
9. $-3 + 7$	**10.** $-2 + 8$	**11.** $-6 + 8$	**12.** $-2 + 7$
13. $-1 - 5$	**14.** $-2 - 3$	**15.** $-5 - 3$	**16.** $-8 - 2$
17. $-4 + 2$	**18.** $-8 + 5$	**19.** $-6 + 4$	**20.** $-9 + 5$
21. $-2 + 5$	**22.** $-1 + 6$	**23.** $-4 + 6$	**24.** $-7 + 10$
25. $-3 - 2$	**26.** $-6 + 5$	**27.** $-4 + 4$	**28.** $8 - 11$
29. $4 - 6$	**30.** $7 - 10$	**31.** $-3 - 2$	**32.** $-9 + 12$
33. $-2 - 3$	**34.** $-4 + 3$	**35.** $-6 + 7$	**36.** $10 - 12$
37. $-1 - 1$	**38.** $-3 - 4$	**39.** $-7 + 8$	**40.** $-9 + 4$

Dealing with more than two numbers

Often we have to do calculations with more than two numbers being added or subtracted. When this happens, do the following:

1. Add up all the positive and negative numbers separately to give two numbers of different signs.
2. Subtract the smaller number from the larger number and keep the sign of the larger number.
   Alternatively, you can use your calculator.

Calculate: (i) $21 + 3 - 8 + 5 - 16$ (ii) $-6 + 3 + 8 - 11 + 5 - 1 - 7$

Solution:

(i) $21 + 3 - 8 + 5 - 16$
        $= 29 - 24$ (add the positive and negative numbers separately)
        $= 5$ (subtract the smaller number, 24, from the larger number, 29, and keep the sign of the larger number, +)

$\boxed{\text{🖩}}$ 21 $\boxed{+}$ 3 $\boxed{-}$ 8 $\boxed{+}$ 5 $\boxed{-}$ 16 $\boxed{=}$

(ii) $-6 + 3 + 8 - 11 + 5 - 1 - 7$
        $= 16 - 25$ (add the positive and negative numbers separately)
        $= -9$ (subtract the smaller number, 16, from the larger number, 25, and keep the sign of the larger number, −)

$\boxed{\text{🖩}}$ 6 $\boxed{+/-}$ $\boxed{+}$ 3 $\boxed{+}$ 8 $\boxed{-}$ 11 $\boxed{+}$ 5 $\boxed{-}$ 1 $\boxed{-}$ 7 $\boxed{=}$

Exercise 3.2 ▼

Calculate each of the following:

1. $8 + 4 - 2 - 5$ 2. $6 + 5 - 1 - 7$ 3. $3 + 5 - 2 - 4$
4. $4 + 2 - 1 - 7$ 5. $8 + 5 - 6 - 10$ 6. $3 + 7 - 4 - 6$
7. $8 - 6 + 4 - 1$ 8. $9 - 8 + 7 - 5$ 9. $10 - 6 - 3 + 4$
10. $-3 - 8 + 7 + 6$ 11. $-4 + 6 - 2 + 5$ 12. $-6 + 3 + 2 - 1$
13. $-3 + 2 + 4 - 5$ 14. $-3 - 4 - 2 + 6$ 15. $6 + 3 - 12 + 5$
16. $-1 - 9 + 6 + 2$ 17. $-6 + 2 + 5 - 1 - 8$ 18. $10 - 13 - 4 - 3 + 10$
19. $-4 + 6 + 1 + 5 + 17 - 15 + 8 - 11$ 20. $-10 + 3 + 17 - 2 + 16 - 5 - 11 + 1$

Multiplication and division

The following two rules are applied when multiplying or dividing integers:

> 1. If the signs are the same, then the answer will be positive.
> 2. If the signs are different, then the answer will be negative.
>
>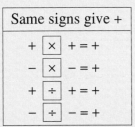
>
>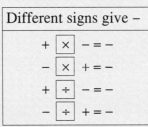

It is good practice to work the sign out first, then multiply or divide the numbers.

Calculate: **(i)** (3)(–4)   **(ii)** –2(–5)   **(iii)** –10 ÷ 5   **(iv)** –12 ÷ –3

Solution:

(i)   (3)(–4)
         = –12   (+ ☒ – = –)

☷ 3 ☒ 4 [+/–] [=]

(ii)   –2(–5)
          = 10   (– ☒ – = +)

☷ 2 [+/–] ☒ 5 [+/–] [=]

(iii)   –10 ÷ 5

    $= \dfrac{-10}{5}$

    = –2   (– ☷ + = –)

☷ 10 [+/–] ☷ 5 [=]

(iv)   –12 ÷ –3

    $= \dfrac{-12}{-3}$

    = 4   (– ☷ – = +)

☷ 12 [+/–] ☷ 3 [+/–] [=]

Note: $\dfrac{-10}{5} = -2$ and $\dfrac{10}{-5} = -2$, therefore $\dfrac{-10}{5}$ or $\dfrac{10}{-5}$ can be written $-\dfrac{10}{5} = -2$.

Exercise 3.3 ▼

Calculate each of the following:

1. –2(2)   **2.** 3(–5)   **3.** –6(–3)   **4.** –5(4)

5. 2(–3)   **6.** –4(–4)   **7.** –8(3)   **8.** (–3)(–5)

9. –12 ÷ 6   **10.** 20 ÷ –4   **11.** –24 ÷ 8   **12.** 20 ÷ –4

13. $\dfrac{-8}{4}$ **14.** $\dfrac{-12}{-3}$ **15.** $\dfrac{-15}{5}$ **16.** $\dfrac{-14}{-7}$

17. (–1)(–1)   **18.** (–3)(–3)   **19.** –28 ÷ –7   **20.** 24 ÷ –3

21. 11(–2)   **22.** –27 ÷ 9   **23.** 21 ÷ –3   **24.** –100 ÷ –20

Exponents: Powers and roots of integers

Note: An **even** number of minus signs give plus when multiplying.
      An **odd** number of minus signs give minus when multiplying.
      The power key on a calculator is y^x.

Calculate: **(i)** $(-3)^2$ **(ii)** $(-4)^3$ **(iii)** $(-2)^4$

Solution:

(i) $(-3)^2$
         $= -3 \times -3$
         $= 9$

(ii) $(-4)^3$
          $= -4 \times -4 \times -4$
          $= -64$

(iii) $(-2)^4$
           $= -2 \times -2 \times -2 \times -2$
           $= 16$

 3 $\boxed{+/-}$ $\boxed{x^2}$ $\boxed{=}$ 4 $\boxed{+/-}$ $\boxed{y^x}$ 3 $\boxed{=}$ 2 $\boxed{+/-}$ $\boxed{y^x}$ 4 $\boxed{=}$

Exercise 3.4 ▼

Calculate each of the following:

1. 3^2 **2.** 5^2 **3.** 7^2 **4.** 1^2 **5.** 2^3

6. 3^3 **7.** 4^3 **8.** $(-2)^2$ **9.** $(-4)^2$ **10.** $(-5)^2$

11. $(-6)^2$ **12.** $(-1)^2$ **13.** $(-1)^3$ **14.** $(-1)^4$ **15.** $(-7)^2$

16. $(-3)^3$ **17.** $(-2)^3$ **18.** $(-10)^2$ **19.** $(-8)^2$ **20.** $(-12)^2$

Order of operations

The order of operations for integers is the same as that for natural numbers.

The memory aid for the order of operations is BEMDAS:

1	2	3	4
B	E	M D	A S

Brackets, **E**xponents, **M**ultiplication and **D**ivision, **A**ddition and **S**ubtraction.

Calculate: **(i)** $5 \times 4 - 30 \div 6 + 3$ **(ii)** $4 + 54 \div -9$

Solution:

(i) $5 \times 4 - 30 \div 6 + 3$

$= 20 - 5 + 3$ (multiplication and division)

$= 23 - 5$ (addition)

$= 18$ (subtraction)

 $5 \;\boxed{\times}\; 4 - 30 \;\boxed{\div}\; 6 + 3 \;\boxed{=}$

(ii) $4 + 54 \div -9$

$= 4 - 6$ (division)

$= -2$ (subtraction)

 $4 \;\boxed{+}\; 54 \;\boxed{\div}\; 9 \;\boxed{+/-}\; \boxed{=}$

Exercise 3.5 ▼

Calculate each of the following:

1. $3 \times 5 + 2$	**2.** $4 + 2 \times 3$	**3.** $5 + 2 \times 4 + 1$
4. $20 \div 4 + 3$	**5.** $3 + 8 \div 4$	**6.** $6 \div 3 + 10 \div 2$
7. $15 \div 5 + 2$	**8.** $24 \div 6 - 1$	**9.** $5 \times 2 + 20 \div 5$
10. $6 \div 2 + 6 \times 3$	**11.** $3 \times 2 - 15 \div 3$	**12.** $4 \times 5 - 30 \div 5$
13. $20 \div 2 - 2 \times 4$	**14.** $8 - 12 \div 6$	**15.** $7 - 15 \div 3$
16. $5(4) + 2(-6)$	**17.** $3(5) - 2(4)$	**18.** $10(2) - 4(-3)$
19. $5(-2) + 4(3) + 1$	**20.** $6(-2) - 5(-3) - 3$	**21.** $5(-4) + 4(3)$
22. $-20 \div -5$	**23.** $14 \div -7$	**24.** $-10 \div 2$
25. $-12 \div -4 + 2$	**26.** $15 \div -3 + 1$	**27.** $-30 \div 6 + 7$
28. $36 \div 9 + 5(2) - 11$	**29.** $6(-1) + 12 \div 2$	**30.** $-20 \div -2 \times 4$

Example ▼

Calculate: **(i)** $15 \div (9 - 6)$ **(ii)** $3(-2)^3$ **(iii)** $2(1 - 4)^2 - 5(6 - 2)$

Solution:

(i) $15 \div (9 - 6)$

$= 15 \div 3$ (brackets)

$= 5$ (division)

 $15 \;\boxed{\div}\; \boxed{(}\; 9 \;\boxed{-}\; 6 \;\boxed{)}\; \boxed{=}$

(ii) $3(-2)^3$

$= 3(-8)$ (exponents)

$= -24$ (multiplication)

$3 \;\boxed{\times}\; 2 \;\boxed{+/-}\; \boxed{y^x}\; 3 \;\boxed{=}$

(iii) $2(1-4)^2 - 5(6-2)$

$\quad = 2(-3)^2 - 5(4)$ (brackets)

$\quad = 2(9) - 5(4)$ (exponents)

$\quad = 18 - 20$ (multiplication)

$\quad = -2$ (subtraction)

$\boxed{\text{▦}}\;\boxed{2}\;\boxed{\times}\;\boxed{(}\;\boxed{1-4}\;\boxed{)}\;\boxed{x^2}\;\boxed{-5}\;\boxed{\times}\;\boxed{(}\;\boxed{6-2}\;\boxed{)}\;\boxed{=}$

Note: A minus sign on its own outside a bracket can be replaced with -1.

For example, $-(8-5) = -1(8-5) = -1(3) = -3$.

In other words, a minus sign outside a bracket means multiply by -1.

Exercise 3.6 ▼

Calculate each of the following:

1. $3(4+2)$	**2.** $5(6-2)$	**3.** $2(8-5)$
4. $(3+5) \div 2$	**5.** $(18-4) \div 7$	**6.** $(21+3) \div 8$
7. $24 \div (6+2)$	**8.** $20 \div (12-2)$	**9.** $(20 \div 5) \div (5-1)$
10. $(8+4) \div (6-3)$	**11.** $(100 \div 2) \div (60 \div 12)$	**12.** $(60 \div 5) \div (45 \div 15)$
13. $5(2 \times 3 - 4)$	**14.** $6(5 \times 3 - 11)$	**15.** $2(2 + 3 \times 4)$
16. $6(2-4)$	**17.** $-3(1-6)$	**18.** $-2(-3+5)$
19. $3(20 \div 5 - 2)$	**20.** $4 + 20 \div (7-2)$	**21.** $8 - 22 \div (9+2)$
22. $-(3-5)$	**23.** $3(2+5) - (4-7)$	**24.** $2(5-7) - (4-8)$
25. 3^2	**26.** $2(3)^2$	**27.** $4(2)^2$
28. $3(-2)^2$	**29.** $2(4)^2$	**30.** $3(-4)^2$
31. $3(2)^2 + 4(2)$	**32.** $3(4)^2 + 2(4) + 5$	**33.** $3(-2)^2 - 5(-2) - 20$
34. $(4-1)^2$	**35.** $(5-8)^2$	**36.** $(100 \div 25)^2$
37. $5(6-2)^2$	**38.** $3(3-5)^2$	**39.** $4(5-3)^2 + 4(3+1)$

In the following problems, calculate the top and bottom first separately before doing the division. The bar, ——, acts exactly like a bracket.

40. $\dfrac{10+2}{5-1}$ 　　 **41.** $\dfrac{2 \times 3 + 8}{5 \times 2 - 3}$ 　　 **42.** $\dfrac{2(5-1)+2}{3 \times 6 - 4 \times 2}$

43. $\dfrac{18 + 2 \times 3}{2(5-1)}$ 　　 **44.** $\dfrac{6 \times 3 + 12 \div 4 + 9}{3(8-1) - 2(4-1)}$ 　　 **45.** $\dfrac{5^2 - 7}{3^2 - 7}$

Chapter test

Calculate each of the following:

1. $10 - 8$
2. $-2 + 5$
3. $4 - 9$
4. $-2 - 4$
5. $-8 + 3$
6. $2 - 3 + 5 - 1$
7. $5(-2)$
8. $-3(-2)$
9. $(-2)^2$
10. $5(-2)^2$
11. $3(-3)^2 - 5(2)^2$
12. $(-1)^3$
13. $(50 \div 10) \div (30 \div 6)$
14. $35 \div (10 - 3)$
15. $(12 - 10)^3$
16. $3(4)^2 + 4(4) + 2$
17. $4(6 - 4)^2$
18. $3(4 - 1)^2 + 5(1 - 5)$
19. $5(2 \times 3 - 4)$
20. $4(3 + 20 \div 5)$
21. $2(-8 + 3)^2$
22. $\dfrac{(4 + 12) \div 2}{2(10 - 8)}$
23. $\dfrac{15 \div 3 + 7}{2(5 - 3)}$
24. $\dfrac{6(5 - 8)}{-3(7 - 4)}$
25. $\dfrac{36 \div (6 - 2) + 1}{5(8 - 9)}$
26. $\dfrac{(4)^2 + 9(\sqrt{4}) - 16}{\sqrt{25} + (2)^2}$
27. $\dfrac{5(-1) - 3(3)^2}{4(3 - 1)}$

FRACTIONS

Fractions

A fraction is written as two whole numbers, one over the other, separated by a bar. For example, $\frac{4}{5}$, $\frac{7}{8}$, $\frac{4}{3}$ and $-\frac{5}{4}$ are fractions.

The top number is called the **numerator** and the bottom number the **denominator**.

Equivalent fractions

Equivalent fractions are fractions that are equal. For example,

$$\frac{1}{2} = \frac{2}{4} = \frac{3}{6} = \frac{4}{8} = \frac{5}{10}.$$

> The top and bottom of a fraction can be multiplied or divided by the same number without changing its value.

Example ▼

Find the missing numbers in these fractions: (i) $\frac{3}{4} = \frac{?}{12}$ (ii) $\frac{10}{15} = \frac{2}{?}$

Solution:

(i) $\frac{3}{4} = \frac{?}{12}$

$\frac{3}{4} = \frac{9}{12}$ (multiply top and bottom by 3)

Therefore the missing number is 9.

(ii) $\frac{10}{15} = \frac{2}{?}$

$\frac{10}{15} = \frac{2}{3}$ (divide top and bottom by 5)

Therefore the missing number is 3.

Exercise 4.1 ▼

Fill in the missing numbers in each of the following:

1. $\frac{1}{4} = \frac{?}{16}$

2. $\frac{1}{2} = \frac{?}{10}$

3. $\frac{3}{4} = \frac{?}{20}$

4. $\frac{2}{3} = \frac{?}{12}$

5. $\frac{3}{?} = \frac{12}{16}$

6. $\frac{4}{?} = \frac{20}{25}$

7. $\frac{12}{24} = \frac{?}{4}$ **8.** $\frac{30}{40} = \frac{3}{?}$ **9.** $\frac{9}{15} = \frac{3}{?}$

10. $\frac{?}{24} = \frac{2}{3}$ **11.** $\frac{?}{30} = \frac{5}{6}$ **12.** $\frac{?}{20} = \frac{1}{4}$

13. $\frac{5}{9} = \frac{?}{27}$ **14.** $\frac{5}{8} = \frac{25}{?}$ **15.** $\frac{4}{7} = \frac{16}{?}$

16. $\frac{40}{?} = \frac{2}{3} = \frac{12}{?}$ **17.** $\frac{?}{24} = \frac{3}{4} = \frac{42}{?}$ **18.** $\frac{?}{45} = \frac{6}{5} = \frac{30}{?}$

Lowest terms

When we can no longer divide the top and bottom evenly by the same whole number, we say that the fraction is in its **lowest terms**. This process is also called **simplifying** or **cancelling down**.

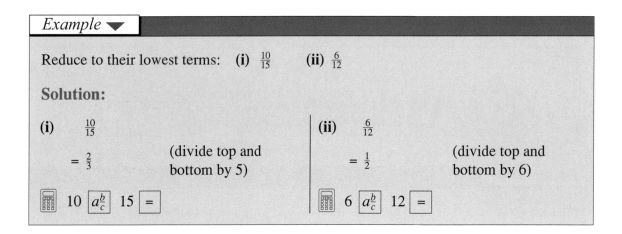

Example ▼

Reduce to their lowest terms: **(i)** $\frac{10}{15}$ **(ii)** $\frac{6}{12}$

Solution:

(i) $\frac{10}{15}$

$= \frac{2}{3}$ (divide top and bottom by 5)

▦ 10 $\boxed{a\frac{b}{c}}$ 15 $\boxed{=}$

(ii) $\frac{6}{12}$

$= \frac{1}{2}$ (divide top and bottom by 6)

▦ 6 $\boxed{a\frac{b}{c}}$ 12 $\boxed{=}$

Exercise 4.2 ▼

Reduce the following fractions to their lowest terms:

1. $\frac{5}{10}$ **2.** $\frac{3}{12}$ **3.** $\frac{15}{25}$ **4.** $\frac{6}{12}$ **5.** $\frac{5}{15}$ **6.** $\frac{3}{15}$

7. $\frac{10}{30}$ **8.** $\frac{15}{20}$ **9.** $\frac{8}{20}$ **10.** $\frac{12}{20}$ **11.** $\frac{14}{21}$ **12.** $\frac{6}{10}$

13. $\frac{28}{35}$ **14.** $\frac{20}{30}$ **15.** $\frac{36}{60}$ **16.** $\frac{25}{100}$ **17.** $\frac{75}{100}$ **18.** $\frac{4}{32}$

19. $\frac{6}{54}$ **20.** $\frac{22}{33}$ **21.** $\frac{16}{48}$ **22.** $\frac{9}{21}$ **23.** $\frac{24}{30}$ **24.** $\frac{21}{24}$

25. $\frac{30}{45}$ **26.** $\frac{32}{48}$ **27.** $\frac{60}{150}$ **28.** $\frac{36}{96}$ **29.** $\frac{56}{70}$ **30.** $\frac{60}{96}$

Types of fractions

1. **Proper fraction**
   If the top is smaller than the bottom, the fraction is called a **proper fraction** or a **bottom-heavy fraction** and is less than 1, for example $\frac{2}{5}$, $\frac{3}{4}$.
2. **Improper fraction**
   If the top is bigger than the bottom, the fraction is called an **improper fraction** or a **top-heavy fraction** and is greater than 1, for example $\frac{4}{3}$, $\frac{7}{5}$.
3. **Mixed fraction**
   Numbers such as $2\frac{3}{4}$ are called **mixed fractions** or **mixed numbers**.

Example ▼

(i) Express $2\frac{3}{4}$ as an improper fraction.

(ii) Express $\frac{19}{5}$ as a mixed fraction.

Solution:

(i) $\quad 2\frac{3}{4}$

$\quad = \frac{11}{4} \qquad (2 \times 4 + 3 = 11)$

[calc] 2 $\boxed{a_c^b}$ 3 $\boxed{a_c^b}$ 4 $\boxed{\text{INV}}$ $\boxed{a_c^b}$

(ii) $\quad \frac{19}{5}$

$\quad = 3\frac{4}{5} \qquad$ (5 into 19 goes three times, remainder 4)

[calc] 19 $\boxed{a_c^b}$ 5 $\boxed{=}$

Note: On some calculators the $\boxed{\text{INV}}$ key is called $\boxed{\text{2nd F}}$ or $\boxed{\text{Shift}}$.

Exercise 4.3 ▼

Express each of the following mixed fractions as an improper (top-heavy) fraction:

1. $2\frac{1}{4}$ 2. $2\frac{3}{5}$ 3. $4\frac{3}{4}$ 4. $3\frac{3}{4}$ 5. $1\frac{2}{5}$ 6. $3\frac{3}{10}$

7. $1\frac{7}{8}$ 8. $3\frac{3}{8}$ 9. $4\frac{2}{5}$ 10. $5\frac{2}{3}$ 11. $4\frac{2}{7}$ 12. $8\frac{3}{5}$

13. $7\frac{3}{4}$ 14. $3\frac{7}{8}$ 15. $6\frac{1}{3}$ 16. $9\frac{5}{8}$ 17. $2\frac{4}{5}$ 18. $7\frac{3}{5}$

19. $5\frac{3}{5}$ 20. $6\frac{3}{4}$ 21. $5\frac{5}{6}$ 22. $2\frac{4}{9}$ 23. $5\frac{3}{10}$ 24. $11\frac{2}{5}$

Express each of the following improper fractions as a mixed fraction:

1. $\frac{7}{4}$ **2.** $\frac{13}{6}$ **3.** $\frac{25}{4}$ **4.** $\frac{11}{3}$ **5.** $\frac{17}{7}$ **6.** $\frac{19}{8}$

7. $\frac{22}{5}$ **8.** $\frac{7}{2}$ **9.** $\frac{3}{2}$ **10.** $\frac{20}{9}$ **11.** $\frac{33}{5}$ **12.** $\frac{41}{6}$

13. $\frac{27}{4}$ **14.** $\frac{45}{8}$ **15.** $\frac{7}{3}$ **16.** $\frac{25}{12}$ **17.** $\frac{40}{13}$ **18.** $\frac{12}{5}$

19. $\frac{35}{8}$ **20.** $\frac{22}{4}$ **21.** $\frac{27}{6}$ **22.** $\frac{27}{12}$ **23.** $\frac{33}{4}$ **24.** $\frac{50}{7}$

Order of operations

The order of operations for fractions is the same as that for natural numbers and integers. Remember: BEMDAS.

However, if you are adding, subtracting, multiplying, dividing, raising to a power or taking a square root of a fraction, it is good practice to write all mixed fractions first as top-heavy (improper) fractions.

Addition and subtraction

To add or subtract fractions, do the following:

> **1.** Express each mixed fraction as a top-heavy fraction.
> **2.** Write each fraction in terms of the same common denominator, preferably the LCM, and simplify.

Write as one fraction: (i) $3\frac{2}{5} - 1\frac{3}{4}$ (ii) $3\frac{1}{3} - 1\frac{5}{6} - 2\frac{1}{4}$

Solution:

(i) $3\frac{2}{5} - 1\frac{3}{4}$

$= \dfrac{17}{5} - \dfrac{7}{4}$

$= \dfrac{4(17) - 5(7)}{20}$

$= \dfrac{68 - 35}{20}$

$= \dfrac{33}{20}$

🖩 3 $\boxed{a\frac{b}{c}}$ 2 $\boxed{a\frac{b}{c}}$ $5 - 1$ $\boxed{a\frac{b}{c}}$ 3 $\boxed{a\frac{b}{c}}$ 4 $\boxed{=}$

(ii) $3\frac{1}{3} - 1\frac{5}{6} - 2\frac{1}{4}$

$= \dfrac{10}{3} - \dfrac{11}{6} - \dfrac{9}{4}$

$= \dfrac{4(10) - 2(11) - 3(9)}{12}$

$= \dfrac{40 - 22 - 27}{12}$

$= \dfrac{40 - 49}{12}$

$= -\dfrac{9}{12} = -\dfrac{3}{4}$

🖩 3 $\boxed{a\frac{b}{c}}$ 1 $\boxed{a\frac{b}{c}}$ $3 - 1$ $\boxed{a\frac{b}{c}}$ 5 $\boxed{a\frac{b}{c}}$ 6

$- 2$ $\boxed{a\frac{b}{c}}$ 1 $\boxed{a\frac{b}{c}}$ 4 $\boxed{=}$

Exercise 4.5 ▼

Write each of the following as one fraction:

1. $\frac{1}{2} + \frac{3}{4}$ **2.** $\frac{2}{3} + \frac{1}{2}$ **3.** $\frac{3}{4} + \frac{5}{8}$ **4.** $\frac{3}{4} + \frac{2}{3}$

5. $\frac{5}{6} + \frac{2}{3}$ **6.** $\frac{3}{5} + \frac{2}{3}$ **7.** $\frac{2}{3} + \frac{3}{4} + \frac{5}{6}$ **8.** $\frac{5}{8} - \frac{1}{4}$

9. $\frac{2}{3} - \frac{1}{2}$ **10.** $\frac{3}{4} - \frac{2}{5}$ **11.** $\frac{2}{5} - \frac{3}{10}$ **12.** $\frac{5}{8} - \frac{3}{4}$

13. $\frac{5}{12} - \frac{2}{3}$ **14.** $\frac{5}{6} - \frac{7}{8}$ **15.** $\frac{2}{7} - \frac{3}{5}$ **16.** $2\frac{1}{4} + 3\frac{1}{3}$

17. $2\frac{3}{4} + 2\frac{1}{8}$ **18.** $4\frac{1}{5} + 1\frac{1}{4}$ **19.** $2\frac{3}{8} + 3\frac{1}{4}$ **20.** $4\frac{3}{5} + 2\frac{1}{10}$

21. $3\frac{1}{3} + 2\frac{4}{5}$ **22.** $4\frac{1}{2} - 3\frac{2}{3}$ **23.** $2\frac{3}{5} - 1\frac{2}{3}$ **24.** $3\frac{1}{3} - 2\frac{5}{6}$

25. $4\frac{1}{3} - 2\frac{5}{12}$ **26.** $2\frac{3}{10} - 3\frac{2}{5}$ **27.** $2\frac{1}{3} - 5\frac{3}{4}$ **28.** $3\frac{1}{4} + 2\frac{1}{3} - 3\frac{7}{12}$

29. $4\frac{1}{2} - 2\frac{3}{8} + 1\frac{1}{4}$ **30.** $3\frac{1}{4} - 2\frac{1}{8} + 2\frac{1}{2}$ **31.** $4\frac{1}{12} - 3\frac{11}{12} + 2\frac{5}{6}$ **32.** $4\frac{1}{5} - 2\frac{7}{10} - 3\frac{11}{20}$

33. $-2\frac{1}{5} + 3\frac{7}{10} - 4\frac{1}{15}$ **34.** $\frac{19}{8} - \frac{3}{2} + \frac{14}{3} - \frac{23}{6}$ **35.** $3\frac{1}{5} + \frac{17}{10} - 2\frac{3}{20} - \frac{3}{5}$ **36.** $1 - \frac{2}{3}$

37. $2 - \frac{5}{6}$ **38.** $3 - 2\frac{3}{4}$ **39.** $4 - 1\frac{1}{5}$ **40.** $3\frac{1}{9} + 2\frac{5}{18} - 4\frac{1}{2}$

41. $8\frac{1}{4} - 7\frac{5}{8} - 1 + \frac{5}{16}$ **42.** $2\frac{1}{2} - \frac{29}{8} - 3 + 1\frac{1}{2}$ **43.** $\frac{19}{3} - 3\frac{5}{12} - 2\frac{7}{18} + 2 - \frac{5}{6}$

Multiplication

To multiply two fractions, do the following:

> **1.** Write each mixed fraction as a top-heavy fraction.
> **2.** Multiply the top by the top and the bottom by the bottom.
> **3.** Simplify this fraction.

Note: We can make the working easier by cancelling **before** multiplying.

Example ▼

Write as one fraction: **(i)** $\frac{3}{7} \times \frac{2}{5}$ **(ii)** $2\frac{1}{2} \times 1\frac{4}{5}$

Solution:

(i) $\frac{3}{7} \times \frac{2}{5}$

$= \frac{6}{35}$ (multiply the top by the top and the bottom by the bottom)

🖩 $3 \;\boxed{a\frac{b}{c}}\; 7 \;\boxed{\times}\; 2 \;\boxed{a\frac{b}{c}}\; 5 \;\boxed{=}$

(ii) $2\frac{1}{2} \times 1\frac{4}{5}$

$= \frac{5}{2} \times \frac{9}{5}$ (make fractions top-heavy)

$= \frac{45}{10}$ (multiply the top by the top and the bottom by the bottom)

$= \frac{9}{2}$ (divide top and bottom by 5)

Alternatively, we can cancel down before multiplying:

$$2\frac{1}{2} \times 1\frac{4}{5} = \frac{\cancel{5}}{2} \times \frac{9}{\cancel{5}\,1} = \frac{9}{2}$$

🖩 $2 \;\boxed{a\frac{b}{c}}\; 1 \;\boxed{a\frac{b}{c}}\; 2 \;\times\; 1 \;\boxed{a\frac{b}{c}}\; 4 \;\boxed{a\frac{b}{c}}\; 5 \;\boxed{=}$

Exercise 4.6 ▼

Write each of the following as one fraction:

1. $\frac{2}{3} \times \frac{5}{7}$ **2.** $\frac{3}{4} \times \frac{1}{5}$ **3.** $\frac{5}{7} \times \frac{3}{4}$ **4.** $\frac{3}{5} \times \frac{5}{9}$

5. $\frac{2}{3} \times \frac{4}{7}$ **6.** $\frac{5}{6} \times \frac{9}{10}$ **7.** $1\frac{1}{2} \times \frac{5}{8}$ **8.** $2\frac{1}{2} \times 1\frac{1}{5}$

9. $1\frac{1}{4} \times \frac{2}{3}$ **10.** $3\frac{1}{2} \times \frac{7}{6}$ **11.** $2\frac{1}{2} \times \frac{3}{5}$ **12.** $2\frac{3}{4} \times 1\frac{3}{11}$

13. $2\frac{2}{3} \times 3\frac{3}{4}$ **14.** $\frac{2}{3} \times \frac{3}{4} \times \frac{5}{8}$ **15.** $2\frac{1}{4} \times 1\frac{5}{11} \times 1\frac{1}{2}$ **16.** $2\frac{1}{3} \times \frac{2}{3} \times \frac{5}{8}$

Division

To divide one fraction by another fraction, do the following:

> **1.** Write each mixed fraction as a top-heavy fraction.
> **2.** Turn the fraction we are dividing by upside down and multiply.

Example ▼

Write as one fraction: (i) $2\frac{1}{3} \div 1\frac{5}{6}$ (ii) $2\frac{3}{5} \div 4$

Solution:

(i) $\quad 2\frac{1}{3} \div 1\frac{5}{6}$

$\quad = \frac{7}{3} \div \frac{11}{6}$

$\quad = \frac{7}{3} \times \frac{6}{11}$

$\quad = \frac{42}{33}$

$\quad = \frac{14}{11}$

(ii) $\quad 2\frac{3}{5} \div 4$

$\quad = \frac{13}{5} \div \frac{4}{1}$

$\quad = \frac{13}{5} \times \frac{1}{4}$

$\quad = \frac{13}{20}$

Note: $4 = \frac{4}{1}$ as a top-heavy fraction

▦ 2 $a\frac{b}{c}$ 3 $a\frac{b}{c}$ 5 $\div$ 4 $=$

Exercise 4.7 ▼

Write each of the following as one fraction:

1. $\frac{3}{5} \div \frac{4}{7}$ **2.** $\frac{2}{5} \div \frac{1}{3}$ **3.** $\frac{2}{3} \div \frac{5}{3}$ **4.** $\frac{4}{5} \div \frac{3}{5}$

5. $\frac{3}{8} \div \frac{1}{4}$ **6.** $\frac{7}{9} \div \frac{14}{3}$ **7.** $\frac{1}{2} \div \frac{1}{4}$ **8.** $\frac{8}{3} \div \frac{2}{3}$

9. $1\frac{1}{5} \div 3\frac{3}{5}$ **10.** $2\frac{1}{4} \div 3\frac{3}{5}$ **11.** $\frac{2}{3} \div 1\frac{2}{3}$ **12.** $1\frac{1}{2} \div 1\frac{3}{4}$

13. $1\frac{4}{5} \div 2\frac{7}{10}$ **14.** $4\frac{1}{4} \div 1\frac{5}{12}$ **15.** $5\frac{1}{4} \div 10\frac{1}{2}$ **16.** $2\frac{5}{8} \div \frac{3}{4}$

17. $4\frac{4}{5} \div 1\frac{1}{7}$ **18.** $4\frac{1}{3} \div 1\frac{6}{7}$ **19.** $3\frac{1}{8} \div \frac{5}{12}$ **20.** $8 \div 2\frac{1}{2}$

21. $4 \div \frac{1}{5}$ **22.** $3\frac{1}{2} \div 10$ **23.** $3\frac{1}{8} \div \frac{5}{16}$ **24.** $6\frac{1}{4} \div 1\frac{7}{8}$

Exponents: Powers of fractions

Just as $2^3 = 2 \times 2 \times 2 = 8$, so $(\frac{4}{5})^3 = \frac{4}{5} \times \frac{4}{5} \times \frac{4}{5} = \frac{64}{125}$.

Simply multiply the top by the top by the top and the bottom by the bottom by the bottom.
Fractions to other powers can be calculated in the same way.
Always write mixed fractions as top-heavy fractions first.

Example ▼

Write **(i)** $(\frac{1}{2})^3$ **(ii)** $(1\frac{1}{2})^2$ as fractions without powers.

Solution:

(i) $\quad (\frac{1}{2})^3$

$\quad = \frac{1}{2} \times \frac{1}{2} \times \frac{1}{2}$

$\quad = \frac{1}{8}$

$\boxed{\text{📟}}$ $\boxed{1}$ $\boxed{a^b_c}$ $\boxed{2}$ $\boxed{\times}$ $\boxed{1}$ $\boxed{a^b_c}$ $\boxed{2}$ $\boxed{\times}$ $\boxed{1}$ $\boxed{a^b_c}$ $\boxed{2}$ $\boxed{=}$

(ii) $\quad (1\frac{1}{2})^2$

$\quad = (\frac{3}{2})^2 \qquad$ (top-heavy)

$\quad = \frac{3}{2} \times \frac{3}{2} = \frac{9}{4}$

$\boxed{\text{📟}}$ $\boxed{1}$ $\boxed{a^b_c}$ $\boxed{1}$ $\boxed{a^b_c}$ $\boxed{2}$ $\boxed{\times}$ $\boxed{1}$ $\boxed{a^b_c}$ $\boxed{1}$ $\boxed{a^b_c}$ $\boxed{2}$ $\boxed{=}$

To avoid having to key in the same number again you can use the memory in your calculator.
To store a number in the memory you press $\boxed{\text{Min}}$ or $\boxed{\text{STO}}$ or $\boxed{x \to M}$.
To recall a number from memory you press $\boxed{\text{MR}}$ or $\boxed{\text{RCL}}$ or $\boxed{\text{RM}}$.

Threfore, to calculate $(\frac{1}{2})^3$ do the following:

Press 1 $\boxed{a^b_c}$ 2 $\boxed{\text{MIN}}$ and, if you want, clear the screen by pressing $\boxed{\text{C}}$.

Now press: $\boxed{\text{MR}}$ $\boxed{\times}$ $\boxed{\text{MR}}$ $\boxed{\times}$ $\boxed{\text{MR}}$ $\boxed{=}$

Note: Do not use the $\boxed{x^2}$ or $\boxed{y^x}$ keys when dealing with fractions.
Write each of the following as fractions without powers:

Exercise 4.8 ▼

1. $(\frac{1}{2})^2$
2. $(\frac{2}{3})^2$
3. $(\frac{3}{4})^2$
4. $(\frac{4}{5})^2$
5. $(\frac{1}{4})^2$

6. $(\frac{1}{3})^2$
7. $(\frac{1}{3})^3$
8. $(\frac{1}{5})^3$
9. $(\frac{3}{5})^3$
10. $(\frac{5}{4})^2$

11. $(1\frac{1}{3})^2$
12. $(1\frac{3}{4})^2$
13. $(3\frac{1}{3})^2$
14. $(2\frac{2}{5})^2$
15. $(1\frac{1}{2})^3$

16. $(1\frac{4}{5})^2$
17. $(\frac{2}{3})^3$
18. $(2\frac{1}{2})^3$
19. $(-\frac{1}{2})^2$
20. $(-\frac{2}{3})^2$

Write as one fraction **(i)** $\frac{1}{2} \times \frac{3}{4} + \frac{5}{16}$ **(ii)** $\frac{6}{5}(\frac{5}{12} + \frac{1}{4})$

(i) $\quad \frac{1}{2} \times \frac{3}{4} + \frac{5}{16}$

$\quad = \frac{3}{8} + \frac{5}{16}$ $\qquad$ (multiplication first)

$\quad = \frac{11}{16}$ $\qquad$ (addition)

▣ $1 \boxed{a_c^b} 2 \boxed{\times} 3 \boxed{a_c^b} 4 + 5 \boxed{a_c^b} 16 \boxed{=}$

(ii) $\quad \frac{6}{5}(\frac{5}{12} + \frac{1}{4})$

$\quad = \frac{6}{5}(\frac{2}{3})$ $\qquad$ (brackets first)

$\quad = \frac{12}{15}$ $\qquad$ (multiplication)

$\quad = \frac{4}{5}$ $\qquad$ (simplify)

▣ $6 \boxed{a_c^b} 5 \boxed{\times}$

$\boxed{(} 5 \boxed{a_c^b} 12 + 1 \boxed{a_c^b} 4 \boxed{)} \boxed{=}$

Notes:

1. In doing the following exercise, keep the order of operations, BEMDAS, in mind.

2. When '**of**' occurs between two fractions, it can always be replaced by '**multiplication with a bracket around the two fractions**'.
For example, $\frac{3}{4} \div \frac{2}{3}$ of $\frac{5}{8} = \frac{3}{4} \div (\frac{2}{3} \times \frac{5}{8})$,
and work on the brackets first.

Write each of the following as one fraction:

1. $\frac{1}{4} \times \frac{3}{5} + \frac{7}{10}$

2. $\frac{3}{2} \times \frac{1}{5} + \frac{3}{10}$

3. $\frac{3}{4} \times \frac{5}{3} + \frac{1}{2}$

4. $\frac{5}{2}(\frac{7}{10} - \frac{3}{5})$

5. $\frac{3}{4}(\frac{1}{2} + \frac{1}{3})$

6. $\frac{1}{2} + \frac{2}{3} \times \frac{5}{4}$

7. $\frac{2}{3} \div \frac{4}{9} + \frac{1}{2}$

8. $\frac{1}{2} + \frac{1}{4} \div \frac{2}{3}$

9. $1\frac{5}{16} + 2\frac{1}{4} \div 3\frac{3}{5}$

10. $(4\frac{2}{3} - 2\frac{3}{4}) \div 1\frac{8}{15}$

11. $\frac{3}{4}(1\frac{1}{5} \div 3\frac{3}{5})$

12. $(2\frac{1}{5} - 1\frac{3}{10}) \div (\frac{1}{2} + \frac{2}{5})$

13. $(2\frac{1}{2} - 1\frac{3}{4}) \div (1\frac{1}{4} - 1\frac{1}{8})$

14. $\frac{4}{9}(\frac{3}{4} \times \frac{2}{3} + \frac{5}{8})$

15. $\frac{3}{17}(\frac{3}{5} + \frac{2}{5} \div \frac{3}{4})$

16. $\frac{5}{6}$ of $3\frac{1}{3} + \frac{2}{3}$

17. $\frac{4}{5}$ of $6\frac{2}{3} - \frac{1}{2}$

18. $\frac{3}{4} \div \frac{3}{4}$ of $\frac{3}{8}$

19. $(\frac{1}{2} + \frac{1}{3})^2$

20. $(\frac{1}{2})^2 + (\frac{1}{3})^2$

21. $8(\frac{1}{2})^2$

22. $\dfrac{\frac{3}{4} + \frac{1}{2}}{\frac{1}{3} + \frac{1}{4}}$

23. $\dfrac{\frac{2}{5} + \frac{3}{4}}{1\frac{1}{5} + 2\frac{1}{4}}$

24. $\dfrac{\frac{1}{3}(\frac{1}{2} + \frac{1}{5})}{\frac{1}{5}(\frac{1}{2} + \frac{1}{3})}$

25. $(\frac{3}{4} - \frac{1}{2})^2 \div \frac{5}{8}$

26. $\dfrac{2\frac{1}{2} + \frac{7}{10} - \frac{1}{5}}{3\frac{1}{4} - 1\frac{2}{3} - \frac{1}{12}}$

27. $\dfrac{(9\frac{1}{2} - 7\frac{5}{8}) \div 1\frac{2}{7}}{1\frac{1}{4}(2\frac{2}{3} + \frac{1}{4})}$

Practical problems

The following questions are all of a practical nature, and all require the use of fractions for their solution:

28. Calculate $\frac{2}{3}$ of €7.20 + $\frac{3}{4}$ of €10.40.

29. In a class of thirty-two pupils, $\frac{5}{8}$ are boys. How many girls are there in the class?

30. Tea is packed in $\frac{1}{4}$ kg packets. How many packets of tea can be made up from a box of tea weighing 50 kg?

31. A box contains 240 oranges. However, $\frac{1}{8}$ of them are found to be bad. How many of the oranges are good?

32. A cask of wine contains 40 litres. The wine is to be poured into glasses holding $\frac{2}{5}$ litres each. How many glasses will the cask fill, if none is spilt?

33. The total number of marks available in a maths test was 72. *A* received $\frac{2}{3}$ of the total marks, *B* received $\frac{5}{8}$, and *C* received $\frac{3}{4}$. Calculate how many marks *A*, *B* and *C* received.

34. Mary has a roll of ribbon 20 m in length. She cuts nine pieces off it, each of length $1\frac{3}{4}$ m. What length remains on the roll?

35. In a club, three-fifths of the members are girls. The remaining 180 members are boys. How many members are there altogether?

36. In a class, $\frac{2}{5}$ come to school by car, $\frac{1}{3}$ come by train, and the rest walk. What fraction of the class walk to school?

One quantity as a fraction of another

To express one quantity as a fraction of another quantity, do the following:

> 1. Make sure that both quantities are in the same units, and remove the units.
> 2. Put the first number over the second number to form a fraction.
> 3. Simplify this fraction.

Example ▼

A girl spent three hours on revision one evening. She spent 45 minutes studying mathematics. What fraction of the revision time was spent studying mathematics?

Solution:
First change 3 hours into minutes.
3 hours = 3 × 60 = 180 minutes.
45 minutes as a fraction of 180 minutes = $\frac{45}{180}$ = $\frac{1}{4}$ (🖩 45 $\boxed{a\frac{b}{c}}$ 180 $\boxed{=}$)

Express the first number as a fraction of the second number:

1. 15; 20   **2.** 18; 30   **3.** 28; 42   **4.** 20; 100

5. 20; 32   **6.** 9; 27   **7.** 15; 90   **8.** 14; 56

Express the first quantity as a fraction of the second quantity:

9. 35c; €1.05   **10.** 4 days; 2 weeks   **11.** 50 cm; 1 m   **12.** 750 m; 1 km

13. 90c; €3   **14.** 20 minutes; 1 hour   **15.** 800 g; 1 kg   **16.** 15 hours; 2 days

17. 18 seconds; $1\frac{1}{2}$ minutes   **18.** 8 mm; 2 cm   **19.** 12 days; 4 weeks

20. 8 months; 2 years

21. A man spent $2\frac{1}{2}$ hours gardening on Saturday morning. He spent 60 minutes trimming the hedge, 50 minutes cutting grass, and the rest of the time weeding. What fraction of this time did he spend
    (i) trimming the hedge   **(ii)** cutting the grass   **(iii)** weeding?

22. In a bag containing 240 marbles, 80 are red, 72 are green, 48 are blue, and the remainder are white. What fraction of these marbles are
    (i) red   **(ii)** green   **(iii)** blue   **(iv)** white?

Chapter test

Express each of the following as one fraction:

1. $\frac{3}{4} + \frac{5}{6}$ **2.** $\frac{5}{2} + \frac{6}{5} - \frac{10}{3}$ **3.** $8\frac{3}{4} - 6\frac{5}{8}$

4. $1\frac{1}{3} \times 1\frac{7}{8}$ **5.** $4\frac{1}{5} \times 2\frac{1}{7}$ **6.** $\frac{2}{3} \div \frac{4}{9}$

7. $2\frac{1}{4} \div 3\frac{3}{5}$ **8.** $\frac{3}{4} \times \frac{5}{2} + \frac{7}{8}$ **9.** $\frac{1}{4}(\frac{1}{2} + \frac{2}{3})$

10. $\frac{3}{2}(\frac{4}{9} - \frac{1}{3})$ **11.** $(2\frac{1}{3} + 5\frac{1}{3}) \div 3\frac{5}{6}$ **12.** $(2\frac{5}{6} - \frac{1}{2}) \div (3\frac{1}{4} - 1\frac{1}{2})$

13. $\frac{3}{4}(\frac{1}{2} + \frac{2}{3} - \frac{5}{6})$ **14.** $(5\frac{1}{3} - 3\frac{2}{5}) \div 2\frac{9}{10}$ **15.** $(\frac{1}{4} + \frac{1}{2})^2$

16. $\dfrac{\frac{3}{4} + \frac{1}{2}}{\frac{7}{6} + \frac{4}{3}}$ **17.** $\dfrac{1\frac{3}{4} \times \frac{4}{5}}{2\frac{1}{3} - 1\frac{2}{5}}$ **18.** $\dfrac{\frac{2}{3}(\frac{1}{2} + \frac{5}{6})}{\frac{1}{4}(\frac{1}{3} + \frac{5}{9})}$

19. Express 240 as a fraction of 300.

20. Express 4 hours and 40 minutes as a fraction of 6 hours.

21. A boy spent $\frac{2}{5}$ of his money in one shop and $\frac{1}{4}$ of his money in another shop. What fraction of his money had he left?

22. The profits of a business are €24,000. It is shared between two partners, *A* and *B*. If *A* receives $\frac{3}{8}$ of the profits and *B* the remainder, how much does
    (i) *A* receive   **(ii)** *B* receive?

23. In a youth club, $\frac{3}{5}$ of the members are girls. The remaining 150 members are boys. How many members are there in the club altogether?

DECIMALS

Decimals and place value

A decimal is another way of writing a fraction. Decimals are used for parts of a number that are smaller than 1. The decimal point separates a number into its whole-number part and its fractional part.

For example, consider the numbers 256.7, 45.83, and 1.478.

hundreds	tens	units	.	tenths	hundredths	thousandths	separate parts
2	5	6	.	7			$= 200 + 50 + 6 + \frac{7}{10}$
	4	5	.	8	3		$= 40 + 5 + \frac{8}{10} + \frac{3}{100}$
		1	.	4	7	8	$= 1 + \frac{4}{10} + \frac{7}{100} + \frac{8}{1000}$

Fractions with 10, 100, 1,000 etc. on the bottom can easily be written as decimals.
For example, $\frac{7}{10} = 0.7$, $\frac{3}{100} = 0.03$, $\frac{23}{1000} = 0.023$
(These decimals can be verified on your calculator.)
Other fractions can be written as decimals by simply dividing the bottom into the top, using your calculator.
For example, $\frac{2}{5} = 0.4$, $\frac{3}{8} = 0.375$ $\frac{5}{4} = 1.25$

Exercise 5.1 ▼

Write each of the following as a decimal:

1. $\frac{2}{10}$
2. $\frac{3}{10}$
3. $\frac{1}{100}$
4. $\frac{7}{100}$
5. $\frac{4}{100}$

6. $\frac{3}{100}$
7. $\frac{9}{1000}$
8. $\frac{6}{10}$
9. $\frac{6}{100}$
10. $\frac{2}{100}$

11. $\frac{1}{1000}$
12. $\frac{7}{1000}$
13. $\frac{9}{100}$
14. $\frac{8}{10}$
15. $\frac{3}{1000}$

16. $\frac{56}{10}$
17. $\frac{23}{100}$
18. $\frac{4}{100}$
19. $\frac{2}{1000}$
20. $\frac{27}{1000}$

21. $\frac{3}{5}$
22. $\frac{1}{2}$
23. $\frac{1}{5}$
24. $\frac{1}{8}$
25. $\frac{5}{8}$

26. $\frac{7}{8}$
27. $\frac{5}{2}$
28. $\frac{3}{2}$
29. $\frac{7}{4}$
30. $\frac{7}{5}$

31. $\frac{3}{20}$
32. $\frac{12}{5}$
33. $\frac{13}{4}$
34. $\frac{13}{16}$
35. $\frac{24}{50}$

36. $2\frac{1}{5}$
37. $4\frac{1}{2}$
38. $2\frac{3}{4}$
39. $1\frac{7}{40}$
40. $1\frac{3}{16}$

Order of operations

The order of operations for decimals is the same as that for integers.
Keep BEMDAS in mind.

Example ▼

Calculate: (i) $5(2.3) + 2.1$ (ii) $3.2 - 23.52 \div 4.2$
              (iii) $8(5.6 - 2.5)$ (iv) $5(0.4 + 0.2)^2$

Solution:

(i) $5(2.3) + 2.1$
     $= 11.5 + 2.1$ (multiplication)
     $= 13.6$ (addition)

⌨ 5 × 2.3 + 2.1 =

(ii) $3.2 - 23.52 \div 4.2$
     $= 3.2 - 5.6$ (division)
     $= -2.4$ (subtraction)

⌨ 3.2 − 23.52 ÷ 4.2 =

(iii) $8(5.6 - 2.5)$
     $= 8(3.1)$ (brackets)
     $= 24.8$ (multiplication)

⌨ 8 × (5.6 − 2.5) =

(iv) $5(0.4 + 0.2)^2$
     $= 5(0.6)^2$ (brackets)
     $= 5(0.36)$ (exponents)
     $= 1.8$ (multiplication)

⌨ 5 × (0.4 + 0.2) x^2 =

Exercise 5.2 ▼

Calculate each of the following:

1. $4.6 + 3.2 + 1.7$
2. $10.3 + 4.8 - 8.9$
3. $3(4.5) + 8.4$
4. $8(2.7) - 10.5$
5. $9.62 \div 3.7$
6. $12.88 \div 4.6 + 1.2$
7. $6.3 + 0.42 \div 0.07$
8. $2.1 + 3.4(6.5)$
9. $3(8.2) + 2(5.4)$
10. $5(8.7) - 7(3.4)$
11. $8(5.6 - 2.4)$
12. $2.7(7.3 - 5.1)$
13. $(38.48 - 7.43) \div 6.9$
14. $1.2 - 3.75 - 28.35 \div 6.3$
15. $5.5 \div 0.25 + 4.5 \div 0.9$
16. $2.45(16.32 - 11.28)$
17. $6.2(3.4 - 5.2)$
18. $50.46 \div (10.1 - 1.4)$

19. $(11.23 + 7.4) \div (15.58 - 3.16)$ **20.** $1.5(4.1 + 3.1 \times 5.2)$ **21.** $4.5(0.036 \div 0.06 + 0.4)$

22. $3.1(1.84 \div 0.8 + 2.7)$ **23.** $(2.4 + 1.3)(2.4 - 1.3)$ **24.** $(2.4)^2 + (0.3)^2$

25. $(1.6)^2 - (0.8)^2$ **26.** $3(0.2)^2 + 4(0.5)^2$ **27.** $6.4(1.2 + 1.3)^2$

28. $\dfrac{2.2 + 4.4}{0.11}$ **29.** $\dfrac{3.04 + 4.76}{0.29 - 0.05}$ **30.** $\dfrac{10(7.168 + 2.832)}{8(8.762 - 5.637)}$

31. $\dfrac{1.5(15.6 \div 0.4)}{1.3(6.25 \times 2.4)}$ **32.** $\dfrac{5(3.584 + 1.416)}{4(9.278 - 6.153)}$ **33.** $\dfrac{(2.7 - 0.3)(2.7 + 0.3)}{(1.2)^2}$.

34. $\sqrt{7.84}$ **35.** $\sqrt{2(14.3) + 5.04}$ **36.** $\sqrt{22.4 \div 3.5 + 2.01}$

37. $\dfrac{\sqrt{7.29} + \sqrt{1.44}}{\sqrt{1.69}}$ **38.** $\dfrac{\sqrt{17.64} + (0.8)^2}{2(4.84)}$ **39.** $\dfrac{3(5.6) + 1.6}{\sqrt{37.21} + \sqrt{3.61}}$

40. $\sqrt{\dfrac{9}{16}}$ **41.** $\sqrt{\dfrac{4}{25}}$ **42.** $\sqrt{\dfrac{9}{25}} \times \sqrt{\dfrac{25}{16}}$

43. $\dfrac{2}{\sqrt{0.25}}$ **44.** $\dfrac{13}{\sqrt{6.25}}$ **45.** $\dfrac{1}{(0.4)^2}$

46. **(i)** $\sqrt{0.25}$ **(ii)** $\dfrac{1}{\sqrt{0.25}}$ **(iii)** $\sqrt{\dfrac{1}{0.25} + 1.76}$

Decimal places

The number of digits after the decimal point, including zeros, is the number of decimal places. Decimal numbers can be rounded off to a given number of decimal places with the following steps:

1. Count the digits after the decimal point to the required number of decimal places.
2. Look at the next digit to the right.
   (i) If it is 5 or more, increase the previous digit by 1.
   (ii) If it is less than 5, leave the previous digit as it is.
3. Remove all the digits to the right.

Write the numbers   **(i)** 24.3847   **(ii)** 0.7802   correct to:

(a) one decimal place   **(b)** two decimal places   **(c)** three decimal places.

Solution:

(i) 24.3 8 4 7
①②③④

(ii) 0.7 8 0 2
①②③④

(a) 24.4   (1 d.p.)
(b) 24.38   (2 d.p.)
(c) 24.385   (3 d.p.)

(a) 0.8   (1 d.p.)
(b) 0.78   (2 d.p.)
(c) 0.780   (3 d.p.)

Note: In **(ii) (c)**, the zero is included to show that the number is correct to three decimal places.

Exercise 5.3 ▼

Round off each of the following numbers to **(i)** one decimal place **(ii)** two decimal places **(iii)** three decimal places:

1. 5.3742	**2.** 3.3787	**3.** 0.9834	**4.** 0.0768
5. 7.4367	**6.** 0.0813	**7.** 23.8016	**8.** 6.4874
9. 27.5076932	**10.** 0.677	**11.** 6.7148	**12.** 29.3042
13. 10.1702	**14.** 8.41	**15.** 2.0068	**16.** 3.996

Write each of the following numbers correct to the nearest whole number:

17. 17.53	**18.** 11.43	**19.** 124.801	**20.** 12.72
21. 13.47	**22.** 9.04	**23.** 4.493	**24.** 204.32

25. Write the number 4,784.74 correct to the:
(i) nearest whole number **(ii)** nearest 10 **(iii)** nearest 100 **(iv)** nearest 1,000.

Estimation and approximation

Being able to estimate the answer to a problem before using your calculator to make an exact calculation is an important skill. The estimate of the answer will show whether an error has been made, which could easily happen if you press a wrong key on your calculator.

By rounding each of the numbers to its nearest whole number, calculate an approximate answer for:

$$\frac{48.27 + 12.146}{14.82 - 3.02}$$

Find the exact answer using your calculator.

Solution:

If you write each number correct to the nearest whole number, the problem now reduces to:

$$\frac{48 + 12}{15 - 3} = \frac{60}{12} = 5$$

Therefore, 5 is an approximate answer.

$$\frac{48.27 + 12.146}{14.82 - 3.02} = \frac{60.416}{11.8} = 5.12$$

Therefore, the exact answer is 5.12 (very close to our estimate).

Exercise 5.4 ▼

In each of the following questions, round off each number to its nearest whole number and calculate an approximate answer. Then, using your calculator or otherwise, find the exact answer:

1. $4.81 + 7.25$
2. $8.73 - 5.82$
3. 3.8×5.3
4. $48.36 \div 7.8$
5. $4.15(11.1 - 4.3)$
6. $2.9 \times 4.1 + 3.04$
7. $19.89 \div 5.2 + 2.17$
8. $3.04 + 39.78 \div 3.9$
9. $4.9 \times 3.1 + 8.316 \div 1.98$

10. $\dfrac{15.332 + 8.94}{9.1 - 3.18}$

11. $\dfrac{27.9996 - 7.84}{6.86 + 3.12}$

12. $\dfrac{2.9 \times 11.4 + 2.196}{21.018 \div 3.1}$

13. $\dfrac{3.95 \times 8.42 + 3.953}{1.8 \times 4.3 + 1.2}$

14. $\dfrac{3.1 \times 5.9 - 0.8 \times 3.4405}{1.8 \times 2.4 - 1.2}$

15. $\dfrac{30.317}{\sqrt{24.7009}}$

Writing decimals as fractions

To write a decimal as a fraction, do the following:

1. Write the decimal number over 1.
2. Multiply the top and bottom by 10, 100, 1,000 etc. until the top is a whole number.
3. Simplify this fraction (if possible).

Example ▼

Write: (i) 0.8 (ii) 0.55 (iii) 1.125 as fraction in their lowest terms.

Solution:

(i) 0.8

$$= \frac{0.8}{1}$$

$$= \frac{8}{10}$$

$$= \frac{4}{5}$$

$$\left(\boxed{\text{▦}} \; 8 \; \boxed{a\frac{b}{c}} \; 10 \; \boxed{=} \right)$$

(ii) 0.55

$$= \frac{0.55}{1}$$

$$= \frac{55}{100}$$

$$= \frac{11}{20}$$

$$\left(\boxed{\text{▦}} \; 55 \; \boxed{a\frac{b}{c}} \; 100 \; \boxed{=} \right)$$

(iii) 1.125

$$= \frac{1.125}{1}$$

$$= \frac{1,125}{1,000}$$

$$= \frac{9}{8}$$

$$\left(\boxed{\text{▦}} \; 1125 \; \boxed{a\frac{b}{c}} \; 1000 \; \boxed{=} \right)$$

Exercise 5.5 ▼

Express each of the following decimals as a fraction in its lowest terms:

1. 0.4	**2.** 0.7	**3.** 0.6	**4.** 0.2	**5.** 0.9
6. 0.25	**7.** 0.75	**8.** 0.15	**9.** 0.35	**10.** 0.55
11. 0.125	**12.** 0.375	**13.** 1.1	**14.** 2.3	**15.** 3.8
16. 0.05	**17.** 2.45	**18.** 3.24	**19.** 2.80	**20.** 0.0625
21. 1.16	**22.** 3.625	**23.** 2.44	**24.** 1.08	**25.** 2.05

Chapter test

Calculate each of the following:

1. $3.45 + 5.28 + 1.27$ **2.** $8.24 - 5.73$ **3.** $3 \times 2.6 + 1.3$

4. $5.4 \div 0.9$ **5.** $13.8 \div 0.03$ **6.** $8.28 \div 1.15$

7. $8(5.6 - 2.4)$ **8.** $2.2(3.4 - 1.9)^2$ **9.** $3.5(8.29 - 5.09)^2$

10. $\sqrt{5.4 \times 3.2 + 2.08}$ **11.** $(1.2)^2 - (0.8)^2$ **12.** $(1.01)^2 - (0.99)^2$

13. $\sqrt{\dfrac{81}{100}}$ **14.** $\dfrac{3.4 + 4.76}{0.29 - 0.05}$ **15.** $\dfrac{2.2(8.168 + 2.832)}{2.42 \times 4}$

16. $\dfrac{\sqrt{7.84} + 1.5 \times 3.2}{0.95(5.2 - 1.2)}$ **17.** $\dfrac{\sqrt{33.64} + 23.32}{\sqrt{11.56} + 0.5 \times 3.6}$ **18.** $\dfrac{28.8 \div 2.4 + 9.75}{\sqrt{1.44} + 3.5 \times 1.8}$

19. **(i)** $\dfrac{1}{(0.2)^2}$ **(ii)** $\dfrac{1}{(0.2)^2} - 4.75$ **(iii)** $\sqrt{\dfrac{1}{(0.2)^2} - 4.75}$

20. **(i)** $(0.6)^2$ **(ii)** $1 - (0.6)^2$ **(iii)** $\dfrac{4}{1 - (0.6)^2}$ **(iv)** $\sqrt{\dfrac{4}{1 - (0.6)^2}}$

21. **(i)** $\dfrac{1}{(0.25)^2}$ **(ii)** $\dfrac{1}{(0.125)^2}$ **(iii)** $\sqrt{\dfrac{1}{(0.25)^2}} + \sqrt{\dfrac{1}{(0.125)^2}}$

22. $a = \sqrt{\dfrac{9.555}{2.1} + (4.3)^2}$, $b = \sqrt{(2.5)^2 - (0.7)^2}$

Calculate: **(i)** a **(ii)** b **(iii)** $a \div b$ **(iv)** $\sqrt{a^2 + b^2 + 0.36}$

In each of the following questions, round off each number to its nearest whole number and calculate an approximate answer. Then, using your calculator or otherwise, find the exact answer:

23. $\dfrac{7.8 \times 4.32 - 13.671}{1.1 \times 4.01 - 2.161}$ **24.** $\dfrac{13.6 \times 3.1 + 5.732}{14.72 \div 4.6 + 2.94}$

25. $\dfrac{3.1 \times 10.4 + 2.977}{18.24 \div 5.7 + 2.1 \times 3.8}$ **26.** $\dfrac{\sqrt{35.7604} + 4.2 \times 5.8 - 2.12}{\sqrt{8.9401} + 1.16}$

Express each of the following decimals as a fraction in its lowest terms:

27. 0.5 **28.** 0.1 **29.** 0.3 **30.** 1.5 **31.** 1.2

32. 1.8 **33.** 2.25 **34.** 3.2 **35.** 3.45 **36.** 1.875

Calculate each of the following to two decimal places:

37. $\sqrt{142}$ **38.** $(14.92)^2$ **39.** $\sqrt{33.49} + (2.29)^3$

40. $(4.37)^2 \times \dfrac{1}{2.05} + \sqrt{50.9}$ **41.** $\sqrt{78.24} \div (3.2)^2$

CHAPTER 6

ALGEBRA 1

Basic algebra

When we perform mathematical operations with letters instead of numbers, we call it algebra. In many ways algebra is just arithmetic with letters, and the signs $+$, $-$, $\times$ and $\div$ are used with the same meanings as in arithmetic. The basic laws of arithmetic are also true in algebra.

Shorthand used in algebra

a	means	$1 \times a$ or $1a$ or a^1
$-a$	means	$-1 \times a$ or $-1a$ or $-a^1$
$4a$	means	$4 \times a$ or $(a + a + a + a)$
$\dfrac{a}{2}$	means	$a \div 2$ or $\frac{1}{2}a$
ab	means	$a \times b$
abc	means	$a \times b \times c$
$3ab$	means	$3 \times a \times b$ or $(ab + ab + ab)$
a^2	means	$a \times a$
a^3	means	$a \times a \times a$
$5a^2$	means	$5 \times a \times a$ or $(a^2 + a^2 + a^2 + a^2 + a^2)$
$(3a)^2$	means	$3a \times 3a$ or $3 \times a \times 3 \times a$ or $3 \times 3 \times a \times a$
$4a^2b^3$	means	$4 \times a \times a \times b \times b \times b$ or $(a^2b^3 + a^2b^3 + a^2b^3 + a^2b^3)$

Words used in algebra

Variable:	When letters are used to stand for different numbers they are called '**variables**' or '**unknowns**'.
Constant:	Anything that has a fixed value (can't be changed) is called a '**constant**'. 5, -3 and $\frac{1}{2}$ are constants, because their values do not change.
Term:	A '**term**' is a single unit containing one or more variables, often with a constant in front or a constant on its own. $5x$, $3ab$, $4x^2y$, $-pq$, 7 and $\dfrac{a}{b}$ are examples of terms.
Coefficient:	The number in front of a term is called the '**coefficient**' of the term. In the term $5x$, 5 is the coefficient of x. In the term $-4pq$, -4 is the coefficient of pq. In the term $-y$, -1 is the coefficient of y (as $-y = -1y$).

Expression:	A collection of terms separated by plus signs or minus signs is called an '**expression**'.
	$3x^2 - 5x + 2$ is an expression with three terms.
	$2p^2 - 7pq$ is an expression with two terms.
Like terms:	Terms that use the same letter, or arrangement of letters, are called '**like terms**'. The only difference is the coefficient (number in front) of the term.
	$3x$, $2x$ and $-x$ are like terms.
	$5ab$, $4ab$ and $-ab$ are like terms.
	$8x^2y$, $3x^2y$ and $-x^2y$ are like terms.
	(The powers of each letter must be the same.)
Note:	The letters in a term are usually written in alphabetical order.
	For example, we would write $4ab$ rather than $4ba$.
	However, the order of the letters within the term is not important.

Terms that are not the same are called 'unlike terms'.
For example, $3a$ and $5b$ are unlike terms.

Addition and subtraction

The golden rule in algebra

Only terms that are the same can be added or subtracted

In other words, 'only like terms can be added or subtracted.'

Adding and subtracting like terms is often called 'collecting like terms' or 'simplifying the expression.'

Example ▼

Simplify each of the following:

(i) $8x + 5x + x$

(ii) $10a - 11a + 4a - a$

(iii) $8x + 5y + 3x - 9y$

(iv) $3xy + 8xy - 7xy$

(v) $8pq - 13qp$

(vi) $8x + 3y - 7 + 2y - 5x + 10$

(vii) $2x^3 - 8x^2 + 6x - x^2 + 5x - 3$

Solution:

(i) $\quad 8x + 5x + x$

$\quad = 8x + 5x + 1x \qquad$ (rewrite x as $1x$)

$\quad = 14x \qquad\qquad\qquad$ (simplify)

(ii) $10a - 11a + 4a - a$

$= 10a + 4a - 11a - 1a$ (group + and − terms together)

$= 14a - 12a$ (simplify + and − terms)

$= 2a$ (simplify)

(iii) $8x + 5y + 3x - 9y$

$= 8x + 3x + 5y - 9y$ (group like terms together)

$= 11x - 4y$ (simplify like terms)

($11x - 4y$ cannot be simplified further, as $11x$ and $-4y$ are different terms.)

(iv) $3xy + 8xy - 7yx$

$= 3xy + 8xy - 7xy$ (rewrite in alphabetical order)

$= 11xy - 7xy$ (simplify + terms)

$= 4xy$ (simplify)

(v) $8pq - 13qp$

$= 8pq - 13pq$ (rewrite in alphabetical order)

$= -5pq$ (simplify)

(vi) $8x + 3y - 7 + 2y - 5x + 10$

$= 8x - 5x + 3y + 2y - 7 + 10$ (group like terms together)

$= 3x + 5y + 3$ (simplify like terms)

(vii) $2x^3 - 8x^2 + 6x - x^2 + 5x - 3$

$= 2x^3 - 8x^2 - x^2 + 6x + 5x - 3$ (group like terms together)

$= 2x^3 - 8x^2 - 1x^2 + 6x + 5x - 3$ (write $-x^2$ as $-1x^2$)

$= 2x^3 - 9x^2 + 11x - 3$ (simplify like terms)

Exercise 6.1 ▼

Simplify each of the following (positive terms only):

1. $a + a + a + a$
2. $x + x + x + x + x$
3. $5x + 3x$
4. $6a + 2a + a$
5. $m + 2m + 3m$
6. $5p + p + 4p$
7. $2ab + 5ab$
8. $3pq + 2pq + pq$
9. $x^2 + x^2 + x^2$
10. $3x^2 + 2x^2 + x^2$
11. $8x + 3x + 5 + 2$
12. $5a + 4a + 2 + 4$
13. $5y + 4y + 1 + 7$
14. $3a + 5 + 6a + 2$
15. $3x + 5 + 3x + 4 + x + 1$
16. $7x + 10 + 2x + 5 + x + 3$
17. $4x + 8 + 5x + 5 + 2x + 2$
18. $5x + 15 + 3x + 3 + x + 4$
19. $2x^2 + 3x + 4 + 3x^2 + 4x + 2$
20. $5x^2 + 5x + 10 + 2x^2 + 4x + 8$
21. $x^3 + 3x^2 + 5x + 3x^2 + 6x + 3$
22. $2x^3 + 6x^2 + 8x + x^2 + 3x + 4$
23. $3x^2 + 12x^2 + 3x + 2x^2 + 8x + 2$
24. $6x^3 + 9x^2 + 12x + 4x^2 + 6x + 8$
25. $5x + 2x + 3y + y$
26. $3x + x + 6y + y$
27. $3x + 2y + 5 + x + y + 2$
28. $5x + 2y + 4 + x + 3y + 5$

These problems include positive and negative terms:

29.	$8x - 5x$	**30.**	$4a - 3a$
31.	$3x - 5x$	**32.**	$2y - 6y$
33.	$8a + 3a - 4a - 2a$	**34.**	$5x - 3x + 4x - x$
35.	$-10x + 11x - 3x + 5x$	**36.**	$8x - 3x - 2x - 4x$
37.	$10x + 15 - 3x - 9$	**38.**	$8x - 3x + 6 - 2$
39.	$7x - 3x + 8 - 10$	**40.**	$6x - 2x + 26 - 11$
41.	$7x - 2x + 4 - 3x - 7$	**42.**	$8x - 8 - 2x - 4 - 3x + 11$
43.	$2 + 5x - 15 + 12 - 7x + 4$	**44.**	$3x + 27 - 6 - 4x - 17$
45.	$x^2 + 3x - x - 6$	**46.**	$2x^2 - 8x + 3x - 12$
47.	$5x^2 - 10x + 3x - 6$	**48.**	$4x^2 - 16x - 10x + 5$
49.	$x^3 + 3x^2 + 2x - x^2 - 3x - 2$	**50.**	$x^3 - 6x^2 + 8x + 2x^2 - 6x + 8$
51.	$2x^3 - 8x^2 - 2x + 3x^2 - 12x - 3$	**52.**	$6x^3 - 9x^2 + 12x - 4x^2 + 6x - 8$
53.	$2 - 8x - 4x^2 - 3x + 12x^2 - 6x^3$	**54.**	$1 - 2x - x^2 - 4x + 6x^2 - 4x^3$
55.	$8x + 9y + 10 - 6x + 2y - 7$	**56.**	$x - 2y + 10 + 3x - 5y - 11$
57.	$3xy + 4xy - 5xy - xy$	**58.**	$6ab + 12bc - 2ba - 9cb$
59.	$4abc + 3bac + 2cab$	**60.**	$16xy + 5x - 4xy + 2x - 7xy$
61.	$8p^2 + 4pq - 5p^2 - 2pq$	**62.**	$3a^2b + 5a^2b - 6a^2b$
63.	$6a^2b + 2a^2b + 8ab^2 - 5ab^2$	**64.**	$6pqr - 8pqr + 2pqr$

Removing brackets 1

To remove brackets with a number outside the bracket, do the following:

> **1.** Multiply each term inside the bracket by the number outside the bracket.
> **2.** Any term not in a bracket is brought down to the next line unchanged.
> **3.** Simplify (add and subtract terms that are the same).

No sign or number in front of a bracket means that every term is multiplied by 1 or left unchanged. If the number outside the bracket is negative, then the sign of every term inside the brackets will change. In particular, a minus sign on its own outside the bracket means that every term inside the bracket is multiplied by -1; or in practice simply change the sign of every term inside the bracket.

For example:

$$-(-2x^2 + 3x - 4) = -1(-2x^2 + 3x - 4) = 2x^2 - 3x + 4$$

(every sign is changed)

Note: Removing brackets is called '**expanding the brackets**'.

Simplify: **(i)** $3(1 - x + 2x^2) - 3(1 - x - 2x^2)$ **(ii)** $q - 4(3q - 7) - (26 - 11q) + q$

Solution:

(i) $3(1 - x + 2x^2) - 3(1 - x - 2x^2)$

$= 3(1 - x + 2x^2) - 3(1 - x - 2x^3)$
$= 3 - 3x + 6x^2 - 3 + 3x + 6x^2$
$= 12x^2$

(ii) $q - 4(3q - 7) - (26 - 11q) + q$

$= q - 4(3q - 7) - 1(26 - 11q) + q$
$= q - 12q + 28 - 26 + 11q + q$
$= 13q - 12q + 28 - 26$
$= q + 2$

Exercise 6.2 ▼

Remove the brackets in each of the following:

1. $2(x + 4)$
2. $3(2x + 5)$
3. $4(x^2 + 3x)$
4. $5(2x^2 + 3x + 4)$
5. $-2(3x + 5)$
6. $-5(-2x + 8)$
7. $-3(x - 4)$
8. $-(x - 3)$
9. $-3(-2x^2 + 3x - 2)$
10. $-4(x^2 - 3x + 4)$
11. $4(3x + 2y)$
12. $-3(2p - 3q - 4)$

Remove the brackets and then simplify each of the following:

13. $3(2x + 4) + 2(5x + 3)$
14. $3(2x + 1) + 5(x + 2) + 7$
15. $4(2x + 3) + 2(4x + 6)$
16. $4(x + 2) + 3(x + 4) + x + 10$
17. $3(2x + 4) + 7 - 3(x + 5) - 2x - 4$
18. $3(4x + 14) - 3 - 2(x + 1) - 5(7 + 2x)$
19. $11x - 3(6 - x) + 13 - 5(2x - 1)$
20. $3x - 4(2x - 7) - (26 - 6x)$
21. $7(6 - x) + 21 + 5(x - 7) - 3(8 - x)$
22. $5(2x - 5) - 3(x - 4) + 2(3 - x) + 10$
23. $3p + 2(4 - p) + 3(p - 5) - 2p + 6$
24. $-2q + 5(1 + 3q) + 3q - (14q + 3)$
25. $5(q + 4) - 3q - 29 + 3(q + 3)$
26. $3a + 4(3 - 2a) - 7 - (2 - 5a)$
27. $5(2x^2 - 3x + 2) - 3(3x^2 - 6x + 2)$
28. $2(1 - 3x - x^2) - (2 - 6x - 3x^2)$
29. $5(1 - x + 2x^2) - 5(1 - x - 2x^2) - 18x^2$
30. $4(2x^2 - 3x - 5) - 4(2x^2 - 3x - 6)$
31. $2(x + y) + 3(2x + 3y)$
32. $3(3x - 2y + 4) - (4x - 3y + 6)$
33. $5(2x - y) - 4(x - 3) + 3(y - 5)$
34. $-2(y + 4) + 3x + 2(3 + 2y) - (3x - 2)$
35. $4x - [4x - 2(2x - 2)]$
36. $3x - [6x - (3x + 3)] - 2$

Index notation

Powers:

Terms	Written	Pronounced
$a \cdot a$	a^2	'a squared' or 'a to the power of 2'
$a \cdot a \cdot a$	a^3	'a cubed' or 'a to the power of 3'
$a \cdot a \cdot a \cdot a$	a^4	'a to the power of 4'
$a \cdot a \cdot a \cdot a \cdot a$	a^5	'a to the power of 5' etc.

In the terms a^2, a^3, a^4 and a^5, the small numbers 2, 3, 4 and 5 are called '**indices**'. a is called the base.

For example, consider the term a^6: 6 is called the index of the power of a.

Note: $a = a^1$, but we usually leave out the 1.

Multiplication of powers:

$$a^4 \cdot a^3 = (a \cdot a \cdot a \cdot a) \cdot (a \cdot a \cdot a)$$
$$= a \cdot a \cdot a \cdot a \cdot a \cdot a \cdot a$$
$$= a^7$$
$$\text{i.e. } a^4 \cdot a^3 = a^{4+3} = a^7$$

$$x \cdot x^3 = (x) \cdot (x \cdot x \cdot x)$$
$$= x \cdot x \cdot x \cdot x$$
$$= x^4$$
$$\text{i.e. } x \cdot x^3 = x^1 \cdot x^3 = x^1 \cdot x^3 = x^{1+3} = x^4$$

Rule:

> When multiplying powers of the same numbers,
> **add** the indices.
> In general: $a^m \cdot a^n = a^{m+n}$

Note: The rule does not apply to different numbers or variables.

Multiplying terms

> The order to follow when multiplying terms in algebra is:
> **1.** sign   **2.** numbers   **3.** letters (separately)

When you are multiplying, it is good practice to group the numbers and the **same** letters together, putting the letters in alphabetical order.

Simplify each of the following:

(i) $(3x)(5x)$ **(ii)** $-3a(2a)$ **(iii)** $4x^2 \cdot x$

(iv) $(-4x^2y)(5xy)$ **(v)** $3pq(-7p^2qr)$

(i) $(3x)(5x)$
$$= 3 \cdot 5 \cdot x^1 \cdot x^1$$
$$= 15x^2$$

(ii) $-3a(2a)$
$$= -3 \cdot 2 \cdot a \cdot a$$
$$= -6a^2$$

(iii) $4x^2 \cdot x$
$$= 4 \cdot x \cdot x \cdot x$$
$$= 4x^3$$

(iv) $(-4x^2y)(5xy)$
$$= -4 \cdot 5 \cdot x^2 \cdot x \cdot y \cdot y$$
$$= -20x^3y^2$$
$$(x^2 \cdot x = x^3 \quad \text{and} \quad y \cdot y = x^2)$$

(v) $3pq(-7p^2qr)$
$$= 3 \cdot -7 \cdot p \cdot p^2 \cdot q \cdot q \cdot r$$
$$= -21p^3q^2r$$
$$(p \cdot p^2 = p^3 \quad \text{and} \quad q \cdot q = q^2)$$

Exercise 6.3 ▼

Simplify each of the following:

1. $2x \cdot 5x$ **2.** $(4x)(3x)$ **3.** $7x(x)$

4. $x \cdot x^2$ **5.** $5x \cdot 3x^2$ **6.** $3a^2 \cdot 2a$

7. $4x^2(2x)$ **8.** $7x \cdot 3x^2$ **9.** $(10a^2)(-2a)$

10. $(5a^2)(-3a)$ **11.** $2x \cdot 3x \cdot 5x$ **12.** $2x \cdot 4x \cdot x$

13. $2p \cdot 2p \cdot 2p$ **14.** $x \cdot 2x \cdot 5x$ **15.** $5x(-4x^2)$

16. $(-x)(-x)$ **17.** $(-3x)(4x)(-5x)$ **18.** $(3a)(-2a)(-5a)$

19. $4ab(3a^2b^2)$ **20.** $5(2x)(3x)$ **21.** $(-2pq)(-5pq)$

22. $(3xy)(xy)$ **23.** $-3x^2 \cdot 2xy^2 \cdot -5y$ **24.** $-x \cdot -x \cdot -x$

25. $p \cdot 3p \cdot -3p^2$ **26.** $(2x)(3xy)(4y)$ **27.** $(5x^2)(-3xy)(2y^2)$

28. $(8xy)(xy)(4x)$ **29.** $(2xy)(x)(3y)$ **30.** $(-4x^2y)(-5xy^2)$

31. If $6x(4x^2) = kx^3$, find the value of k.

Removing brackets 2

To remove brackets with a term outside the bracket, do the following:

1. Multiply each term inside the bracket by the term outside the bracket.
2. Any term not in a bracket is brought down to the next line unchanged.
3. Simplify (add and subtract terms that are the same).

Simplify: **(i)** $2x(3x^2 - 6x + 2) - 3(2x^2 - 8x - 4)$ **(ii)** $5x(x + y) + 2xy - 3y(x - 2y)$

Solution:

(i)
$$2x(3x^2 - 6x + 2) - 3(2x^2 - 8x - 4)$$
$$= 6x^3 - 12x^2 + 4x - 6x^2 + 24x + 12$$
$$= 6x^3 - 12x^2 - 6x^2 + 4x + 24x + 12$$
$$= 6x^3 - 18x^2 + 28x + 12$$

(ii)
$$5x(x + y) + 2xy - 3y(x - 2y)$$
$$= 5x^2 + 5xy + 2xy - 3xy + 6y^2$$
$$= 5x^2 + 7xy - 3xy + 6y^2$$
$$= 5x^2 + 4xy + 6y^2$$

Exercise 6.4 ▼

Remove the brackets and then simplify each of the following:

1. $x(x + 2) + 3(x + 2)$
2. $x(x + 3) + 3(x + 3)$
3. $2x(x + 5) + 3(x + 5)$
4. $3x(x + 2) + 5(x + 2)$
5. $x(x + 4) - 2(x + 4)$
6. $2x(x - 1) - 3(x - 1)$
7. $3x(x - 5) - 4(x - 5)$
8. $5x(2x - 3) - 4(2x - 3)$
9. $2x(2x + 3) + 3(2x + 3)$
10. $3x(3x - 2) + 2(3x - 2)$
11. $x(x^2 + 3x + 4) + 2(x^2 + 3x + 4)$
12. $2x(x^2 + 5x + 3) + 3(x^2 + 5x + 3)$
13. $x(x^2 - 2x + 1) - 3(x^2 - 2x + 1)$
14. $3x(2x^2 - 3x - 5) - 2(2x^2 - 3x - 5)$
15. $4x(2x^2 - 3x + 6) + 6(2x^2 - 4x)$
16. $5x^2(x + 4) - 2x(x^2 + 3) - 3(x^3 + 5x^2 - 2x)$
17. $3a(2a + 3) - 2a(3a + 5) + a$
18. $a(a + 1) + 2a(a - 3) + 6a - 3a^2$
19. $2x(x + y) + 3y(x + y)$
20. $3x(2x + y) + 2y(2x + y)$
21. $5x(2x - y) - 2y(2x - y)$
22. $x(x - y) + y^2 + y(x - y)$
23. $2x(x - 4y) - 2x^2 - 5y^2 + 8y(x + y)$
24. $3x(2x + 4y) + 6y^2 - 6y(x + y)$
25. $2(a^2 + 3a) - a(2a + 5) + a$
26. $3a(2a + 1) - 7a - 2(4 + 2a^2) + 4(2 + a)$
27. $a(b + c) - b(c - a) - c(a - b)$
28. $2a(b + c) - 2b(c + a) - 2c(a - b)$
29. $a(a - b) + b(a - b) + b^2$
30. $2[a(a + b) + b(b - a)]$

Multiplying expressions

To multiply two expressions, do the following:

1. Multiply each term separately in the second expression by each term in the first expression.
2. Simplify (add and subtract terms that are the same).

Note: Multiplication is often indicated by brackets.

(i) Remove the brackets and simplify: $(x - 3)(x + 5)$

(ii) Multiply $2x^2 - 3x + 4$ by $x - 3$

Solution:

(i) $(x - 3)(x + 5)$

$= x(x + 5) - 3(x + 5)$

$= x^2 + 5x - 3x - 15$

$= x^2 + 2x - 15$

(ii) $(x - 3)(2x^2 - 3x + 4)$

$= x(2x^2 - 3x + 4) - 3(2x^2 - 3x + 4)$

$= 2x^3 - 3x^2 + 4x - 6x^2 + 9x - 12$

$= 2x^3 - 3x^2 - 6x^2 + 4x + 9x - 12$

$= 2x^3 - 9x^2 + 13x - 12$

Note: $(x + 3)^2 = (x + 3)(x + 3) = x(x + 3) + 3(x + 3) = x^2 + 3x + 3x + 9 = x^2 + 6x + 9$

Exercise 6.5 ▼

Remove the brackets and simplify each of the following:

1. $(x + 1)(x + 2)$ **2.** $(x + 3)(x + 4)$ **3.** $(x + 5)(x + 6)$

4. $(x + 2)(x + 7)$ **5.** $(x + 4)(x + 8)$ **6.** $(2x + 3)(x + 4)$

7. $(3x + 2)(5x + 1)$ **8.** $(4x - 3)(2x - 1)$ **9.** $(2x + 5)(x - 3)$

10. $(3x - 1)(2x + 3)$ **11.** $(2x - 1)(x - 4)$ **12.** $(4x + 3)(3x - 5)$

13. $(2x - 5)(x + 4)$ **14.** $(5x - 2)(2x - 1)$ **15.** $(4x + 3)(x - 4)$

16. $(x + 4)(x^2 + 2x + 3)$ **17.** $(x + 3)(2x^2 + 3x + 2)$

18. $(x + 2)(3x^2 + 2x + 4)$ **19.** $(x + 4)(2x^2 + x + 5)$

20. $(x + 1)(3x^2 + x + 1)$ **21.** $(x + 5)(2x^2 + 5x + 3)$

22. $(2x + 3)(x^2 + 2x + 3)$ **23.** $(3x + 1)(2x^2 + x + 4)$

24. $(x - 3)(x^2 - 3x + 2)$ **25.** $(x - 2)(2x^2 - 3x - 4)$

26. $(2x - 1)(x^2 - 2x - 5)$ **27.** $(3x - 2)(2x^2 - x + 3)$

28. $(2x - 5)(2x^2 + 2x - 3)$ **29.** $(1 - 2x)(2 - 2x - x^2)$

30. $(x + 2)^2$ **31.** $(2x + 3)^2$

32. $(2x - 5)^2$ **33.** $(3x - 1)^2$

34. $(x + 3)(x + 2) + (x - 4)(1 - x) + 5(1 - 2x)$ **35.** $(x + 1)(x^2 - x + 1) + (1 - x)(x^2 + x + 1)$

36. $(x + 1)(x + 2)(x + 3)$

Addition and subtraction of algebraic fractions

Algebraic fractions that have numbers as denominators can be added or subtracted in exactly the same way as in arithmetic, i.e. we express the fractions with the lowest common denominator.

Algebraic fractions are added or subtracted with the following steps:

1. Put brackets on the top of each fraction.
2. Find the LCD of the numbers on the bottom.
3. Proceed in exactly the same way as in arithmetic.
4. Simplify the top (add and subtract terms that are the same).

Example ▼

Express as a single fraction:

(i) $\dfrac{x+2}{3} + \dfrac{x+5}{4}$

(ii) $\dfrac{3x-4}{5} - \dfrac{2x-3}{4} - \dfrac{1}{2}$

Solution:

(i)

$$\dfrac{x+2}{3} + \dfrac{x+5}{4}$$

$$= \dfrac{(x+2)}{3} + \dfrac{(x+5)}{4} \qquad \text{(put brackets on top)}$$
(the LCD is 12)

$$= \dfrac{4(x+2) + 3(x+5)}{12} \qquad \text{(do the same as in arithmetic)}$$

$$= \dfrac{4x+8+3x+15}{12} \qquad \text{(remove the brackets on top)}$$

$$= \dfrac{7x+23}{12} \qquad \text{(simplify the top)}$$

(ii)

$$\dfrac{3x-4}{5} - \dfrac{2x-3}{4} - \dfrac{1}{2}$$

$$= \dfrac{(3x-4)}{5} - \dfrac{(2x-3)}{4} - \dfrac{(1)}{2} \qquad \text{(put brackets on top)}$$
(the LCD is 20)

$$= \dfrac{4(3x-4) - 5(2x-3) - 10(1)}{20} \qquad \text{(do the same as in arithmetic)}$$

$$= \dfrac{12x-16-10x+15-10}{20} \qquad \text{(remove brackets on top)}$$

$$= \dfrac{2x-11}{20} \qquad \text{(simplify the top)}$$

Express each of the following as a single fraction:

1. $\dfrac{7}{2} + \dfrac{4}{3}$

2. $\dfrac{3}{4} + \dfrac{5}{3}$

3. $\dfrac{1}{5} + \dfrac{3}{4}$

4. $\dfrac{5}{3} + \dfrac{1}{6} - \dfrac{7}{9}$

5. $\dfrac{5}{8} - \dfrac{3}{4} + \dfrac{1}{2}$

6. $\dfrac{7}{5} - \dfrac{9}{10} + \dfrac{11}{15}$

7. $\dfrac{x}{2} + \dfrac{x}{3}$

8. $\dfrac{x}{4} + \dfrac{x}{3}$

9. $\dfrac{x}{5} + \dfrac{x}{4}$

10. $\dfrac{2x}{3} + \dfrac{x}{6} - \dfrac{4x}{9}$

11. $\dfrac{3x}{8} + \dfrac{x}{2} - \dfrac{3x}{4}$

12. $\dfrac{x}{2} + \dfrac{3x}{4} - \dfrac{5x}{3}$

13. $\dfrac{x+5}{2} + \dfrac{x+1}{3}$

14. $\dfrac{x+5}{4} + \dfrac{x+4}{3}$

15. $\dfrac{x+2}{5} + \dfrac{x+7}{10}$

16. $\dfrac{x+4}{2} + \dfrac{x+5}{4}$

17. $\dfrac{2x+3}{6} + \dfrac{x+1}{4}$

18. $\dfrac{2x+3}{7} + \dfrac{x+1}{3}$

19. $\dfrac{5x-1}{4} + \dfrac{2x-3}{5}$

20. $\dfrac{2x-3}{4} + \dfrac{3x+6}{2}$

21. $\dfrac{5x-3}{2} - \dfrac{3x-4}{3}$

22. $\dfrac{5x+1}{6} - \dfrac{2x-3}{4}$

23. $\dfrac{2x-1}{3} - \dfrac{x+4}{5}$

24. $\dfrac{2x+5}{3} - \dfrac{4x-3}{2}$

25. $\dfrac{x+2}{3} + \dfrac{x+5}{2} + \dfrac{3}{4}$

26. $\dfrac{3x+2}{8} - \dfrac{x}{4} + \dfrac{x+1}{2}$

27. $\dfrac{5x-1}{4} + \dfrac{x}{3} - \dfrac{5}{6}$

28. $\dfrac{2x-4}{7} + \dfrac{2x}{21} - \dfrac{x-4}{3}$

29. $\dfrac{3x-5}{2} + \dfrac{2x+3}{6} - \dfrac{2x-1}{3}$

30. $\dfrac{5x}{3} - \dfrac{1}{6} + \dfrac{2-3x}{2}$

31. Show that $\dfrac{3x+5}{6} - \dfrac{2x+3}{4} = \dfrac{1}{12}$

32. Show that $\dfrac{4x+3}{6} - \dfrac{6x+4}{9} = \dfrac{1}{18}$

Dividing terms

Dividing terms in algebra is similar to dividing numbers in arithmetic.

When dividing one term by another, do the following:

> Divide top and bottom by common factors.

Note: This is a very important technique needed when finding factors.

Example ▼

Simplify: **(i)** $\dfrac{10ab}{2b}$ **(ii)** $\dfrac{12x^2y}{3x}$

Solution:

(i) $\dfrac{10ab}{2b}$

$= \dfrac{\overset{5}{\cancel{10}}a\overset{1}{\cancel{b}}}{\underset{1}{\cancel{2}}\underset{1}{\cancel{b}}} = 5a$ (divide top and bottom by $2b$)

(ii) $\dfrac{12x^2y}{3x}$

$= \dfrac{12xxy}{3x}$

$= \dfrac{\overset{4}{\cancel{12}}\overset{1}{\cancel{x}}xy}{\underset{1}{\cancel{3}}\underset{1}{\cancel{x}}} = 4xy$ (divide top and bottom by $3x$)

Exercise 6.7 ▼

Simplify each of the following:

1. $\dfrac{20ab}{5b}$ **2.** $\dfrac{10xy}{2y}$ **3.** $\dfrac{21pq}{7q}$ **4.** $\dfrac{12ab}{6a}$ **5.** $\dfrac{16a}{8}$

6. $\dfrac{28p}{7}$ **7.** $\dfrac{15x}{5}$ **8.** $\dfrac{6pq}{3pq}$ **9.** $\dfrac{x^2}{x}$ **10.** $\dfrac{x^2y}{xy}$

11. $\dfrac{a^2}{a^2}$ **12.** $\dfrac{3pq}{3pq}$ **13.** $\dfrac{5ab}{5ab}$ **14.** $\dfrac{22a^2}{11a}$ **15.** $\dfrac{6x^2y}{3xy}$

16. $\dfrac{18a^3b}{6a^2b}$ **17.** $\dfrac{24ab^2}{8ab}$ **18.** $\dfrac{30p^2q}{15p^2}$ **19.** $\dfrac{12a^2b^2}{6b^2}$ **20.** $\dfrac{25xy^2z}{5y^2z}$

Evaluating expressions (substitution)

A **substitute** is used to replace something. In football, a substitute replaces another player. In algebra when we replace letters with numbers when evaluating expressions we call it **substitution**. When you are substituting numbers in an expression, it is good practice to put a bracket around the number that replaces the letter. (Remember: **BEMDAS**.)

Example ▼

(i)   Evaluate: $3(x + y) + 2(a + 3b) + (y - x)^2$ when $a = 1$, $b = 2$, $x = 3$ and $y = 5$.

(ii) When $p = -2$ and $q = 3$, find the value of $\dfrac{p^2 + 4q}{2(q + 1)}$.

Solution:

(i)
$$3(x + y) + 2(a + 3b) + (y - x)^2$$
$$= 3(3 + 5) + 2[1 + 3(2)] + (5 - 3)^2$$
$$= 3(8) + 2(1 + 6) + (2)^2$$
$$= 3(8) + 2(7) + 4$$
$$= 24 + 14 + 4$$
$$= 42$$

(ii)

Top	Bottom
$= p^2 + 4q$	$= 2(q + 1)$
$= (-2)^2 + 4(3)$	$= 2(3 + 1)$
$= 4 + 12$	$= 2(4)$
$= 16$	$= 8$

Thus, $\dfrac{\text{top}}{\text{bottom}} = \dfrac{16}{8} = 2$

Exercise 6.8 ▼

When $a = 1$, $b = 2$, $c = 3$, $x = 4$, $y = 5$, and $z = 6$, find the value of:

1. $a + b + c$
2. $x + y + z$
3. $2a + 3b + 4c$
4. $3x + 2y + z$
5. $3x + 2$
6. abc
7. xyz
8. $2ab + 3xy$
9. $3xz + 5bx$
10. $10ax + 3by$
11. $3(a + b) + 4(x + y)$
12. $3(2b + a) + 2(3x + 2y)$
13. $x^2 + y^2$
14. $2a^2 + 3b^2 + 4c^2$
15. $(a + b)^b$
16. $\dfrac{x + z}{b + c}$
17. $\dfrac{2z + cx}{bc + 2a}$
18. $\left(\dfrac{2abc}{z}\right)^c$
19. $\dfrac{2y + 3x}{3c + b}$
20. $\dfrac{x^2 + c^2}{y^2}$
21. $\dfrac{5(y + a)}{3(a^2 + b^2)}$
22. $x^3 + x^2 + x + 4$
23. $(b + c)^b + 2(a + b)$
24. $2(b^2c + bc^2)$

When $p = 2$, $q = -1$, $r = 3$, $s = -2$, $u = 4$, and $v = -3$, find the value of:

1. $p + q$
2. $3p + 2q$
3. $5u - 3v$
4. $5r + 2p$
5. $2u - 3s + 4$
6. $p + 3q + 1$
7. $4p - 3q + 7$
8. $u^2 + s^2$
9. $-3q + 4p + 2r$
10. $2pr + 3r - q$
11. $3p(r - 5)$
12. $p^2 + 2pr + r^2$
13. pqr
14. $2pq - 3rs$
15. $3(p + r) + 2(r + u)$
16. $p^2 + q^2 + r^2$
17. $3r^2 + 2u^2$
18. $(r + p)^p$
19. $(r + s)^u$

20. $5p - 3q + 7$
21. $p^3 + u^2 + 2r$
22. $\dfrac{u + p}{r}$
23. $\dfrac{6u - 2s}{3p - q}$

24. $\dfrac{2(r + 2p)}{pu - 3pq}$
25. $\dfrac{pqs + 2pr}{2(r - p)}$
26. $\dfrac{p(2p - q)}{q^2(p^2 + 2q)}$
27. $\left(\dfrac{4pu}{p + 2r}\right)^p$

28. When $x = 2$ and $y = -1$, find the value of $\dfrac{5(x - y)}{3(x^2 + y^2)}$.

29. When $x = 9$, find the value of $x^2 - 15\sqrt{x} - 3(x + 1)$.

Chapter test

1. **(a)** When $x = 1$, $y = 2$, and $z = 3$, find the value of $\dfrac{2x + 3y + 6z + 2}{3z + y - 4x}$.
   (b) Simplify $2(3q - 5) - 2q + 3(q - 2) - (6q - 12) + 4$.
   (c) Multiply $x^2 - 5x + 4$ by $x - 4$.
2. **(a)** Multiply $2x^2 - 2x + 1$ by $x + 1$.
   (b) Simplify $3(x + 4) - 5(2x + 3) + 2(5x - 6)$ and **then** find its value when $x = 5$.
   (c) When $y = 2$, show that $10y(y + 1) - 9(y + 2) - 24 = 0$.
3. **(a)** When $p = 3$ and $q = 2$, show that $p^2 - q^2 = (p - q)(p + q)$.
   (b) Multiply $2x^2 - 3x + 4$ by $x - 3$.
   (c) Simplify $3x(2x^2 - 4x + 4) - 6(x^3 - 2x^2 + 2x - 1)$.
   (d) Write as one fraction $\dfrac{x + 3}{4} + \dfrac{x + 5}{3}$.
4. **(a)** When $a = 2$ and $b = -1$, find the value of:
   (i) $(a - b)^a$ **(ii)** $\dfrac{a(2a - b)}{b^2(a^2 + 2b)}$.
   (b) Simplify:
   (i) $3x(5 - x) + 4x(x - 4) + x$
   (ii) $5x(x + 2y - 1) - 3(x^2 + 4xy - 2) + (5x + 2xy) - 2x^2$

(c) Multiply $x^2 - 5x - 3$ by $x - 2$.

(d) Write as one fraction $\dfrac{4x-3}{5} - \dfrac{x}{2} + \dfrac{1}{10}$.

5. **(a)** When $x = -1$ and $y = 3$, find the value of $\dfrac{5x - 3y^2}{4(y - x)}$.

(b) Simplify $2(5a + 3b + 2c) - 2(8a - b + c) + 2(3a - b - c)$.

(c) Multiply $x^2 - 5x + 6$ by $x - 3$.

(d) Write as one fraction $\dfrac{3x+2}{4} - \dfrac{x+3}{2} + \dfrac{7}{8}$.

(e) x people share the cost of travelling y km in z cars.

The amount, €A, each has to pay is given by the formula $A = \dfrac{z\left(8 + \dfrac{y}{5}\right)}{x}$.

Find the value of A when $x = 17$, $y = 300$, and $z = 18$.

6. **(a)** If $x = 4$, find the value of $x^2 + 9\sqrt{x} - 16$.

(b) Multiply $3x^2 - 6x + 2$ by $2x + 5$.

(c) Simplify $2x(3x + 5y - 5) - 5y(y + 2x) + 5(2x + y^2)$.

(d) Write as one fraction $\dfrac{2x+3}{5} + \dfrac{x-1}{4} - \dfrac{3}{20}$.

(e) A car increases its speed from u km/h to v km/h in a time t hrs.

The distance, d km, that it has travelled is given by the formula $d = \dfrac{t}{4}(u + v)$.

Calculate d when $t = 12$, $u = 3$, and $v = 7$.

SIMPLE EQUATIONS

Equation

> An equation is a statement in which two **different** algebraic
> expressions are equal.

For example, $3x + 1 = x + 13$ is an equation.

Note: $x + x = 2x$ is an identity, not an equation, because the two expressions are the same.

Solution of an equation

To solve an equation means to find the value of the letter that makes both sides equal in value. The aim is to end up with 'letter' = 'number'. The number that makes both sides equal in value is called the '**solution**' or '**root**' of the equation.

Consider the equation $x + 2 = 7$.

When $x = 5$, both sides are equal to 7.
We say that 5 is the solution or root of the
equation $x + 2 = 7$.

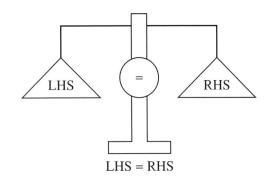

The two sides of an equation can be thought of as scales '**in balance**'. The scale will stay '**balanced**' provided we do the same thing to both sides. In the same way we do the same thing to both sides of an equation until we end up with:

> 'letter' = 'number'.

Then we say the equation is '**solved**'.

When solving an equation we can:

1. **add** or **subtract** the same quantity to both sides.
   (In practice this involves moving a term from one side to another side and changing its sign.)
2. **multiply** or **divide** both sides by the same quantity.

Remember: You must carry out the same operation on each side of the equation to keep it in 'balance'. It is good practice to check your answer by substitution.

Solve for x: $-3x = 12$

Solution:
$$-3x = 12$$
$$3x = -12 \qquad \text{(multiply both sides by } -1\text{)}$$
$$\frac{3x}{3} = \frac{-12}{3} \qquad \text{(divide both sides by 3)}$$
$$x = -4$$

Solve for x: $2x + 3 = 11$ and verify your solution

Solution:
$$2x + 3 = 11$$
$$2x + 3 - 3 = 11 - 3 \qquad \text{(subtract 3 from both sides)}$$
$$2x = 8$$
$$\frac{2x}{2} = \frac{8}{2} \qquad \text{(divide both sides by 2)}$$
$$x = 4$$

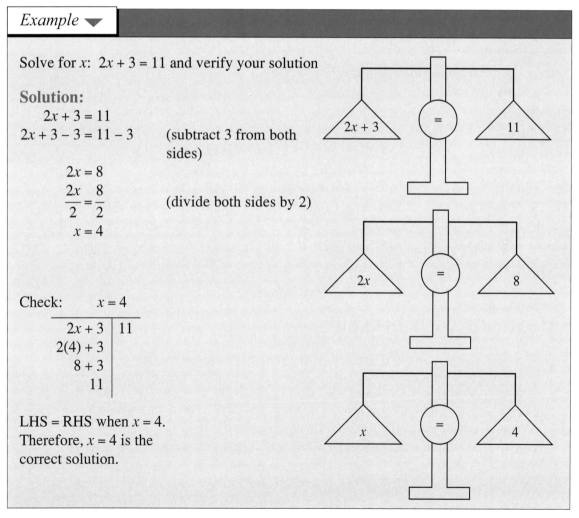

Check: $x = 4$

$2x + 3$	11
$2(4) + 3$	
$8 + 3$	
11	

LHS = RHS when $x = 4$.
Therefore, $x = 4$ is the correct solution.

Note: LHS means left-hand side and RHS means right-hand side.

It is not necessary to draw the scales to solve an equation, but always keep balance in mind.

Example ▼

Solve for x: $6x - 7 = 2x + 13$

Solution:

$$6x - 7 = 2x + 13$$
$$6x - 7 + 7 = 2x + 13 + 7 \qquad \text{(add 7 to both sides)}$$
$$6x = 2x + 20 \qquad \text{(simplify each side)}$$
$$6x - 2x = 2x + 20 - 2x \qquad \text{(subtract } 2x \text{ from both sides)}$$
$$4x = 20 \qquad \text{(simplify each side}$$
$$\frac{4x}{4} = \frac{20}{4} \qquad \text{(divide both sides by 4)}$$
$$x = 5$$

Exercise 7.1 ▼

Solve each of the following equations:

1. $5x = 10$	**2.** $3x = 12$	**3.** $2x = 6$
4. $4x = 20$	**5.** $10x = 30$	**6.** $6x = 30$
7. $-7x = -21$	**8.** $-5x = -10$	**9.** $-2x = -12$
10. $-3x = -33$	**11.** $2x = -4$	**12.** $5x = -15$
13. $-3x = 18$	**14.** $-4x = 20$	**15.** $5x = 0$
16. $2x = 0$	**17.** $7x - 5 = 16$	**18.** $3x - 7 = 8$
19. $2x + 16 = 24$	**20.** $5x - 8 = 22$	**21.** $5x - 2 = -12$
22. $10 = 3x + 1$	**23.** $4x = 28 - 3x$	**24.** $5x = 12 + 8x$
25. $7x = 26 - 6x$	**26.** $2x + 14 = 26 - 4x$	**27.** $7x + 40 = 2x - 10$
28. $8x + 2 = 5x - 16$	**29.** $7x + 11 = 3x + 27$	**30.** $2x - 5 = 1 - x$

Equations with brackets

Equations that contain brackets are solved with the following steps:

1. Remove the brackets.
   (any term not in a bracket is moved down to the next line unchanged)
2. Move all the letters to the left and the numbers to the right.
   (change the sign of each letter and number that changes side)
3. Simplify the sides.
4. Divide both sides by the number in front of the letter.
   (If the number in front of x is negative it is good practice to first multiply both sides by -1.)

Solve for x: $11 - 7(x + 2) = 5(x - 3)$

Solution:

$11 - 7(x + 2) = 5(x - 3)$

$11 - 7x - 14 = 5x - 15$	(remove the brackets)
$-7x - 5x = -15 - 11 + 14$	(letters to the left, numbers to the right)
$-12x = -12$	(simplify both sides)
$12x = 12$	(multiply both sides by -1)
$\dfrac{12x}{12} = \dfrac{12}{12}$	(divide both sides by 12)
$x = 1$	

Exercise 7.2 ▼

Solve each of the following solutions:

1. $3(x + 4) = 18$
2. $5(x - 2) = 10$
3. $3(x + 4) = 2(x + 8)$
4. $6(x + 3) = 4(x + 5)$
5. $7(x - 2) = 4(x + 1)$
6. $4(x + 4) = 2(x + 3)$
7. $5(x - 3) + 7(x + 2) = 11$
8. $5(x + 4) - 3(x - 4) = 40$
9. $3(x - 1) + 5(x + 1) = 18$
10. $4(x - 1) - 3(x - 2) = 6$
11. $5(x - 1) - 2(x + 2) = 3$
12. $4(x + 5) - 2(x + 3) = 12$
13. $3x + 4(x - 6) + 3 = 0$
14. $x + 2(x + 1) = 11$
15. $10(x + 4) - 3(2x + 5) - 1 = 0$
16. $5(2x + 3) - 4 = 4(2x + 1) + 11$
17. $4(x - 3) + 3(x + 7) = 16$
18. $3(2x + 1) - 3(x + 4) = 0$
19. $5(x + 4) - 3(x - 4) = 3x + 29$
20. $2(7 + x) - 4(x + 3) = 15(x - 1)$
21. $7(x - 6) + 2(x - 7) = 5(x - 4)$
22. $4(x - 3) - 2(x - 1) = 3(x - 2)$
23. $2 - 6(2 - x) = 5(x + 3) - 23$
24. $5 - 4(x - 3) = x - 2(x - 1)$
25. $1 + 4(2x - 6) - 3(x + 4) = 0$
26. $5 = 3(3 - 2x) + 4(6 - 2x)$
27. $11 + 4(3x - 1) = 5(2x + 1) + 2(2x - 5)$
28. $8 + 2(2x - 11) - 2x = 4(x - 4)$
29. $5(3x - 2) + 1 - 3(2x + 1) = 2(x + 1)$
30. $2 + 5(3x - 1) = 4(2x - 3) + 2(x - 3)$

Equations with fractions

Equations with fractions are solved with the following steps:

1. Put brackets on top.
2. Multiply each part of the equation by the LCD of the numbers on the bottom.
3. Divide the bottom into the top (this removes all fractions).
4. Proceed as when solving previous equations.

Example ▼

Solve for x: $\dfrac{2x}{3} + \dfrac{x}{4} = \dfrac{11}{6}$

Solution:

The LCD of 3, 4 and 6 is 12. Therefore we multiply each part of the equation by 12.

$$\dfrac{(2x)}{3} + \dfrac{(x)}{4} = \dfrac{(11)}{6} \qquad \text{(put brackets on top)}$$

$$\dfrac{12(2x)}{3} + \dfrac{12(x)}{4} = \dfrac{12(11)}{6} \qquad \text{(multiply each part by 12)}$$

$$4(2x) + 3(x) = 2(11) \qquad \text{(divide the bottom into the top)}$$

$$8x + 3x = 22 \qquad \text{(remove the brackets)}$$

$$11x = 22 \qquad \text{(simplify the left-hand side)}$$

$$\dfrac{11x}{11} = \dfrac{22}{11} \qquad \text{(divide both sides by 11)}$$

$$x = 2$$

Example ▼

Solve for x: $\dfrac{x+1}{2} = \dfrac{2x+1}{10} + \dfrac{x+2}{3}$

Solution:

The LCD of 2, 10 and 3 is 30. Therefore we multiply each part of the equation by 30.

$$\dfrac{(x+1)}{2} = \dfrac{(2x+1)}{10} + \dfrac{(x+2)}{3} \qquad \text{(put brackets on top)}$$

$$\dfrac{30(x+1)}{2} = \dfrac{30(2x+1)}{10} + \dfrac{30(x+2)}{3} \qquad \text{(multiply each part by 30)}$$

$$15(x+1) = 3(2x+1) + 10(x+2) \qquad \text{(divide the bottom into the top)}$$

$$15x + 15 = 6x + 3 + 10x + 20 \qquad \text{(remove brackets)}$$

$$15x - 6x - 10x = 3 + 20 - 15 \qquad \text{(letters to the left, numbers to the right)}$$

$$-x = 8 \qquad \text{(simplify both sides)}$$

$$x = -8 \qquad \text{(multiply both sides by } -1)$$

Note: If a part of the equation is not a fraction, it can be changed into fraction form by putting it over 1.

For example, $5 = \dfrac{5}{1}$, $2x = \dfrac{2x}{1}$, $x + 3 = \dfrac{x+3}{1}$.

Exercise 7.3 ▼

Solve each of the following equations:

1. $\dfrac{x}{2} + \dfrac{x}{3} = \dfrac{5}{2}$

2. $\dfrac{x}{4} + \dfrac{x}{2} = \dfrac{15}{4}$

3. $\dfrac{x}{3} + \dfrac{x}{4} = \dfrac{7}{12}$

4. $\dfrac{x}{4} + \dfrac{x}{5} = \dfrac{27}{20}$

5. $\dfrac{x}{2} - \dfrac{x}{5} = \dfrac{3}{10}$

6. $\dfrac{x}{3} - \dfrac{x}{5} = \dfrac{2}{3}$

7. $\dfrac{2x}{5} + \dfrac{x}{3} = \dfrac{22}{15}$

8. $\dfrac{3x}{4} - \dfrac{2x}{3} = \dfrac{5}{12}$

9. $\dfrac{2x}{5} = \dfrac{3}{2} + \dfrac{x}{4}$

10. $\dfrac{4x}{9} - \dfrac{x}{2} = \dfrac{2}{3}$

11. $\dfrac{x+2}{4} + \dfrac{x-3}{2} = \dfrac{1}{2}$

12. $\dfrac{x+4}{3} = \dfrac{x+1}{4} + \dfrac{1}{6}$

13. $\dfrac{3x+4}{2} - \dfrac{4x-11}{5} = 0$

14. $\dfrac{x-3}{4} + \dfrac{4}{3} = \dfrac{3x-1}{6}$

15. $\dfrac{x+4}{3} - \dfrac{x+2}{4} = \dfrac{7}{6}$

16. $\dfrac{x-8}{7} + \dfrac{x-3}{3} - \dfrac{5}{21} = 0$

17. $\dfrac{2x-3}{3} - \dfrac{1}{6} = \dfrac{x+2}{4}$

18. $\dfrac{x-5}{3} + \dfrac{1}{15} = \dfrac{x-2}{5}$

19. $\dfrac{3x-1}{2} - \dfrac{x}{4} = \dfrac{9}{2}$

20. $\dfrac{x}{5} - \dfrac{x-3}{6} = \dfrac{11}{15}$

21. $\dfrac{3x-1}{2} = \dfrac{x+8}{3} + \dfrac{x-1}{6}$

22. $\dfrac{2x-3}{10} + \dfrac{x-2}{5} - \dfrac{1}{2} = 0$

23. $\dfrac{3x-1}{3} - \dfrac{5-3x}{4} = \dfrac{2x-1}{6}$

24. $\dfrac{x-1}{4} - \dfrac{1}{20} = \dfrac{2x-3}{5}$

25. $\dfrac{x+2}{4} - \dfrac{x-2}{2} = 3$

26. $\dfrac{x+5}{5} = \dfrac{5-x}{10} + 5$

27. $\dfrac{x-2}{2} = 5 - \dfrac{x+10}{9}$

28. $\dfrac{2x+1}{6} = \dfrac{4x-5}{2} + x$

29. $\dfrac{x+9}{2} - 1 = \dfrac{2x+8}{3}$

30. $\dfrac{x-1}{3} + \dfrac{x-3}{4} = x - 4$

Chapter test

Solve each of the following equations:

1. $3x = 12$ 2. $5x = 15$ 3. $2x = 10$

4. $7x = 0$ 5. $7x - 5 = 16$ 6. $3x - 7 = 8$

7. $5x - 8 = 22$ 8. $9x - 6 = 5x - 2$ 9. $4x + 14 = 26 - 2x$

10. $8x - 12 = 3x - 2$ 11. $5(2x - 3) = 3(x - 4) + 11$ 12. $7(x + 2) + 5(x - 3) = 11$

13. $8(x - 4) - 6 = 2(x + 5)$ 14. $11x - 3(6 - x) = 3 + 5(2x - 1)$

15. $3(3x - 5) = 5(x + 2) - 8x + 11$ 16. $2(7x - 8) = 5(4x - 3) + 5$

17. $5(4 - 3x) - 2(10 - x) = 5x$ 18. $3(3x - 2) - 2(5 + 3x) - 2 = 0$

19. $\dfrac{x}{2} + \dfrac{x}{3} = \dfrac{5}{6}$ 20. $\dfrac{x}{3} + \dfrac{x}{4} = \dfrac{7}{3}$ 21. $\dfrac{x}{3} = \dfrac{2x}{7} + \dfrac{5}{21}$

22. $\dfrac{2x}{3} - \dfrac{3x}{5} = \dfrac{2}{15}$ 23. $\dfrac{x}{5} + \dfrac{7}{10} = \dfrac{11x}{20}$ 24. $\dfrac{3x}{4} - \dfrac{x}{5} = \dfrac{33}{10}$

25. $\dfrac{x+2}{3} + \dfrac{x+5}{4} = \dfrac{5}{2}$ 26. $\dfrac{x-1}{5} + \dfrac{x+3}{2} = \dfrac{17}{5}$ 27. $\dfrac{2x+1}{2} + \dfrac{x+5}{3} + \dfrac{19}{6} = 0$

28. $\dfrac{x-2}{6} + \dfrac{3x-7}{5} = \dfrac{x}{3}$ 29. $\dfrac{2x+3}{5} = \dfrac{x+3}{4} + \dfrac{x+1}{20}$ 30. $\dfrac{x+5}{4} - \dfrac{x-3}{7} = 2$

THE 24-HOUR CLOCK AND TIMETABLES

The 24-hour clock

To avoid confusion, timetables generally use the 24-hour clock instead of a.m. and p.m. In the 24-hour clock system, all times are written using four digits. The first two digits show the number of hours past midnight, and the last two digits show the number of minutes past the hour. Nowadays a colon is used to separate the hours from the minutes.

13:00 would be pronounced 'thirteen hours' or 'thirteen hundred hours'.
15:21 would be pronounced 'fifteen twenty-one' or 'fifteen twenty-one hours'.
07:30 would be pronounced 'seven thirty' or 'seven thirty hours'.

Note: The 24-hour clock runs from 00:00 hours (midnight) to 24:00 hours (midnight again). Therefore 00:00 = 24:00.

Adding and subtracting times in the 24-hour clock system

> **Remember:** 1 hour = 60 minutes.

Example ▼

(i) A train left Dublin at 18:31 hours. It arrived in Drogheda 39 minutes later. At what time did the train arrive in Drogheda?

(ii) A train left Kildare at 10:45 hours and arrived in Mallow at 13:07 hours. How many hours and minutes did the journey take?

Solution:

(i) Add 39 minutes to 18:31

$$18:31$$
$$00:39$$
$$\overline{18:70}$$
$$= 19:10$$

$18:70 = 18:00 + 00:70$
$= 18:00 + 01:10$
$= 19:10$

> 70 minutes
> = 1 hour and 10 minutes

The train arrived in Drogheda at 19:10.

(ii) The problem here is that the number of minutes in the earlier time is greater than the number of minutes in the later time. This problem is solved by one of three methods:

Method 1:
'Transfer one hour into the minutes column.'

$$\begin{array}{r} 13:07 \\ -10:45 \\ \hline \end{array} = \begin{array}{r} 12:67 \\ -10:45 \\ \hline 2:22 \end{array}$$

Therefore the time taken is:
2 hours and 22 minutes

Method 2:
'Add the same number of minutes to both times to make the earlier time an even number of hours.'

$$\begin{array}{r} 13:07 \\ -10:45 \\ \hline \end{array} = \begin{array}{r} 13:22 \\ -11:00 \\ \hline 2:22 \end{array}$$ (add 15 minutes to both times)

Therefore the time taken is:
2 hours 22 minutes

Method 3:
'Divide the time up.'

	Hours	Minutes
10:45 to 11:00		15
11:00 to 13:00	2	
13:00 to 13:07		7
	2	22

Therefore the time taken is:
2 hours and 22 minutes

Exercise 8.1 ▼

1. Find the duration, in hours and minutes, of each of the following journeys.
   All times are printed using the 24-hour clock system.

Depart	Arrive
18:00	21:00
06:30	11:30
15:07	17:07
14:40	18:40
15:15	17:20
17:48	20:50

Depart	Arrive
11:18	14:49
09:02	13:18
00:05	05:11
18:24	22:40
15:22	19:54
13:07	17:08

Depart	Arrive
15:50	18:30
17:40	21:20
09:35	11:25
12:57	17:42
18:39	22:19
21:43	23:33

Depart	Arrive
16:34	22:12
12:52	16:40
11:48	14:17
09:17	17:05
07:23	12:19
19:41	23:25

2. A bus left Limerick at 09:35 hours and arrived in Dublin at 12:10 hours. How many hours and minutes did the journey take?

3. A train leaves Dublin at 07:42 hours and arrives in Killarney at 11:22 hours. How many hours and minutes does the journey take?

4. A coach left Dublin at 17:15 hours. It arrived in Maynooth 47 minutes later. At what time did the coach arrive in Maynooth?

5. A train arrived in Waterford from Dublin at 17:35. The journey took 2 hours and 20 minutes. At what time did the train leave Dublin?

6. Ian sets his video recorder to record a film. The film begins at 20:40 and ends at 22:15.
   (a) Calculate the running time of the film.
   (b) If Ian uses a new 240-minutes tape, how much recording time will be left on the tape?

7. A lorry must reach its destination by 17:15 and the journey takes 3 hours and 20 minutes. What is the latest time at which the driver should set out?

8. A ferry journey takes $3\frac{3}{4}$ hours, and the ferry was due to leave at 21:50 hours. However, it was delayed by $1\frac{1}{2}$ hours. What time did the ferry arrive at its destination?

9. A school's lessons begin at 09:00 hours and end at 15:40 hours, with a 65-minute break at lunchtime and a 20-minute break in mid-morning. If there are nine lessons of equal length, how long is a lesson?

10. A pupil arrived home from school at 17:10. She immediately began her maths homework, which took 35 minutes. She then took a 20-minute break. After this she spent 30 minutes studying history, then she took a 12-minute break and spent 25 minutes each on science, English, and Irish. Complete the following table:

Arrived home	Finished maths	Finished first break	Finished history	Finished second break	Finished science	Finished English	Finished Irish
17:10			18:35				

11. A turkey needs to be cooked for lunch at 13:45. The cooking time is 20 minutes per kilogram, plus 30 minutes. If the turkey weighs 6 kg, what is the latest time at which the turkey should be put in the oven?

Timetables

Transport timetables are usually printed in the 24-hour clock system using a two-way table. Frequently the separator is left out: for example 17:23 is given as 1723.

Example ▼

Below is an extract from the Galway to Dublin bus timetable:

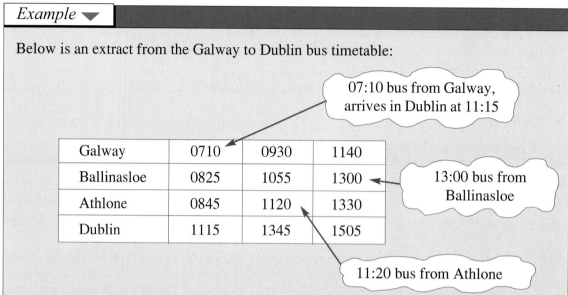

07:10 bus from Galway, arrives in Dublin at 11:15

Galway	0710	0930	1140
Ballinasloe	0825	1055	1300
Athlone	0845	1120	1330
Dublin	1115	1345	1505

13:00 bus from Ballinasloe

11:20 bus from Athlone

(i) Calculate the difference in travelling time to Dublin between the 07:10 bus and the 09:30 bus.

(ii) Calculate how long it takes the 11:20 bus from Athlone to get to Dublin.

(iii) John lives in Ballinasloe and needs to catch the 13:00 bus to Athlone. It takes him 17 minutes to walk from his house to the bus stop in Ballinasloe. What is the latest time at which he can leave his house to catch the 13:00 bus, if he has to walk?

Solution:

(i)

```
  11:15        Therefore the 07:10 bus      13:45        Therefore the 09:30 bus takes
 −07:10        takes 4 hours and 5         −09:30        4 hours and 15 minutes.
 ──────        minutes.                    ──────
  4:05                                      4:15
```

Therefore the 09:30 bus from Galway takes 10 minutes longer to travel to Dublin.

(ii)

```
  13:45        Therefore the 11:20 bus from Athlone takes
 −11:20        2 hours and 25 minutes to get to Dublin.
 ──────
  2:25
```

(iii) John needs to leave his house at 17 minutes before 13:00 at the latest.
In other words, he has to leave his house at 12:43 at the latest.

```
  12:60
 −00:17
 ──────
  12:43
```

1. Calculate the time it takes for the bus to travel between each station:

Letterkenny	06:50
Monaghan	07:43
Castleblayney	08:29
Carrickmacross	09:04
Slane	10:09
Ashbourne	10:51
Dublin	11:27

2. Find the time taken by the train to travel from Pearse Station to each station:

Pearse Station	1732
Connolly Station	1736
Howth Junction	1745
Malahide	1753
Skerries	1805
Drogheda	1817
Dundalk	1835

3. This is an extract from a railway timetable:

Dublin	Departing	0810	1245	1730
Port Laoise	Departing	0905	1350	1815
Thurles	Departing	0940	1430	1900
Mallow	Departing	1045	1540	1955
Killarney	Departing	1200	1620	2040
Tralee	Arriving	1235	1650	2115

(i) How long, in hours and minutes, does it take to go from Dublin to Tralee on each train?

(ii) Find the difference in time between the fastest and the slowest train from Dublin to Tralee.

(iii) It takes Colman 12 minutes to travel from his home to the railway station in Port Laoise. What is the latest time at which he can leave his house to catch the 08:10 train from Dublin to Tralee at Port Laoise railway station?

4. Here is an extract from the Westport to Dublin train timetable:

Westport	Departing	0710	1320	1740
Castlebar	Departing	0727	1338	1755
Claremorris	Departing	0748	1359	1814
Athlone	Departing	0928	1540	1949
Dublin	Arriving	1050	1655	2110

(i) How long does it take the 07:10 train from Westport to arrive in Dublin?

(ii) Which train—the 07:10, the 13:20, or the 17:40—takes the shortest time to travel from Westport to Dublin?

(iii) Jane arrives at the railway station in Castlebar at 12:58. How long will she have to wait to catch the next train to Athlone?

5. Below is an extract from the timetable of a private coach service between Arklow and Bray:

Arklow	0700	1020	1115	1410	1840
Rathdrum	0725	1048	1143	1437	1859
Wicklow	0744	1110	1204	1455	1916
Rathnew	0750	1117	1212	1501	1922
Greystones	0811	1137	1229	1522	1941
Bray	0830	1202	1258	1550	2005

(i) If Mary arrives twelve minutes late for the 10:20 bus from Arklow, how long must she wait for the next coach to Wicklow? What time will she arrive in Wicklow ?
(ii) Which coach is the fastest from Arklow to Bray?
(iii) Which coach is the slowest from Arklow to Bray?
(iv) What is the difference in time between the fastest coach and the slowest coach from Arklow to Bray?
(v) Ciara lives near Rathdrum. It takes her eleven minutes to travel to the bus stop in Rathdrum. What is the latest time she can leave her home to catch the 07:50 coach to Greystones? When she reaches Greystones she has to walk for eight minutes to reach her place of work. Calculate how long she spent travelling from her home to her place of employment.

6. Below is an extract from the northbound DART timetable:

Pearse Station	0715	0735		
Tara Street	0717		0757	
Connolly Station	0720			
Clontarf	0724			
Killester	0728			

(i) Calculate the time it takes to travel from Pearse Station to Killester.
(ii) Trains from Pearse Station depart every twenty minutes. Complete the train timetable for the next three trains. (Assume that each train takes the same time between stops as shown in the timetable).
(iii) What time does the 07:55 from Pearse Station reach Clontarf?
(iv) What time does the 08:17 from Tara Street reach Connolly Station?
(v) Aideen arrives in Clontarf at 07:32. How long does she have to wait to catch the next train to Killester? What time does she arrive in Killester?

7. Use the timetable below, which gives details of trains travelling from Waterford to Dublin, to answer the following questions:

Weekdays							Sunday	
Waterford	dep.	0600	0740	1050	1525	1815	0950	1805
Thomastown	dep.	0628	0803	1115	1550	1840	1014	1830
Kilkenny	dep.	0648	0820	1130	1605	1858	1027	1845
Muine Bheag	dep.	0706	0840	1153	1628	1921	1050	1908
Carlow	dep.	0720	0853	1207	1641	1940	1103	1922
Athy	dep.	0734	0907	1221	1656	1954	1119	1941
Kildare	dep.	0755	0924	1243	1715	2015	1139	2002
Droichead Nua	dep.	—	—	1251	1723	2023	—	—
Dublin (Heuston Station)	arr.	0830	0955	1320	1750	2050	1210	2035

(a) How many trains travel each weekday?
(b) If I arrive ten minutes late for the 10:50 train from Waterford, how long must I wait for the next train?
(c) Which train is the fastest from Waterford to Dublin?
(d) Which train is the slowest from Waterford to Dublin?
(e) Which is the first train on a weekday a person should take to reach Droichead Nua?
(f) How long does it take the 15:25 train from Waterford to reach Carlow?
(g) A man lives in Kilkenny and has an appointment in Kildare at 14:00. If it takes him twenty minutes to reach the railway station, what is the latest time at which he must leave home to keep the appointment?
(h) Which trains serve Droichead Nua on Sunday?
(i) How much longer does it take to travel to Athy from Thomastown on the 18:15 train than on the 06:00?

DISTANCE, SPEED, AND TIME

Distance, speed and time

There are three formulas to remember when dealing with problems involving distance (D), speed (S), and time (T). It can be difficult to remember these formulas; however, the work can be made easier using a triangle and the memory aid 'Dad's Silly Triangle'.

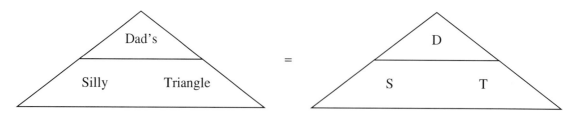

1. $\text{Speed} = \dfrac{\text{Distance}}{\text{Time}}$ **2.** $\text{Time} = \dfrac{\text{Distance}}{\text{Speed}}$ **3.** $\text{Distance} = \text{Speed} \times \text{Time}$

Consider the triangle on the right. By covering the quantity required, D, S or T, any of the three formulas above can be found by inspection.

Note: Speed here means 'average speed'.

Common units of speed:

1. kilometres per hour, written as km/h.
2. metres per second, written as m/s.

Note: 'per' means 'divided by'.

Converting minutes to hours

To convert minutes to hours **divide by 60**.
For example, 48 minutes = $\frac{48}{60}$ h = $\frac{4}{5}$ h or 0.8 h.

However, the following occur quite often and are easy to memorise:

30 minutes = $\frac{1}{2}$ hour	20 minutes = $\frac{1}{3}$ hour	50 minutes = $\frac{5}{6}$ hour
15 minutes = $\frac{1}{4}$ hour	40 minutes = $\frac{2}{3}$ hour	12 minutes = $\frac{1}{5}$ hour
45 minutes = $\frac{3}{4}$ hour	10 minutes = $\frac{1}{6}$ hour	24 minutes = $\frac{2}{5}$ hour

Example ▼

(i) A train takes 2 hours and 30 minutes to travel a distance of 250 km.
Calculate the average speed of the train in km/h.

(ii) A cyclist travels $2\frac{1}{4}$ km at an average speed of 15 m/s.
How long does the journey take?

(iii) A car travels for 3 hours and 20 minutes at an average speed of 75 km/h.
How far does it travel?

Solution:

(i) Time has to be expressed in hours.
2 hours and 30 minutes = $2\frac{1}{2}$ hours

$\text{Speed} = \dfrac{\text{Distance}}{\text{Time}}$

$= \dfrac{250}{2\frac{1}{2}}$

$= \dfrac{500}{5}$ (Multiply top and bottom by 2)

$= 100$

Therefore average speed is 100 km/h

(ii) km has to be expressed in m.
$2\frac{1}{4}$ km = 2250 m

$\text{Time} = \dfrac{\text{Distance}}{\text{Speed}}$

$= \dfrac{2250}{15}$

$= 150$

Therefore time taken = 150 seconds
(or $2\frac{1}{2}$ minutes)

(iii) Time has to be expressed in hours. 3 hours and 20 minutes = $3\frac{1}{3}$ hours.

$$\text{Distance} = \text{speed} \times \text{time}$$
$$= 75 \times 3\frac{1}{3}$$
$$= 250$$

Therefore the distance travelled = 250 km.

1. The tables below show some information on problems concerning distance, speed, and time. Complete the tables:

Distance	Speed	Time
240 km		3 hours
360 km	90 km/h	
	70 km/h	2 hours
320 km		5 hours
216 km	72 km/h	
232 km	58 km/h	
1,080 m	12 m/s	
400 m		80 seconds
	15 m/s	200 seconds
	60 km/h	$3\frac{1}{2}$ hours

Distance	Speed	Time
240 km		2 hours and 30 mins
72 km	16 km/h	
150 km		1 hour and 30 mins
280 km		3 hours and 30 mins
300 m		40 seconds
	64 km/h	3 hours and 15 mins
	90 km/h	1 hour and 20 mins
50 km		1 hour and 15 mins
	75 km/h	1 hour and 40 mins
90 km		45 mins

2. How long does it take a bus to travel 260 km at an average speed of 52 km/h?

3. A tractor travels 45 km in 3 hours. Calculate its average speed in km/h.

4. A car travelled for 5 hours at an average speed of 60 km/h. Calculate the distance it travelled.

5. (a) Express 2 hours and 30 minutes in hours.
   (b) A train starts a journey of 180 km at 14:15 and completes the journey at 16:45. Calculate the average speed of the train in km/h.

6. A bus travelled at an average speed of 100 km/h between 12:55 and 14:25. What distance did it travel?

7. Find the average speed of a car that completes a journey of 208 km in 3 hours 15 minutes.

8. A girl ran a distance of 3,600 m in 15 minutes. Calculate her average speed in m/s.

9. A motorcyclist begins a journey of 280 km at 15:00. If the average speed is 80 km/h, find the time at which the journey is completed.

10. (a) Express 4 hours and 15 minutes in hours.
   (b) A train starts a journey of 255 km at 09:40 and completes the journey at 13:55. What was the average speed of the train?

11. A car travels 54 km in 45 minutes. Calculate its average speed in km/h.

12. A train travels 52 km in 40 minutes. How far will it travel in 1 hour 10 minutes at the same average speed?

13. A non-stop journey of 305 km began at 09:10 and ended at 14:15.
Calculate the average speed in km/h.

14. A train began a non-stop journey of 147 km at 10:50 and completed the journey at 12:35.
How long did the journey take, in hours and minutes?
Calculate the average speed of the train in km/h.

15. A non-stop bus left Cork at 12:24 and arrived in Dublin at 15:09.
   (i) For how long was the bus travelling?
   (ii) By leaving Cork at 12:24 the bus was 34 minutes late. At what time was it due to leave Cork?
   (iii) The distance travelled was 258.5 km.
      Calculate the average speed of the bus in km/h.

Two-part questions

Two-part questions on distance, speed and time involve two separate journeys. In these questions we need the total distance travelled for both journeys and the total time for both journeys. We then use the formula:

$$\text{Overall average speed for both journeys} = \frac{\text{Total distance for both journeys}}{\text{Total time for both journeys}}$$

Example ▼

A bus travelled a distance of 300 km at an average speed of 75 km/h. It then travelled for 2 hours at an average speed of 72 km/h. Calculate:

(i) the time taken for the first journey
(ii) the distance travelled in the second journey
(iii) the total distance travelled
(iv) the total time taken
(v) the overall average speed.

Solution:

(i) In the first journey, the time is required:

$$\text{Time} = \frac{\text{Distance}}{\text{Speed}}$$

$$= \frac{300}{75}$$

$$= 4 \text{ hours}$$

(ii) In the second journey, the distance is required:

$$\text{Distance} = \text{speed} \times \text{time}$$

$$= 72 \times 2$$

$$= 144 \text{ km}$$

(iii) Total distance travelled = distance for the first journey + distance for the second journey

$$= 300 + 144 = 444 \text{ km}$$

(iv) Total time = time for the first journey + time for the second journey

$$= 4 + 2 = 6 \text{ hours}$$

(v) Overall average speed for both journeys $= \dfrac{\text{Total distance for both journeys}}{\text{Total time for both journeys}}$

$$= \frac{444}{6} = 74 \text{ km/h}$$

Exercise 9.2 ▼

1. A train travels for 4 hours at an average speed of 80 km/h and then for 3 hours at an average speed of 90 km/h. Calculate the total distance travelled.

2. A man walked for 3 hours at an average speed of 5 km/h and then cycled at an average speed of 18 km/h for 2 hours. What distance did he cover altogether?

3. A plane flies for 2 hours at an average speed of 400 km/h and then for 4 hours at an average speed of 250 km/h. Find the total distance travelled and the overall average speed.

4. A car travels 100 km at an average speed of 50 km/h and then 180 km at an average speed of 60 km/h. Calculate (*a*) the total distance travelled; (*b*) the total time taken; (*c*) the overall average speed.

5. A bus travels for 300 km at an average speed of 75 km/h and then 162 km at an average speed of 81 km/h. Calculate (*a*) the total time taken; (*b*) the total distance travelled; (*c*) the overall average speed.

6. A woman drove her car for 200 km at an average speed of 80 km/h and then for 60 km at an average speed of 40 km/h. Find (*a*) the total time taken; (*b*) the total distance travelled; (*c*) the overall average speed.

7. A car travels 200 km at an average speed of 50 km/h and then travels 360 km at an average speed of 60 km/h. Calculate:
  (i) the total distance travelled
  (ii) the total time taken
  (iii) the overall average speed.

8. A train travels for 2 hours at an average speed of 80 km/h and then for 3 hours at an average speed of 90 km/h. Calculate:
  (i) the total distance travelled
  (ii) the total time taken
  (iii) the overall average speed.

9. A bus travelled a distance of 120 km at an average speed of 40 km/h. It then travelled for 4 hours at at an average speed of 61 km/h. Calculate:
  (i) the time taken for the first journey
  (ii) the distance travelled in the second journey
  (iii) the total distance travelled
  (iv) the total time taken
  (v) the overall average speed.

10. On an outward journey of 280 km a driver takes $3\frac{1}{2}$ hours. On the return journey she takes a short cut, driving at an average speed of 104 km/h, and this takes one hour less than the outward journey. Calculate the overall average speed.

11. A lorry travels 189 km in $3\frac{1}{2}$ hours. It then travels for $4\frac{1}{2}$ hours at an average speed of 70 km/h.
  (a) How far has it travelled altogether?
  (b) What is the total time taken?
  (c) What is the overall average speed?

12. On an outward journey of 330 km a driver takes 6 hours, and on the return journey he takes one hour less. Calculate:
  (a) the average speed of the outward journey.
  (b) the average speed of the return journey.
  (c) the total time and the total distance.
  (d) the overall average speed.

PERCENTAGES

Percentages, fractions, and decimals

The words '**per cent**' mean 'per 100' or 'in every 100'. The symbol for per cent is %.
So 15 per cent means '15 in every 100,' written as 15% for short.
A percentage is a fraction with 100 on the bottom. It tells you 'an amount out of 100'.

Percentages, fractions and decimals are linked:

$$7\% \quad = \quad \frac{7}{100} \quad = \quad 0.07$$

$$\uparrow \qquad\qquad \uparrow \qquad\qquad \uparrow$$

percentage   fraction   decimal

Changing percentages to fractions and decimals

To change a percentage into a fraction do the following:

Write the number as a fraction with 100 on the bottom and simplify this fraction.

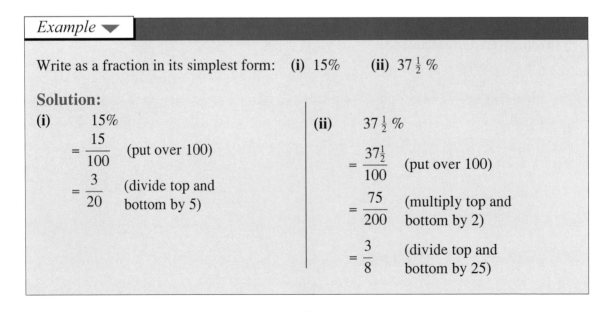

Example ▼

Write as a fraction in its simplest form: **(i)** 15%   **(ii)** $37\frac{1}{2}$ %

Solution:

(i)   15%

$= \dfrac{15}{100}$ (put over 100)

$= \dfrac{3}{20}$ (divide top and bottom by 5)

(ii) $37\frac{1}{2}$ %

$= \dfrac{37\frac{1}{2}}{100}$ (put over 100)

$= \dfrac{75}{200}$ (multiply top and bottom by 2)

$= \dfrac{3}{8}$ (divide top and bottom by 25)

To change a percentage into a decimal do the following:

> Divide the number by 100.

The working can be done in your head (move the decimal points two places to the left), or you can use your calculator.

Example ▼

Write as decimals: **(i)** 32%   **(ii)** $27\frac{1}{2}\%$

Solution:

(i)   32%

$$= \frac{32}{100}$$

$$= 0.32$$

(ii) $27\frac{1}{2}\%$

$$= \frac{27.5}{100}$$

$$= 0.275$$

Exercise 10.1 ▼

Write each of the following percentages as:
(i) a fraction in its simplest form and   **(ii)** a decimal:

1. 20%	**2.** 30%	**3.** 50%	**4.** 25%	**5.** 10%
6. 5%	**7.** 40%	**8.** 75%	**9.** 80%	**10.** 60%
11. 35%	**12.** 45%	**13.** 65%	**14.** 95%	**15.** 55%
16. 12%	**17.** 4%	**18.** 15%	**19.** 2%	**20.** 88%
21. 120%	**22.** 150%	**23.** 110%	**24.** 180%	**25.** 225%
26. $12\frac{1}{2}\%$	**27.** $62\frac{1}{2}\%$	**28.** $7\frac{1}{2}\%$	**29.** $17\frac{1}{2}\%$	**30.** 18.4%

Write each of the following as a fraction in its lowest terms:

31. $33\frac{1}{3}\%$	**32.** $66\frac{2}{3}\%$	**33.** $16\frac{2}{3}\%$	**34.** $83\frac{1}{3}\%$	**35.** $\frac{1}{2}\%$

Changing fractions and decimals to percentages

To change a fraction or a decimal to a percentage do the following:

> Multiply the fraction or decimal by 100 and put the percentage symbol, %, at the end.

Example ▼

Write as percentages: (i) 0.42 (ii) $\frac{3}{5}$ (iii) $\frac{3}{40}$

Solution:

(i) 0.42
$= 0.42 \times 100\%$
$= 42\%$

(ii) $\frac{3}{5}$
$= \frac{3}{5} \times 100\%$
$= 60\%$

(iii) $\frac{3}{40}$
$= \frac{3}{40} \times 100\%$
$= 7\frac{1}{2}\%$

Exercise 10.2 ▼

Write each of the following as a percentage:

1. 0.23
2. 0.37
3. 0.18
4. 0.06
5. 2.4
6. $\frac{1}{2}$
7. $\frac{1}{4}$
8. $\frac{3}{4}$
9. $\frac{2}{5}$
10. $\frac{9}{10}$
11. $\frac{17}{20}$
12. $\frac{33}{50}$
13. $\frac{9}{25}$
14. $\frac{3}{2}$
15. $\frac{6}{5}$
16. $\frac{2}{25}$
17. $1\frac{1}{4}$
18. $\frac{27}{25}$
19. $\frac{7}{40}$
20. $\frac{1}{8}$
21. $\frac{1}{3}$
22. $\frac{7}{8}$
23. $\frac{1}{12}$
24. $\frac{2}{3}$
25. $\frac{9}{16}$

Expressing one quantity as a percentage of another

To express one quantity as a percentage of another quantity do the following:

1. Write both quantities in the same units and remove the units.
2. Put the first number over the second number to form a fraction.
3. Multiply this fraction by 100 and put in the percentage symbol, %, at the end.
   In short:

$$\frac{\text{first number}}{\text{second number}} \times 100\%$$

Express: (i) 80 c as a percentage of €2.40   (ii) 400 m as a percentage of 2 km.

Solution:

(i) **1.** €2.40 = 240 c

2. $\dfrac{80}{240}$

3. $\dfrac{80}{240} \times 100\%$

= $33\frac{1}{3}\%$

(ii) **1.** 2 km = 2,000 m

2. $\dfrac{400}{2000}$

3. $\dfrac{400}{2000} \times 100\%$

= 20%

Exercise 10.3 ▼

In each of the following, express the first quantity as a percentage of the second:

1. 15, 20   **2.** 20, 50   **3.** 3, 5   **4.** 60, 300
5. 12, 15   **6.** 36, 300   **7.** 20, 8   **8.** 18, 12
9. 15 cm, 60 cm   **10.** 300 m, 1 km   **11.** 4 mm; 2 cm   **12.** 900 g, 2 kg
13. 80 cm, 2 m   **14.** 750 m, 5 km   **15.** €1.50; €7.50   **16.** 18 hours; 3 days
17. 60°, 180°   **18.** €1.26, €8.40   **19.** €1.20, €1   **20.** 60 km/h; 80 km/h
21. 63 c; €1.80   **22.** 800 g, $2\frac{1}{2}$ kg   **23.** 700 cm^3, 2 litres   **24.** 640 kg, 4 tonnes
25. There are 15 girls in a class of 25. What percentage of the class are girls? What percentage are boys?
26. A boy gains 142 marks out of 200 marks in an exam. What percentage is this?
27. There are 40 red, 60 green, 100 blue and 50 white marbles in a bag. What percentage of the total number of marbles is each colour?
28. Which is the better record, 20 wins in 25 or 30 wins in 40?
29. An auctioneer received €4,100 as commission when she sold a house for €164,000. What percentage commission did the auctioneer receive for selling the house?
30. An article that costs €240 is increased in price by €60.
What is the increase as a percentage of the old price?
What is the increase as a percentage of the new price?

Finding the percentage change in a quantity

Often we have to express a change in a quantity as a percentage change.
Always express the change in the quantity as a percentage of the original quantity, using the following formula:

$$\begin{array}{|c|} \hline \text{Percentage change} \\ \text{in a quantity} \end{array} = \frac{\text{Change in quantity}}{\text{Original quantity}} \times 100\%$$

Example ▼

(i) A woman's salary was increased from €40,000 to €44,800.
Calculate her percentage increase in salary.

(ii) A man went on a diet and reduced his weight from 120 kg to 111 kg.
Calculate his percentage decrease in weight.

Solution:

(i)   increase = €44,800 – €40,000
= €4,800

Percentage increase in salary
$$= \frac{\text{increase in salary}}{\text{original salary}} \times 100\%$$
$$= \frac{4,800}{40,000} \times 100\%$$
$$= 12\%$$

(ii)   decrease = 120 kg – 111 kg
= 9 kg

Percentage decrease in weight
$$= \frac{\text{decrease in weight}}{\text{original weight}} \times 100\%$$
$$= \frac{9}{120} \times 100\%$$
$$= 7\tfrac{1}{2}\%$$

Exercise 10.4 ▼

Calculate the percentage increase or decrease in each of the following quantities:

	Original quantity	New quantity		Original quantity	New quantity		Original quantity	New quantity
1.	25 kg	30 kg	**7.**	800 kg	856 kg	**13.**	50 cm	46.5 cm
2.	40 m	60 m	**8.**	€120	€109.20	**14.**	€250	€212.50
3.	60 marks	45 marks	**9.**	250 m	215 m	**15.**	72 marks	81 marks
4.	50 c	45 c	**10.**	475 pupils	513 pupils	**16.**	€2,700	€3,064.50
5.	€4.20	€4.41	**11.**	€1.60	€1.40	**17.**	360 kg	240 kg
6.	25 litres	22 litres	**12.**	80 km/h	84 km/h	**18.**	120 litres	40 litres

19. In 1998 a school had 450 pupils on the roll. In 1999 the number of pupils had increased to 477. Calculate the percentage increase in the number of pupils attending the school.

20. A maths book had 350 pages. A new edition was published with 343 pages. Calculate the percentage decrease in the number of pages in the book.

21. A man's salary was increased from €30,900 to €33,063.
Calculate his percentage increase in salary.

22. A car, including 4 passengers, had a weight of 1,680 kg. Two of the passengers got out of the car and the weight was reduced to 1,478.4 kg. Calculate **(i)** the weight of the two passengers who got out and **(ii)** the percentage decrease in weight.

23. During a fever, the temperature of a child rose from 98.8°F to 104.2°F.
Calculate the percentage increase in temperature, correct to one decimal place.

Finding a given percentage of a quantity

There are several ways to find percentages of quantities. Here are two methods:

Method 1:
1. Divide by 100 (this gives 1%).
2. Multiply this by the percentage asked for in the question.

Method 2:
1. Write the percentage as a decimal (or a fraction)
2. Multiply the quantity by the decimal (or the fraction).

Example ▼

Find 12% of €284.

Solution:

Method 1:

1. $1\% = € \dfrac{284}{100} = €2.84$

2. $12\% = €2.84 \times 12$
$= €34.08$

Method 2:

1. $12\% = 0.12$ (as a decimal)
2. Therefore 12% of €284
$= €284 \times 0.12 = €34.08$

If you prefer to use fractions, or use them sometimes, the following occur frequently and can be useful to learn:

$$50\% = \tfrac{1}{2}, \quad 25\% = \tfrac{1}{4}, \quad 10\% = \tfrac{1}{10}, \quad 33\tfrac{1}{3}\% = \tfrac{1}{3}, \quad 20\% = \tfrac{1}{5},$$
$$75\% = \tfrac{3}{4}, \quad 12\tfrac{1}{2}\% = \tfrac{1}{8}, \quad 5\% = \tfrac{1}{20}, \quad 66\tfrac{2}{3}\% = \tfrac{2}{3}, \quad 2\tfrac{1}{2}\% = \tfrac{1}{40}.$$

Exercise 10.5 ▼

Find:

1. 10% of €380
2. 20% of €150
3. 25% of €3.36
4. 75% of €72.40
5. 5% of €120
6. 50% of 184 m
7. $12\tfrac{1}{2}\%$ of 400 m
8. 30% of €270.50
9. 35% of €520.20
10. 45% of 168.80
11. 11% of €350
12. 13% of $2\tfrac{1}{2}$ km
13. 31% of €120
14. 48% of €250
15. 8% of €50
16. 17% of €140
17. $7\tfrac{1}{2}\%$ of 6,160
18. $2\tfrac{1}{2}\%$ of €80.40
19. $33\tfrac{1}{3}\%$ of 900 m
20. $66\tfrac{2}{3}\%$ of €180
21. A school concert raised €2,480 for charity. After a vote it was decided to give 20% to charity A, 25% to charity B, 40% to charity C, and the remainder to charity D. How much was given to each charity?
22. Add 18% of €35 and 14% of €23.

Percentage increase or decrease

A change in a quantity, whether an increase or a decrease, is often described by a percentage. We will use two methods to increase or decrease a quantity by a percentage.

Example ▼

In 1994 the population of a town was 5,400. In 1998 it increased by 12%. What was the population of the town in 1998?

Solution:

Method 1:

$$1\% = \frac{5400}{100} = 54$$

Therefore $12\% = 54 \times 12 = 648$

Therefore the population in 1998
$= 5,400 + 648 = 6,048$

Method 2:

As a percentage, the population in 1998 is:

$100\% + 12\% = 112\%$ of the population in 1994.

Therefore the population in 1998
$= 112\%$ of 5,400
$= 1.12 \times 5,400 = 6,048$

A machine was bought for €15,000. During the year its value depreciated by 15%. Calculate the value of the machine at the end of the year.

Solution:

Method 1:

$$1\% = \frac{€15,000}{100} = €150$$

$15\% = €150 \times 15 = €2,250$

Therefore the value of the machine after a year

$= €15,000 - €2,250$

$= €12,750$

Method 2:

As a percentage the new value is:

$100\% - 15\% = 85\%$ of the old value.

Therefore the value of the machine after a year

$= 85\%$ of €15,000

$= €15,000 \times 0.85$

$= €12,750$

Exercise 10.6 ▼

1. Increase each of these amounts by 12%:
   (i) 300   **(ii)** 40   **(iii)** 120   **(iv)** 60   **(v)** 4,000

2. Decrease each of these amounts by 6%:
   (i) 200   **(ii)** 48   **(iii)** 15   **(iv)** 5,200   **(v)** 240

3. John weighs 125 kg before going on a diet. He sets himself a target of losing 8% of his original weight. What is his target weight?

4. Sarah earns €425 per week. She receives a pay rise of 7%.
   How much does she earn each week after the pay rise?

5. A bus ticket now costing €28 is due to rise by 12% in the new year.
   What will the price of the bus ticket be in the new year?

6. Apples cost 60c each. The shop reduces the price by 5%. Calculate the new price.

7. A lorry is carrying 750 kg of sand. For safety reasons, it has to reduce its load by 18%.
   Calculate the new weight the lorry is carrying after the reduction.

8. During a sale, a shop reduces the price of all goods by 15%. Calculate the sale price of the following four items:
   (a) a fridge costing €120   **(b)** a carpet costing €250.
   (c) a television set costing €550   **(d)** a woman's coat costing €785.

9. Because of low sales, a firm reduces its work force by
   (a) 18% of the factory workers and **(b)** 24% of the office staff. If 350 people work in the factory and 50 people work in the office, how many people will work in the firm after the reductions?

10. A car costing €20,000 depreciates (loses its value) each year based on its value at the beginning of each year. It depreciates by:
    10% in its first year, 8% in its second year, and 5% in its third year.
    Copy and complete the table to find the value of the car after three years.

New price	€20,000
Value after 1 year	
Value after 2 years	
Value after 3 years	

Percentage profit, loss, and discount

Percentage profit and loss

Profit and loss are often given as a percentage of the cost price. This is useful when we need to compare profit or loss on different items. Percentage profit or loss is calculated with the following formulas:

$$\text{Percentage profit} = \frac{\text{profit}}{\text{cost price}} \times 100\%$$

$$\text{Percentage loss} = \frac{\text{loss}}{\text{cost price}} \times 100\%$$

Note: It is usual in the business world to express profit or loss as a percentage of the selling price. However, in solving problems in arithmetic, always give profit or loss as a percentage of the cost price, unless instructed to do otherwise.

Example ▼

A dealer bought a piano for €4,000 and sold it for €5,000.

(i) Calculate the amount of profit made.
(ii) Express the profit as a percentage of (**a**) the cost price and (**b**) the selling price

Solution:
(i) Profit = selling price − cost price = €5,000 − €4,000 = €1,000

(ii)

(a) $\dfrac{\text{Percentage profit}}{\text{on cost price}} = \dfrac{\text{profit}}{\text{cost price}} \times 100\% = \dfrac{1000}{4000} \times 100\% = 25\%$

(b) $\dfrac{\text{Percentage profit}}{\text{on selling price}} = \dfrac{\text{profit}}{\text{selling price}} \times 100\% = \dfrac{1000}{5000} \times 100\% = 20\%$

Discount

A **discount** is a reduction in the selling price. Percentage discount is calculated as follows:

$$\text{Percentage discount} = \frac{\text{discount}}{\text{selling price}} \times 100\%$$

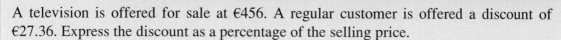

Example ▼

A television is offered for sale at €456. A regular customer is offered a discount of €27.36. Express the discount as a percentage of the selling price.

Solution:

Selling price = €456   discount = €27.36

$$\text{Percentage discount} = \frac{\text{discount}}{\text{selling price}} \times 100\% = \frac{27.36}{456} \times 100\% = 6\%$$

Exercise 10.7 ▼

Complete the following tables:

	Cost price	Selling price	Profit	Loss	Percentage profit or loss of the cost price
1.	€8	€10		—	
2.	€120	€108	—		
3.	€405	€486		—	
4.	€180	€153	—		
5.	€120	€129.60		—	
6.		€31.50	—	€3.50	
7.		€90	€10	—	
8.		€508	€108	—	
9.		€100	—	€50	
10.		€360	€144	—	
	Cost price	Selling price	Profit	Loss	Percentage profit or loss of the selling price
11.	€40	€ 50		—	
12.	€46	€ 50	—		
13.	€34	€ 40		—	
14.	€114	€120		—	
15.	€6.16	€5.50	—		
16.	€91.20		€28.80	—	
17.	€31		—	€11	
18.	€217		€31	—	
19.	€59		—	€9	
20.	€2,134		€66		

21. A dealer bought a table for €80 and sold it for €100.
   Express the profit as a percentage of **(i)** the cost price and **(ii)** the selling price.

22. A car was bought for €12,000 and sold for €10,200.
   Express the loss as a percentage of the cost price.

23. A motorbike was bought for €1,224 and sold for €1,481.04.
   Express the profit as a percentage of the cost price.

24. A girl bought a watch for €89.60 and sold it for €80.
   Express her loss as a percentage of the selling price.

25. A man bought an article for €150 and sold if for €225. Find the profit.
   Express the profit as a percentage of **(i)** the cost price and **(ii)** the selling price.

In each of the following, calculate the percentage discount:

	Selling price	Discount
26.	€40	€12
27.	€250	€30
28.	€350	€35
29.	€50	€4
30.	€240	€48

	Selling price	Discount
31.	€170	€42.50
32.	€7.60	€3.04
33.	€84	€14.28
34.	€1.20	24c
35.	€12.40	62c

Calculate the price of each of the following after the discount.

	Selling price	Discount
36.	€140	10%
37.	€20	15%
38.	€220	20%
39.	€44	25%
40.	€150	12%

	Selling price	Discount
41.	€120	8%
42.	€24	5%
43.	€72	$12\frac{1}{2}\%z$
44.	€60	$33\frac{1}{3}\%$
45.	€360	$17\frac{1}{2}\%$

46. A shop offers a discount of $12\frac{1}{2}\%$ on an article marked €36. How much is the discount?

Given a percentage of a quantity

In some questions on percentages we will be given an equation in disguise.
When this happens, do the following:

> **1.** Write down the equation given in disguise.
> **2.** From this equation find 1%.
> **3.** Calculate the required percentage.

(i) 85% of a number is 153. Find the number.

(ii) $4\frac{1}{2}\%$ of a number is 36. Find 16% of the number.

Solution:

(i) Equation given in disguise:

$85\% = 153$

$1\% = 1.8$ (divide both sides by 85)

$100\% = 180$ (multiply both sides by 100)

Therefore the number is 180.

Check: 85% of $180 = 0.85 \times 180 = 153$ ✓

(ii) Equation given in disguise:

$4\frac{1}{2}\% = 36$

$9\% = 72$ (multiply both sides by 2)

$1\% = 8$ (divide both sides by 9)

$16\% = 128$ (multiply both sides by 16)

Therefore 16% of the number is 128.

Check: $4\frac{1}{2}\% = 4\frac{1}{2} \times 8 = 36$ ✓

(i) The cost of a train ticket has risen by 5% to €15.96. What was the original price of the ticket?

(ii) A bicycle was sold for €384 at a loss of 20%. Find the original cost of the bicycle.

Solution:

(i) Think of the original price as 100%.

$100\% + 5\% = 105\%$

Therefore $105\% = €15.96$

(equation in disguise)

$1\% = €0.152$

(divide both sides by 105)

$100\% = €15.20$

(multiply both sides by 100)

Therefore the original price was €15.20

Check: 105% of €15.20 = €15.20 × 1.05

= 15.96 ✓

(ii) Think of the original cost as 100%.

$100\% - 20\% = 80\%$

Therefore $80\% = €384$

(equation in disguise)

$1\% = €4.8$

(divide both sides by 80)

$100\% = €480$

(multiply both sides by 100)

Therefore the original cost was €480

Check: 80% of €480 = €480 × 0.80 = €384 ✓

1. 8% of a certain number is 80. Find the number.
2. 20% of a certain sum of money is €60. Find this sum.
3. 15% of a number is 90. Find the number.
4. 40% of a number is 20. Find the number.
5. 8% of a population left a town. If the population is now 2,852, find the population before the 8% left. How many people left the town?
6. $12\frac{1}{2}$% of a certain sum of money is €72. Find the sum of money.
7. A woman received an increase of $2\frac{1}{2}$% in her weekly salary. If the increase was €10, find her new weekly salary.
8. 16% of a sum of money is €48. Find 11% of this sum.
9. 125% of a sum of money is €60. Find this sum.
10. 112% of a sum of money is €280. Find this sum.
11. After an increase of 20%, a motorbike was sold for €2,640. What was the original price?
12. A bicycle was sold for €272 at a loss of 15%. Find the original cost, and the amount of the loss.
13. The price of a holiday is increased by 8% to €583.20. What was the original cost of the holiday?
14. The price of a watch was reduced by 18% in the sales to €172.20. What was the pre-sale price?
15. A piece of elastic was stretched by 15% to a length of 16.1 cm. Calculate its unstretched original length.
16. A man went on a diet and reduced his weight by 8% to 147.2 kg. Calculate his original weight before he went on his diet.
17. A washing machine is advertised at €600 after a price reduction of 20%. What was the price before it was reduced?.
18. By selling a car for €8,840, the owner incurs a loss of 35% on the purchase price. Calculate the purchase price.
19. A solicitor's fee for the sale of a house is $1\frac{1}{2}$% of the selling price. If the fee is €2,610, calculate the selling price.
20. In an election the winning candidate received 154 votes, which represented 55% of the members of a club. The only other candidate received 25% of the votes and the remaining members did not vote.
    (i)   How many members are in the club?
    (ii) How many members voted for the unsuccessful candidate?
    (iii) How many members in the club did not vote in this election?
21. *A* sold an article to *B* for a gain of 10%. *B* sold it to *C* for a gain of 15%. If *C* paid €25.30, how much did *A* and *B* pay for it?

Chapter test

1. Copy and complete the following tables of equivalent percentages, fractions, and decimals:

Percentage	Fraction	Decimal
30%	$\frac{3}{10}$	0.3
20%		
		0.8
15%		
	$\frac{7}{10}$	
		0.4

Percentage	Fraction	Decimal
	$\frac{4}{25}$	
12%		
	$\frac{3}{2}$	
$12\frac{1}{2}\%$		
	$\frac{1}{100}$	
		0.025

2. Express **(i)** 36 as a percentage of 45, **(ii)** 39c as a percentage of €3.

3. Seán scored 63 out of 90 in a maths test and 18 out of 30 in an English test. In which test did he achieve the higher percentage?

4. There are 60 red, 75 green, 120 blue and 45 orange marbles in a bag. What percentage is each colour of the total?

5. (i) A woman bought a second-hand car for €8,600 and sold it for €7,482. Express her loss as a percentage of the cost price.

    (ii) Anne receives €5 in pocket money each week. She saves 25% of this and spends the remainder. How many weeks does it take Anne to save exactly €15?

6. A dealer bought a machine for €7,040 and immediately sold it for €8,000. Calculate his profit, as a percentage of the selling price.

7. In a school of 520 pupils, 35% play games. How many pupils do not play games?

8. A shop offers a discount of $12\frac{1}{2}\%$ on an article marked €50.40. How much is the discount?

9. Find $12\frac{1}{2}\%$ of €3.44 + $33\frac{1}{3}\%$ of €4.80.

10. An article was bought for €54 and sold for a profit of 15%. Calculate the selling price.

11. A computer costs €6,000 when new. In the first year it depreciates by 10%. In the second year it depreciates by 8% of its value at the end of the first year. In the third year it depreciates by 5% of its value at the end of the second year. By completing the table, calculate its value after three years.

New price	€6,000
Value after 1 year	
Value after 2 years	
Value after 3 years	

12. 13% of a number is 156. Find 8% of the number.

13. A girl bought a book for €16.33. If the bookseller made a profit of 15%, how much did he pay for the book?

14. A shopkeeper pays €240 for a bicycle and marks it up so that she makes a profit of 20%. Find the selling price.

During a sale the price of the bicycle is reduced by 5%.

(a) Calculate the price of the bicycle during the sale.

(b) Express the profit during the sale as a percentage of the cost price.

15. Express $\frac{2}{3}$ of 0.48 as a percentage of 2.56.

16. Two cars, P and Q, were brought for €12,000 and €8,000, respectively. Car P was sold at a profit of 15%, while car Q was sold at a loss of 10%. Calculate the overall percentage profit or loss.

17. By selling an article for €535 a shopkeeper makes a profit of 7%. For how much must he sell the article to make a profit of 15%?

18. When 9% of the pupils in a school are absent, 637 are present. How many pupils are on the school roll?

19. A woman sold an item for €392 and in so doing made a profit of 12%. How much did the item cost her?

20. A box containing 40 candles was bought by a shopkeeper. He sold all 40 candles for €1.80 each, which gave him a profit of 20%. How much did the shopkeeper pay for the box of candles?

21. A youth club collects the same membership subscription from each of its 140 members. 15% of the club's members have still to pay their subscription. How many members have not paid their subscription? If the subscriptions not yet paid amount to €50.40, calculate the subscription for each club member.

22. Patrick has €14.25 of his birthday money left after spending 10% of it on chocolate and 15% of it on a magazine.

(i) How much money did Patrick get for his birthday?

(ii) How much did he spend on chocolate?

(iii) What was the price of the magazine?

VAT AND INCOME TAX

VAT I

Value-added tax (VAT) is a tax on goods and services. The rate of VAT is given in the form of a percentage, for example 15% VAT.

Note: Be careful with VAT, as some prices are given inclusive of VAT (the VAT has already been added on), while other prices are given exclusive of VAT (the VAT has not been added on yet).

Example ▼

VAT at 21% is added to a bill of €160. Calculate the total bill, including the VAT.

Solution:

Method 1:

$$1\% = \frac{€160}{100} = €1.60$$

$21\% = €1.60 \times 21 = €33.60$

Therefore the total bill is

$€160 + €33.60 = €193.60$

Method 2:

As a percentage, the new bill is:

$100\% + 21\% = 121\%$ of the bill without VAT.

$= 121\%$ of €160

$= €160 \times 1.21 = €193.60$

Example ▼

A garage bill came to €120. When VAT was added to the bill it amounted to €138. Calculate the rate of VAT.

Solution:

VAT added = bill including VAT − bill excluding VAT

$= €138 − €120 = €18$

$$\text{Rate of VAT} = \frac{\text{VAT added on}}{\text{bill excluding VAT}} \times 100\% = \frac{18}{120} \times 100\% = 15\%$$

Complete the following table, where the bill does not include VAT:

	Bill	**VAT rate**	**VAT**	**Bill including VAT**
1.	€140	10%		
2.	€210	15%		
3.	€136	12%		
4.	€118	13%		
5.	€45	18%		
6.	€540	23%		
7.	€32	21%		
8.	€600	$12\frac{1}{2}\%$		
9.	€1,080	$17\frac{1}{2}\%$		
10.	€150	$8\frac{1}{2}\%$		
11.	€80			€92
12.	€150			€177
13.	€2,500			€3,075
14.	€145		€11.60	
15.	€1,040			€1,170
16.	€105			€127.05

17. A radio costs €124. For how much would it be sold if the rate of VAT is 23%?

18. Calculate the VAT payable on a garage bill of €380 if the rate of VAT is 18%.

19. A magazine is advertised as €4.20 + VAT. If the VAT rate is 15%, what is the selling price of the magazine?

20. VAT at the rate of $12\frac{1}{2}\%$ is added to an electricity bill of €96. Calculate the bill including the VAT.

21. A man bought a coat for €150 + VAT and an electric razor for €80 + VAT. If VAT on clothes is 12% and VAT on electronic equipment is 21%, find how much he paid in total, including the VAT.

22. The price of a watch was €120 + VAT. If the price paid was €134.40, calculate the rate of VAT.

23. An article was priced at €180 + VAT. If a person paid €221.40 for the article, calculate the rate of VAT.

24. A tanker delivered oil to a school. Before the delivery the meter showed 11,360 litres of oil in the tanker. After the delivery, the meter reading was 7,160 litres.

(i) How many litres of oil were delivered to the school?

(ii) Calculate the cost of oil delivered if 1 litre of oil costs 41c.

(iii) When VAT was added to the price of the oil delivered, the bill to the school amounted to €2,083.62. Calculate the rate of VAT added.

VAT 2

Often a price includes VAT, and we have to work in reverse to calculate the VAT or the price before VAT was added on.

Example ▼

A garage bill for repairs to a car came to €295.20, including VAT at 23%. Calculate the bill before VAT was added.

Solution:

Think of the bill before the VAT was added on as 100%.

$$100\% + 23\% = 123\%$$

Therefore 123% = €295.20	(equation given in disguise)
1% = €2.40	(divide both sides by 123)
100% = €240	(multiply both sides by 100)

check: 123% of €240 = €240 × 1.23 = €295.20 ✓

Exercise 11.2 ▼

Complete the following table:

	Price including VAT	VAT rate	Price without VAT	VAT
1.	€275	10%		
2.	€138	15%		
3.	€252	5%		
4.	€968	21%		
5.	€5,535	23%		
6.	€89.60	12%		
7.	423.50	21%		
8.	€63.72	18%		
9.	€56.16	8%		
10.	202.50	$12\frac{1}{2}\%$		

11. The price of a chair is €46 including VAT. If the rate of VAT is 15%, how much does the chair cost without VAT?

12. A table is priced at €767, which includes VAT at 18%. How much does the table cost without VAT?
13. A telephone bill, including VAT at 21%, came to €99.22. Calculate the bill without VAT.
14. With VAT included, a solicitor's bill came to €295.20. If the rate of VAT is 23%, calculate the bill without VAT.
15. A motorbike is priced at €1,086.40, which includes VAT at 12%. Calculate **(i)** the price without VAT **(ii)** the VAT.
16. When a woman bought a television set in a shop, VAT at 23% was added on. If the VAT on the cost of the set was €195.50, what was the price of the television set before VAT was added? What was the price including VAT?
17. A man bought a microwave oven in a shop. The rate of VAT was 18%, and the VAT amounted to €75.60. How much in total did he pay for the microwave oven?
18. A boy bought a calculator for €73.80, which included VAT at 23%. Find the price of the calculator if VAT was reduced to 15%.
19. The selling price of a car was €13,125, which included 25% VAT. Before it was sold, the VAT rate was reduced from 25% to 15%. Find the new selling price of the car.
20. When the rate of VAT was increased from 18% to 23%, the price of a guitar increased by €40. Calculate the price of the guitar, inclusive of the VAT at 23%.

Income tax I

Income tax is a tax taken as a proportion of any money earned. The amount of income tax depends on the amount of money earned, your personal allowances, and the rate of tax. Your **'tax-free allowance'** is the amount of money that you can earn without paying any tax on it. Any income above this, called **'taxable income'**, is the income on which tax is paid.
This leads to the income tax equation:

Gross income – tax-free allowance = taxable income.

Note: Gross income is the amount of money earned **before** any deductions are made. Net income (also called take-home pay) is the amount of money left after all deductions have been taken away.

Example ▼

A person has a gross yearly income of €42,000 and a tax-free allowance of €12,600.

(i) Find the taxable income.
(ii) Income tax is paid at the rate of 40c in the euro, on taxable income. Calculate the amount of tax paid in the year.
(iii) Calculate net income for the year.
(iv) Express tax paid for the year as a percentage of gross income for the year.

Solution:

(i)   Gross income – tax-free allowance = taxable income (income tax equation)

€42,000 – €12,600 = €29,400

Therefore taxable income = €29,400

(ii)   The person has to pay tax on €29,400 at the rate of 40c in the euro.

40% of €29,400 = €29,400 × 0.4 = €11,760

Therefore tax paid for the year = €11,760

(iii)   Net income = gross income – tax paid

= €42,000 – €11,760 = €30,240

Therefore net income for the year = €30,240

(iv)   Tax as a percentage of gross income $= \dfrac{\text{tax}}{\text{gross income}} \times 100\%$

$= \dfrac{11{,}760}{42{,}000} \times 100\% = 28\%$

Note: 40c in the euro is the same as 40%.

Exercise 11.3 ▼

Complete the following table which shows some of the yearly income for ten people:

	Gross income	Tax-free allowance	Taxable income	Rate of tax	Tax paid	Net income
1.	€18,000	€8,000		20c in the €		
2.	€45,500	€12,200		40c in the €		
3.	€24,800	€9,450		24c in the €		
4.	€16,480	€5,280		46c in the €		
5.	€24,240	€7,350		25c in the €		
6.	€34,760	€9,450		32c in the €		
7.	€28,780	€9,542		35c in the €		
8.		€8,345	€16,920	28c in the €		
9.		€6,720	€18,480	22c in the €		
10.		€6,104	€13,405	19c in the €		

11. A woman has a gross yearly income of €27,200 and a tax-free allowance of €6,800.

(i)   Find her taxable income.

(ii)   Income tax is paid at the rate of 20c in the euro on taxable income. Calculate the amount of tax paid in the year.

(iii) Calculate net income for the year.

(iv) Express her tax paid for the year as a percentage of her gross income for the year.

12. A man has a gross yearly income of €38,500 and a tax-free allowance of €7,700.
   (i)   Find his taxable income.
   (ii) Income tax is paid at the rate of 40c in the euro on taxable income. Calculate the amount of tax paid in the year.
   (iii) Calculate net income for the year.
   (iv) Express his tax paid for the year as a percentage of his gross income for the year.

13. A person has a gross yearly income of €24,640 and a tax-free allowance of €5,600.
   (i)   Find their taxable income.
   (ii) Income tax is paid at the rate of 22c in the euro on taxable income. Calculate the amount of tax paid in the year.
   (iii) Calculate net income for the year.
   (iv) Express their net pay for the year as a percentage of gross income for the year.

14. A person has a gross yearly income of €28,672 and a tax-free allowance of €10,752.
   (i)   Find their taxable income.
   (ii) Income tax is paid at the rate of 32c in the euro on taxable income. Calculate the amount of tax paid in the year.
   (iii) Calculate net income for the year.
   (iv) Express their net pay for the year as a percentage of gross income for the year.

15. A person has a gross yearly income of €21,875 and a tax-free allowance of €5,250.
   (i)   Find their taxable income.
   (ii) Income tax is paid at the rate of 25c in the euro on taxable income. Calculate the amount of tax paid in the year.
   (iii) Calculate net income for the year.
   (iv) Express their tax paid for the year as a percentage of gross income for the year.

In some questions we have to split the taxable income into two parts, which are taxed at different rates. Consider the next example:

Example ▼

A woman with an annual gross income of €24,000 has a tax-free allowance of €5,775 per annum. If she pays tax at 25c in the euro on the first €5,400 of taxable income and tax at 40c in the euro on the remainder of taxable income, calculate the total amount of tax payable. Express the total tax payable as a percentage of gross income.

Solution:
Gross income – tax-free allowance = taxable income (income tax equation)

$$€24,000 – €5,775 = €18,225$$

Therefore she must pay tax on €18,225, i.e. her taxable income.

The tax on taxable income is split as follows:

Tax = 25% of €5,400 + 40% of €12,825
   = €5,400 × 0.25 + €12,825 × 0.40
   = €1,350 + €5,130
   = €6,480

Difference
18,225
5,400
12,825

$$\text{Tax as a percentage of gross income} = \frac{\text{tax}}{\text{gross income}} \times 100\% = \frac{6,480}{24,000} \times 100\% = 27\%$$

16. A woman with an annual gross income of €40,000 has a tax-free allowance of €15,000 per annum. If she pays tax at 24c in the euro on the first €10,000 of taxable income and tax at 45c in the euro on the remainder of taxable income, calculate the total amount of tax payable.

17. A man with an annual gross income of €38,000 has a tax-free allowance of €8,500 per annum. If he pays tax at 20c in the euro on the first €5,500 of taxable income and tax at 40c in the euro on the remainder of taxable income, calculate the total amount of tax payable and the net income.

18. A woman with an annual gross income of €25,000 has a tax-free allowance of €8,400 per annum. If she pays tax at 22c in the euro on the first €4,300 of taxable income and tax at 38c in the euro on the remainder of taxable income, calculate the total amount of tax payable.

19. A woman with an annual gross income of €20,200 has a tax-free allowance of €1,640 per annum. If she pays tax at 25c in the euro on the first €6,400 of taxable income and tax at 40c in the euro on the remainder of taxable income, calculate the total amount of tax payable. Express the total tax payable as a percentage of gross income.

20. A man with an annual gross income of €30,000 has a tax-free allowance of €12,240 per annum. If he pays tax at 25c in the euro on the first €5,760 of taxable income and tax at 48c in the euro on the remainder of taxable income, calculate the total amount of tax payable. Express the total tax payable as a percentage of gross income.

Example ▼

A person whose gross salary is €15,000 has a tax-free allowance of €8,000. If she pays €2,450 tax, calculate the rate of tax on taxable income.

Solution:

Gross income – tax free allowance = taxable income (income tax equation)
   €15,000 – €8,000 = €7,000

$$\text{Rate of tax} = \frac{\text{tax}}{\text{taxable income}} \times 100\% = \frac{2450}{7000} \times 100\% = 35\%$$

or the rate of tax is 35c in the euro.

Complete the following table, which shows some of the yearly income of ten people:

	Gross income	Tax-free allowance	Taxable income	Tax paid	Rate of tax on taxable income
21.	€20,000	€8,000		€4,800	
22.	€16,500	€5,500		€2,200	
23.	€45,320	€8,320		€12,950	
24.	€18,318	€4,318		€2,520	
25.	€27,400	€5,300		€5,525	
26.	€32,540	€6,750		€5,673.80	
27.	€23,150	€4,340		€4,514.40	
28.	€16,894	€5,724		€4,244.60	
29.	€22,342	€4,762		€5,625.60	
30.	€25,873	€6,874		€5,129.73	

31. A man has a gross salary of €42,340 and a tax-free allowance of €11,590. Calculate his taxable income. If he pays €9,840 in tax, calculate the rate of tax on his taxable income

32. A woman has a gross salary of €37,510 and a tax-free allowance of €9,750. Calculate her taxable income. If she pays €11,104 in tax, calculate the rate of tax on her taxable income.

33. A man whose gross salary is €23,478 has a tax-free allowance of €6,348. If he pays €3,939.90 in tax, calculate the rate of tax on taxable income.

34. A married couple have a joint gross salary of €67,852. Their combined tax-free allowance is €14,692. If they paid €20,200.80 in tax, express the tax paid as a percentage of their taxable income.

Income tax 2

In some questions we are given the rate of tax on taxable income, the tax paid, and the tax-free allowance, and we are asked to find the gross income. Essentially, we are given an equation in disguise.

These questions are solved with the following steps:

1. Write down the equation given in disguise (i.e. a certain percentage of taxable income).
2. Divide both sides by the given percentage (this gives 1% of taxable income).
3. Multiply both sides by 100% (this gives the taxable income).
4. Substitute this 'taxable income' and the given 'tax-free allowance' in the income tax equation: gross income – tax-free allowance = taxable income.

In some questions we are given the gross income and are asked to find the tax-free allowance. The method is the same, with 'tax-free allowance' replacing 'gross income' in the steps described above.

Example ▼

When income tax is charged at 27c in the euro, a man pays €4,077 in income tax. If his tax-free allowance is €4,500, calculate his gross income.

Solution:
Equation given in disguise:

$$27\% \text{ of taxable income} = €4,077 \quad \text{(equation given in disguise)}$$
$$1\% \text{ of taxable income} = €151 \quad \text{(divide both sides by 27)}$$
$$\text{Therefore taxable income} = €15,100 \quad \text{(multiply both sides by 100)}$$
$$\text{Gross income} - \text{tax-free allowance} = \text{taxable income} \quad \text{(income tax equation)}$$
$$\text{Therefore gross income} = \text{taxable income} + \text{allowances}$$
$$= €15,100 \qquad + €4,500$$
$$= €19,600$$

Therefore his gross salary is €19,600.

Exercise 11.4 ▼

Complete the following table, which shows some of the yearly income figures for ten people:

	Rate of tax on taxable income	Actual tax paid	Tax-free allowance	Gross income
1.	20c in the €	€3,200	€4,500	
2.	25c in the €	€4,800	€4,750	
3.	40c in the €	€3,400	€6,420	
4.	18c in the €	€3,312	€7,180	
5.	22c in the €	€4,268		€26,250
6.	24c in the €	€3,528		€20,672
7.	30c in the €	€4,590		€21,841
8.	42c in the €	€6,132		€20,027
9.	38c in the €	€6,612	€5,428	
10.	27c in the €	€6,752.70		€32,000

11. When income tax is charged at 25c in the euro, a man pays €3,475 in income tax. If his tax-free allowance is €4,500, calculate his gross income.

12. When the rate of tax is 32c in the euro, a man with a tax-free allowance of €6,380 pays €5,600 in income tax. Calculate his gross income.

13. When income tax is charged at 40c in the euro, a woman pays €10,000 in income tax. If her gross income is €32,500, calculate her tax-free allowance.

14. A woman has a gross income of €36,280. When income tax is charged at 20c in the euro, she paid €6,500 in income tax. Calculate her tax-free allowance.

15. A married couple have a tax-free allowance of €12,480 and pay tax at 35c in the euro on the rest of their income. If they pay €14,175 tax in a year, calculate their gross income for that year.

Exercise 11.5 ▼

Chapter test

1. VAT at 21% is added to a bill of €50. Calculate the total bill, including VAT.

2. A bill came to €110. When VAT was added, the bill came to €123.20. Calculate the rate of VAT.

3. A woman buys a coat for €140 + VAT. How much will she pay if VAT is 23%?

4. The price of a table is €138, including VAT at 15%. Calculate the VAT.

5. A gas bill is €108.90, including VAT at 21%. Calculate the VAT.

6. A bill, including VAT at 33%, came to €93.10. Calculate the bill without VAT.

7. A man buys a calculator for €96.80, which includes VAT at 21%. Find the price of the calculator if VAT is reduced to 10%.

8. An electricity meter has a reading of 2,022 units. The previous reading was 1,172. How many units of electricity were used?
The price of electricity is 9.2c per unit. Calculate the price of the units used.
A standing charge of €5.80 is added to the bill, and then VAT at 15% must be paid on the whole bill (including the standing charge). What is the total amount of the bill?

9. Complete the following ESB bill:

Meter reading		Units used	Rate per unit	Description	Amount
Present	Previous				
22,918	21,068		9.5c	Cost of units used	
				Standing charge	€4.25
				VAT @ $12\frac{1}{2}$ %	
				Total due	

10. A person has a gross yearly income of €32,640 and a tax-free allowance of €8,160.
  (i) Find their taxable income.
  (ii) Income tax is paid at the rate of 20c in the euro on taxable income. Calculate the amount of tax paid in the year.

    (iii) Calculate net income for the year.

    (iv) Express their net pay for the year as a percentage of their gross income for the year.

11. A person has a gross yearly income of €32,725 and a tax-free allowance of €6,545.

    (i) Find their taxable income.

    (ii) Income tax is paid at the rate of 40c in the euro on taxable income. Calculate the amount of tax paid in the year.

    (iii) Calculate net income for the year.

    (iv) Express their net pay for the year as a percentage of their gross income for the year.

12. A woman has a gross yearly income of €30,800 and a personal tax-free allowance of €7,000.

    (i) Find her taxable income.

    (ii) Income tax is paid at the rate of 22c in the euro on taxable income. Calculate the amount of tax paid in the year.

    (iii) Calculate net income for the year.

    (iv) Express her tax paid for the year as a percentage of her gross income for the year.

13. A man has a gross yearly income of €43,008 and a tax-free allowance of €16,128.

    (i) Find his taxable income.

    (ii) Income tax is paid at the rate of 32c in the euro on taxable income. Calculate the amount of tax paid in the year.

    (iii) Calculate net income for the year.

    (iv) Express his tax paid for the year as a percentage of his gross income for the year.

14. A man with an annual gross income of €37,590 has a tax-free allowance of €9,480. If he pays tax at 22c in the euro on the first €14,000 of taxable income and 35c in the euro on the remainder of taxable income, calculate the total amount of tax payable.

15. A woman with an annual gross income of €42,300 has a tax-free allowance of €11,480. If she pays tax at 20c in the euro on the first €9,000 of taxable income and 40c in the euro on the remainder of taxable income, calculate the total amount of tax payable and the net income.

16. A man has a gross salary of €39,480 and a tax-free allowance of €12,280. Calculate his taxable income. If he pays €9,792 in tax, calculate the rate of tax on his taxable income.

17. A woman has a gross salary of €31,200 and a tax-free allowance of €12,600. Calculate her taxable income. If she pays €7,440 in tax, calculate the rate of tax on her taxable income.

18. When the rate of tax is 25c in the euro, a man with a tax-free allowance of €9,500 pays €5,050 in income tax. Calculate his gross income.

19. When income tax is charged at 20c in the euro, a woman pays €4,700 in income tax. If her gross income is €34,900, calculate her tax-free allowance.

20. When income tax is charged at 40c in the euro, a man pays €9,960 in income tax. If his tax-free allowances amount to €12,700, calculate his gross income.

ANNUAL AND COMPOUND INTEREST

Interest

Interest is the sum of money that you pay for borrowing money or that is paid to you for lending money. When dealing with interest we use the following symbols:

P = the '**principal**', the sum of money borrowed or invested.
T = the '**time**', the number of years for which the sum of money is borrowed or invested.
R = the '**rate**', the percentage rate per annum at which interest is charged.
I = the '**interest**', the sum of money paid for borrowing or lending money.
A = the '**amount**', the principal and the interest added together: $A = P + I$.

Note: per annum = per year.

Annual interest

Annual interest, as its name suggests, is the interest for borrowing or lending money for one year. We have a formula for calculating the interest for **one** year:

$$I = P\left(\frac{R}{100}\right)$$

Example ▼

€250 was invested for a year at 2.5% per annum. Calculate the interest earned.

Solution:
Given: $P = 250$, $R = 2.5$. Find I.

$$I = P\left(\frac{R}{100}\right) = 250\left(\frac{2.5}{100}\right) = 250(0.025) = 6.25$$

Therefore the interest earned is €6.25.

€540 is borrowed at 8% per annum. Calculate the amount owed after one year.

Solution:
Given: $P = 540$, $R = 8$. Find I and then A.

$$I = P\left(\frac{R}{100}\right) = 540\left(\frac{8}{100}\right) = 540(0.08) = 43.20$$

$$A = P + I = 540 + 43.20 = 583.20$$

Therefore the amount owed after one year is €583.20.

Exercise 12.1 ▼

Complete the following tables:

	€P	R%	€I	€A
1.	1,000	10		
2.	3,000	8		
3.	8,000	5		
4.	5,000	6		
5.	400	3		

	€P	R%	€I	€A
6.	280	4		
7.	320	7		
8.	250	5·5		
9.	80	3·4		
10.	3,240	2·1		

11. €2,000 was invested for a year at 3% per annum. Calculate the interest.
12. €540 was invested for a year at 6% per annum. Calculate the interest.
13. €920 was invested for a year at 8% per annum. Calculate the interest.
14. €1,200 is borrowed at $2\frac{1}{2}$% per annum. Calculate the interest owed after one year.
15. €580 is borrowed at $3\frac{1}{2}$% per annum. Calculate the amount owed after one year.
16. €640 is borrowed at $4\frac{1}{2}$% per annum. Calculate the amount owed after one year.
17. A woman deposited €2,400 in a building society, where she is offered $5\frac{1}{2}$% per annum interest. How much will she have at the end of the year?
18. A man borrowed €5,000 from a bank at a rate of 4% per annum. He agreed to pay off the loan at the end of one year with one payment. How much did he need to pay to clear the loan?
19. A woman borrowed €4,500 from a bank at a rate of $8\frac{1}{2}$% per annum. She agreed to repay €2,200 of the amount outstanding after one year. How much did she still owe the bank after one year?

Inverse problems on annual interest

Often in questions we are asked to find the principal, P, or the interest rate, R. To do this we rearrange the formula for annual interest to get the two formulas:

$$P = \frac{I}{R} \times 100 \qquad\qquad R = \frac{I}{P} \times 100$$

Example ▼

What sum of money will earn €44.80 interest if it is invested at 8% per annum for one year?

Solution:
Given: $I = 44.80$, $R = 8$. Find P.

$$P = \frac{I}{R} \times 100 = \frac{44.80}{8} \times 100 = 560$$

Therefore the sum of money invested is €560.

Alternative method: Write down the equation given in disguise.

Given: 8% = €44.80   (8% of the principal is €44.80)
           1% = €5.60   (divide both sides by 8)
     100% = €560   (multiply both sides by 100)

Therefore the sum of money invested is €560.

Example ▼

€350 was invested for one year and amounted to €362.25. Calculate the rate of interest per annum.

Solution:
Given: $P = 350$, $A = 362.25$. Find I and then find R.

$$I = A - P = 362.25 - 350 = 12.25$$

$$R = \frac{I}{P} \times 100 = \frac{12.25}{350} \times 100 = 3.5$$

Therefore the rate of interest per annum is 3.5%

Complete the following tables:

	€I	€P	R%	€A
1.	24		8	
2.	30	500		
3.	30		3	
4.	32	400		
5.	60		4	
6.	96	1,200		
7.	300		6	
8.	126	1,400		

	€I	€P	R%	€A
9.	31.50		7	
10.	75.60	840		
11.	13.50		2.5	
12.	44.55	810		
13.		600		660
14.		1,800		1,872
15.		2,500		2,562.50
16.		3,200		3,372.80

17. What sum of money will earn €600 interest if it is invested at 4% per annum for one year?

18. €800 was invested for one year and amounted to €856. Calculate the rate of interest per annum.

19. What sum of money will earn €29.25 interest if it is invested for one year at $6\frac{1}{2}\%$ per annum?

20. €720 was invested for a year and amounted to €752.40. Calculate the annual rate of interest.

Given the amount and the annual rate of interest

In some questions we are given the amount and the annual rate of interest and are asked to find the principal, P, and sometimes the interest, I. Essentially we are given an equation in disguise, and from this we can find 1% of the principal and thus find the principal and the interest.

Example ▼

A sum of money, P, invested for a year at 6% per annum amounted to €445.20. Calculate the sum of money invested and the interest earned.

Solution:
Given: $A = 445.20$, $R = 6$. Find P and then I.
Equation in disguise: $106\% = 445.20$ $(100\% + 6\% = 106\%)$
               $1\% = 4.2$ (divide both sides by 106)
             $100\% = 420$ (multiply both sides by 100)
Threrefore the sum of money invested, P, is €420.
$I = A - P = €445.20 - €420 = €25.20$

Complete the following tables. In each question a sum of money, P, is invested for one year and amounts to a sum of money, A, and an interest rate, R, per annum.
(Hint: Write down the equation given in disguise.)

	€A	R%	€P	€I
1.	648	8		
2.	840	5		
3.	530	6		
4.	2,080	4		
5.	4,950	10		
6.	1,635	9		
7.	428	7		
8.	206	3		

	€A	R%	€P	€I
9.	1,479	2		
10.	381.60	6		
11.	2,719.50	11		
12.	950.40	8		
13.	657.20	6		
14.	738.40	4		
15.	279.45	3.5		
16.	825.55	4.5		

17. A sum of money invested for a year at 4% per annum amounted to €4,368. Calculate the sum of money and the interest earned.
18. A woman borrowed a sum of money for a year at 8% per annum. At the end of the year she paid back €7,344. This cleared the loan, including the interest charged. How much did she borrow?

Compound interest

Very often when a sum of money earns interest this interest is added to the principal and earns interest in the next year, and so on. This is called '**compound interest**'. When calculating compound interest, do the following:

Method 1:
Calculate the interest for the **first** year and add this to the principal to form the new principal for the next year. Calculate the interest for **one** year on this new principal and add it on to form the principal for the next year, and so on. The easiest way to calculate each stage is to multiply the principal at the beginning of each year by the factor

$$\left(1 + \frac{R}{100}\right)$$

This will give the principal for the next year, and so on.

Method 2:

Use the formula: $A = P\left(1 + \dfrac{R}{100}\right)^{T}$, where T = the number of years.

It is not necessary to memorise the formula, as compound interest problems are best solved a year at a time (as described in method 1). The examination questions will not require you to calculate compound interest beyond **three** years. Besides, the formula does not work if

(a) the interest rate, R, is changed during the three years, or
(b) money is added or subtracted during the three years.

In the next examples,

P_1 = principal at the beginning of year 1; A_1 = amount at the end of year 1.
P_2 = principal at the beginning of year 2; A_2 = amount at the end of year 2.
P_3 = principal at the beginning of year 3; A_3 = amount at the end of year 3.

Example ▼

Calculate the compound interest on €2,500 for three years at 6% per annum.

Solution:

$1 + \dfrac{R}{100} = 1 + \dfrac{6}{100} = 1 + 0.06 = 1.06$

Method 1:
$P_1 = 2,500$
$A_1 = 2,500 \times 1.06 = 2,650$
$P_2 = 2,650$
$A_2 = 2,650 \times 1.06 = 2,809$
$P_3 = 2,809$
$A_3 = 2,809 \times 1.06 = 2,977.54$
Compound interest $= A_3 - P_1 = €2,977.54 - €2,500 = €477.54$

Method 2: Using the formula
Given: $P = 2,500$, $R = 6$, and $T = 3$. Find A.

$A = P\left(1 + \dfrac{R}{100}\right)^{T}$

$A = 2,500(1.06)^3$
$A = 2,977.54$ ▦ $2,500 \times 1.06 \; \boxed{y^x} \; 3 \; \boxed{=}$
Compound interest $= A - P = €2,977.54 - €2,500 = €477.54$

Calculate the compound interest on each of the following investments:

1. €500 for 2 years at 6% per annum
2. €4,000 for 2 years at 5% per annum
3. €2,500 for 2 years at 8% per annum
4. €3,600 for 2 years at 7% per annum
5. €800 for 2 years at 4% per annum
6. €1,200 for 2 years at 3% per annum
7. €800 for 2 years at 10% per annum
8. €3,000 for 2 years at 8% per annum
9. €350 for 3 years at 10% per annum
10. €2,500 for 3 years at 8% per annum
11. €4,000 for 3 years at 5% per annum
12. €10,000 for 3 years at 6% per annum
13. €80 for 3 years at 5% per annum
14. €20,000 for 3 years at 4% per annum
15. €15,000 for 3 years at 12% per annum
16. €25,000 for 3 years at 6% per annum

17. A person invests €12,400 at 6.5% per annum compound interest for two years. What does the investment amount to at the end of **(i)** one year **(ii)** two years?

(Hint: When $R = 6.5$, $1 + \dfrac{R}{100} = 1 + \dfrac{6.5}{100} = 1 + 0.065 = 1.065$)

18. A man borrowed €7,500 at 8% per annum compound interest. He agreed to pay back the entire loan including interest after three years. How much did he pay back?

19. A woman invests €12,500 for 3 years at 6% per annum compound interest. Calculate the interest earned in: **(i)** the first year **(ii)** the second year **(iii)** the third year.
    How much is her investment worth at the end of three years?

20. €10,000 is invested for one year at 4% per annum. Calculate the interest earned. The initial €10,000 and the interest earned for the year are reinvested for another two years at 4% per annum compound interest. Calculate the value of the investment at the end of the three years.

21. Post Office savings certificates pay 3% per annum compound interest if the money is invested for three years. How much would €20,000 amount to if invested with the Post Office for three years?

22. €4,000 is invested for one year and amounts to €4,200. Calculate the annual rate of interest, R. The €4,200 is then invested at $R\%$ per annum compound interest for two years. Calculate the total interest earned for the three years of the investment.

Compound interest when the rate changes

In some questions the annual interest changes each year. When this happens it is important to remember that the **formula does not work**. Consider the next example.

Example ▼

€8,500 was invested for 3 years at compound interest. The rate for the first year was 6%, the rate for the second year was 8%, and the rate for the third year was 5%. Calculate the amount at the end of the third year and the compound interest earned.

Solution:

The rate changes every year, therefore we cannot use the formula.

$P_1 = 8,500$

$A_1 = 8,500 \times 1.06 = 9,100$ $\qquad \left(1 + \dfrac{R_1}{100} = 1 + \dfrac{6}{100} = 1 + 0{\cdot}06 = 1{\cdot}06\right)$

$P_2 = 9,010$

$A_2 = 9,010 \times 1.08 = 9,730.80$ $\qquad \left(1 + \dfrac{R_2}{100} = 1 + \dfrac{8}{100} = 1 + 0{\cdot}08 = \; = 1{\cdot}08\right)$

$P_3 = 9,730.80$

$A_3 = 9,730.80 \times 1.05 = 10,217.34$ $\qquad \left(1 + \dfrac{R_3}{100} = 1 + \dfrac{5}{100} = 1 + 0{\cdot}05 = \; = 1{\cdot}05\right)$

Therefore the amount after three years is €10,217.34.

Compound interest $= A_3 - P_1 = $ €10,217.34 − €8,500 = €1,717.34
The working can also be shown using a table:

Year	Principal	Amount
1	8,500	8,500 × 1.06 = 9,010
2	9,010	9,010 × 1.08 = 9,730.80
3	9,730.80	9,730.80 × 1.05 = 10,217.34

Compound interest $= A_3 - P_1 = $ €10,217.34 − €8,500 = €1,717.34

1. €8,000 was invested for two years at compound interest. The interest rate for the first year was 4% and for the second was 5%. Calculate the total interest earned.

2. A person invested €3,500 at compound interest for two years. The interest rate for the first year was 5% and for the second was 7%. Calculate the total interest earned.

3. A man borrowed €10,000 at compound interest for two years. The interest rate for the first year was 8% and for the second was 6%. He agreed to pay off the loan, including the interest, after two years. Calculate how much he needed to pay to clear the loan.

4. A woman invested €5,000 at compound interest for two years. The interest rate for the first year was 3% and for the second was 4%. Calculate the value of her investment at the end of two years.

5. €6,500 was invested for three years at compound interest. The interest rate for the first year was 5%, for the second year 8%, and for the third year 12%. Calculate the total interest earned.

6. €7,500 was invested for three years at compound interest. The rate for the first year was 6%, the rate for the second year was 8%, and the rate for the third year was 5%. Calculate the total interest earned.

7. €15,000 was invested for three years at compound interest. The rate for the first year was 8%, the rate for the second year was 12%, and the rate for the third year was 9%. Calculate the amount after three years.

8. €2500 was invested for three years at compound interest. The rate for the first year was 4%, the rate for the second year was 3%, and the rate for the third year was $2\frac{1}{2}\%$. Calculate the amount after three years.

Repayments

In some questions money is repaid at the end of a year. Again, it is important to remember that in this case the **formula does not work**.

Consider the next example, where r_1 = repayment at the end of year 1 and r_2 = repayment at the end of year 2.

A person borrowed €6,000 at 12% per annum compound interest. If they repay €2,000 at the end of each year, how much is outstanding after the second repayment?

Solution:

$$1 + \frac{R}{100} = 1 + \frac{12}{100} = 1 + 0.12 = 1.12$$

$$
\begin{aligned}
P_1 &= 6{,}000 \\
A_1 &= 6{,}000 \times 1.12 \\
&= 6{,}720 \\
r_1 &= 2{,}000 \\
P_2 &= 4{,}720 \\
A_2 &= 4{,}720 \times 1.12 \\
&= 5{,}286.40 \\
r_2 &= 2{,}000.00 \\
&\ 3{,}286.40
\end{aligned}
$$

Therefore the amount outstanding after two years is €3,286.40.

Exercise 12.6 ▼

1. A man borrowed €8,000 at 5% per annum compound interest. If he repays €2,000 at the end of each year, how much is outstanding after the second repayment?
2. A woman borrowed €5,000 at 8% per annum compound interest. If she repays €1,500 at the end of each year, how much is outstanding after the second repayment?
3. A man borrowed €7,500 at 6% per annum compound interest. If he repays €1,500 at the end of each year, how much is outstanding after the second repayment?
4. A man borrowed €10,000 at 3% per annum compound interest. He agreed to repay €2,000 after one year and a further €3,000 at the end of two years. How much is outstanding after the second repayment?
5. A woman borrowed €4,000 at 8% per annum compound interest. She agreed to repay €1,000 after one year and a further €1,500 at the end of two years. How much is outstanding after the second repayment?

Chapter test

1. **(a)** €2,000 was invested for a year at 6% per annum. Calculate the interest earned.
   (b) Calculate the compound interest on €4,500 for two years at 10% per annum
   (c) A sum of money invested for a year at 8% per annum amounted to €2,700. Calculate the sum of money and the interest earned.

2. **(a)** €1,500 was invested for a year at 4% per annum. Calculate the interest earned.
   (b) Calculate the compound interest on €4,200 for two years at 5% per annum.
   (c) What sum of money will earn €432 interest if invested at 8% per annum for one year?

3. **(a)** €2,400 was borrowed at 7% per annum. Calculate the amount owed after one year.
   (b) Calculate the compound interest on €15,000 invested for three years at 6% per annum.
   (c) €2,100 was invested for one year and amounted to €2,289. Calculate the rate of interest per annum.

4. **(a)** €750 was invested for a year at $2\frac{1}{2}$% per annum. Calculate the interest earned.
   (b) Calculate the compound interest on €7,500 for three years at 4% per annum.
   (c) €6,500 was invested for a year and amounted to €6,890.
   Calculate **(i)** the interest earned and **(ii)** the annual rate of interest.

5. **(a)** A woman deposited €2,000 in a building society, where she is offered $4\frac{1}{2}$% per annum. How much will she have at the end of one year?
   (b) €8,000 was invested for three years at compound interest. The interest rate for the first year was 5%, for the second year 8%, and for the third year 12%. Calculate the total interest earned.
   (c) What sum of money will earn €25.20 interest if invested for one year at 3% per annum?

6. **(a)** A man borrowed €2,200 from a bank at a rate of 6% per annum. He agreed to pay off the loan at the end of one year with one payment. How much did he pay to clear the loan?
   (b) €20,000 was invested for three years at compound interest. The interest rate for the first year was 8%, the rate for the second year was 12%, and the rate for the third year was 9%. Calculate the amount after three years.
   (c) A sum of money invested for a year at 4% per annum amounted to €884.
   Calculate **(i)** the sum of money and **(ii)** the interest earned.
   (d) A woman invested €50,000 in a bank for three years at 10% per annum compound interest. At the end of the three years she collected all of her investment but she had to pay 40c in the euro tax on the interest earned for the three years. Calculate at the end of three years:
   (i) the value of her investment
   (ii) the total interest
   (iii) the tax paid.
   Express the tax paid as a percentage of the sum of money invested.
   (e) A woman borrowed €15,000 at 6% per annum compound interest. If she agreed to repay €5,000 at the end of each year, how much is outstanding after the second repayment?

RATIO, PROPORTION, AND FOREIGN EXCHANGE

Ratio

A ratio is a comparison between two similar quantities measured in the same units.
It is written in a given order.
The ratio '7 to 4' is written $7 : 4$ or as a fraction, $\frac{7}{4}$.

Simplifying ratios

A ratio is unchanged if we multiply or divide each part by the same number. It is usual to make each part of the ratio as small as possible. However, each part must be a whole number.

Example ▼

Express each of the following ratios in its simplest form:

(i) $12 : 15$ **(ii)** $14 : 28 : 35$ **(iii)** $2 : 1\frac{1}{2}$
(iv) $0.25 : 0.75$

Solution:
(i) $12 : 15 = 4 : 5$ (divide each part by 3)
(ii) $14 : 28 : 35 = 2 : 4 : 5$ (divide each part by 7)
(iii) $2 : 1\frac{1}{2} = 4 : 3$ (multiply each part by 2)
(iv) $0{\cdot}25 : 0.75 = 25 : 75$ (multiply each part by 100)
                    $= 1 : 3$ (divide each part by 25)

To express one quantity as a ratio of another, do the following:

---

1. Make sure both quantities are in the same units.
2. Remove the units and write the numbers as a ratio.
3. Simplify this ratio.

Express the ratio 800 m to 2 km in its simplest form.

1. First express both in metres.

   2 km = 2,000 m
2. Therefore 800 : 2 km

   $=$ 800 m : 2000 m

   $=$ 800 : 2000   (remove the units)
3. $=$ 8 : 20   (divide each part by 100)

   $=$ 2 : 5   (divide each part by 4)

Exercise 13.1 ▼

Express each of the following ratios in its simplest form:

1. 4 : 8	**2.** 15 : 20	**3.** 3 : 9	**4.** 12 : 30
5. 6 : 10	**6.** 14 : 21	**7.** 15 : 12	**8.** 50 : 30
9. 30 : 25	**10.** 36 : 24	**11.** 40 : 50	**12.** 20 : 100
13. 24 : 16	**14.** 36 : 27	**15.** 88 : 77	**16.** 125 : 200
17. 8 : 12 : 20	**18.** 15 : 20 : 25	**19.** 2 : 8 : 10	**20.** 18 : 24 : 42
21. 20 cm : 50 cm	**22.** €18 : €24	**23.** 12 m : 18 m	**24.** 8 km : 24 km
25. 400 m : 2 km	**26.** 75 cm : 2 m	**27.** 600 cm^3 : 2 L	**28.** 900 g : 1 kg
29. 4 days : 2 weeks	**30.** 2 hours : 40 mins		**31.** 9 months : 2 years
32. 25% : 125%	**33.** 15 mins : 2 hours 30 mins		**34.** 800 kg : $1\frac{1}{2}$ tonnes

35. If $a = 4$, $b = 6$, and $c = 12$, simplify each of the following ratios

    (i) $a : c$ **(ii)** $2b : c$ **(iii)** $a^2 : 2c$ **(iv)** $(a + b) : (2c - a)$
36. In a class of 30 pupils there are 20 girls. Find the ratio of

    (i) the number of boys to the number of girls

    (ii) the number of boys to the number of pupils in the whole class.
37. A girl is 15 years old and her father is 45 years old. Calculate the ratio of

    (i) the girl's age to her father's age now

    (i) the girl's age to her father's age in five years' time

    (iii) the father's age to the girl's age three years ago.
38. A man was earning €400 a week. He received an extra €80 a week in salary. Calculate the ratio of the new salary per week to the old salary per week.
39. A football pitch has a length of 120 m and its width is 80 m. Calculate:

    (i) the ratio of its length to its width

    (ii) the ratio of its length to its perimeter

    (iii) the ratio of its perimeter to its width.
40. A car travelling at 75 km/h overtakes a motorbike travelling at 1 km/min. Calculate, at the moment of overtaking, the ratio of the car's speed to the motorbike's speed.

Express each of the following ratios in their simplest form:

41. $1\frac{1}{2} : 3$ **42.** $1\frac{1}{4} : 2$ **43.** $\frac{1}{3} : 1$ **44.** $\frac{3}{4} : \frac{1}{4}$ **45.** $1\frac{3}{4} : 2\frac{1}{4}$

46. $\frac{2}{5} : 1\frac{1}{5}$ **47.** $\frac{2}{3} : \frac{5}{6}$ **48.** $2\frac{1}{2} : 7\frac{1}{2}$ **49.** $2.5 : 3.5$ **50.** $0.4 : 1.2$

51. $0.25 : 1.25$ **52.** $2.7 : 3.6$

Proportional parts (dividing quantities in a given ratio)

Ratios can be used to divide, or share, quantities.

To divide, or share, a quantity in a given ratio, do the following:

> **1.** Add the ratios to get the total number of parts.
> **2.** Divide the quantity by the total of the parts (this gives one part).
> **3.** Multiply this separately by each ratio.

Example ▼

Divide: **(i)** €28 in the ratio $2 : 5$ **(ii)** 300 kg in the ratio $2 : 5 : 8$

(i) 1. $2 + 5 = 7$ parts

   2.   1 part $= \dfrac{€28}{7} = €4$

   3.   2 parts $= €4 \times 2 = €8$
           5 parts $= €4 \times 5 = €20$

   Therefore €28 divided in the ratio $2 : 5$
           is €8, €20.

   (Check: €8 + €20 = €28.)

(ii) 1. $2 + 5 + 8 = 15$ parts

   2.   1 part $= \dfrac{300\,\text{kg}}{15} = 20\,\text{kg}$

   3.   2 parts $= 2 \times 20\,\text{kg} = 40\,\text{kg}$
           5 parts $= 5 \times 20\,\text{kg} = 100\,\text{kg}$
           8 parts $= 8 \times 20\,\text{kg} = 160\,\text{kg}$

   Therefore 300 kg divided in the ratio
           $2 : 5 : 8$ is 40 kg, 100 kg, 160 kg.

   (Check: 40 kg + 100 kg + 160 kg = 300 kg.)

Divide each of the following quantities in the given ratio:

	Quantity	Ratio			Quantity	Ratio
1.	€18	1 : 2	**11.**	450 pupils	4 : 5
2.	€30	2 : 3	**12.**	260 g	6 : 7
3.	€24	1 : 3	**13.**	150	3 : 2
4.	40 kg	3 : 5	**14.**	€24.36	2 : 1
5.	28 mins	3 : 4	**15.**	€15.30	2 : 3
6.	50 cm	3 : 2	**16.**	€180	2 : 8 : 5
7.	9 months	2 : 1	**17.**	480 g	5 : 4 : 3
8.	36	5 : 4	**18.**	€4,000	5 : 7 : 8
9.	88	7 : 4	**19.**	170 kg	3 : 6 : 8
10.	€120	5 : 3	**20.**	162 cm	4 : 3 : 2

21. Divide €24 into 3 equal parts. Hence, or otherwise, divide €24 in the ratio 1 : 2.
22. Divide €50 in the ratio 7 : 3.
23. A prize of €30 is shared between two people in the ratio 1 : 2. How much does each person receive?
24. €1,040 was divided in the ratio 6 : 7. The larger amount was given to charity. How much was this?
25. The total attendance at a concert over two nights was 450. The nightly attendances were in the ratio of 2 : 3. Find the attendance on the first night.
26. €105 was shared among three people in the ratio 1 : 2 : 4. Calculate the smallest share.
27. A man has two children, a boy aged 8 years and a girl aged 12 years. If he divides €400 in the ratio of their ages, how much does each child get?
28. The sides of a triangle are in the ratio 3 : 4 : 5. If the perimeter of the triangle is 60 cm, find the length of each side.
29. An alloy consists of copper, zinc and tin in the ratio 7 : 4 : 3 (by weight).
    Find the weight of each metal in 84 kg of alloy.
30. Two schools are to receive a grant from the Department of Education in proportion to their number of pupils. If one school has 450 pupils and the other has 720, how would a grant of €56,160 be divided between them?
31. The profits of a business are divided in the ratio of money invested. **A**, **B** and **C** invested €24,000, €16,000 and €12,000, respectively. How much will each receive from a profit of €6,500?

Divide each of the following quantities in the given ratio:

	Quantity	Ratio			Quantity	Ratio
32.	30	$1 : \frac{1}{2}$		**37.**	200 g	$0.3 : 0.7$
33.	28 kg	$1\frac{1}{2} : 2$		**38.**	36 cm	$2\frac{1}{2} : 3\frac{1}{3}$
34.	€300	$2\frac{1}{2} : 5$		**39.**	€44	$1\frac{1}{3} : 2\frac{1}{3}$
35.	40	$0.5 : 1.5$		**40.**	35 g	$\frac{1}{2} : 1 : 2$
36.	24 kg	$0 : 25 : 1.25$		**41.**	€78	$4 : 2 : \frac{1}{2}$

42. Divide 60 in the ratio $1.5 : 2.5 : 3.5$.

43. A man has two children, aged $7\frac{1}{2}$ years and $9\frac{1}{2}$ years. If he decides to divide €170 in the ratio of their ages, how much does each receive?

Given the ratios in disguise

In some questions the ratios are given in disguise.

Example ▼

€560 is shared between A, B and C so that A gets twice as much as B and B gets twice as much as C. How much does each receive?

Solution:
Let the smallest share be 1 part.
Therefore C receives 1 part (smallest share)
and B receives 2 parts (twice as much as C)
and A receives 4 parts (twice as much as B).
Now the requirement is to divide €560 in the ratio $1 : 2 : 4$.

1. $1 + 2 + 4 = 7$ parts

2. $1 \text{ part} = \dfrac{€560}{7} = €80$

3. C's share is 1 part $= €80$
B's share is 2 parts $= €80 \times 2 = €160$
A's share is 4 parts $= €80 \times 4 = €320$
(Check: $€80 + €160 + €320 = €560$.)

1. €120 is shared between A and B. How much does each receive if
    (i) A and B receive equal shares
    (ii) A gets twice as much as B
    (iii) A gets three times as much as B
    (iv) A gets €30 more than B?
2. €280 is divided between A, B and C so that A gets twice as much as B and B gets twice as much as C. How much does each receive?
3. €120 is shared between P, Q and R so that P gets twice as much as Q and Q and R get equal shares. How much does P receive?
4. €42 is divided between A, B and C so that A gets twice as much as B and B gets twice as much as C. How much does B receive?
5. €70 is divided between A, B and C so that A gets twice as much as B and C gets twice as much as A.
    (i) Who received the smallest share?
    (ii) How much does each receive?
6. €300 is divided between X, Y and Z so that Y gets three times as much as X and Z gets twice as much as Y.
    (i) Who received the smallest share?
    (ii) How much does each receive?

Given the value of some of the parts (proportions)

Sometimes we are given the value of some of the parts. Look for the equation given in disguise.

Example ▼

A and B share a sum of money in the ratio 4 : 3. If B's share is €15, calculate:

(i) the total amount shared between A and B
(ii) the amount that A received.

Solution:
(i) $4 + 3 = 7$, so there are 7 parts altogether.

Equation given in disguise: 3 parts $= €15$ (B's share)
                    Therefore 1 part $= €5$ (divide both sides by 3)
                    Therefore 7 parts $= €35$ (multiply both sides by 7)
Therefore the total sum of money shared is €35.
(ii) A's share is 4 parts $= €5 \times 4 = €20$

Note: This problem could also be solved using fractions.
Given: $\frac{3}{7}$ total $= €15$, therefore $\frac{1}{7}$ total $= €5$, etc.

1. A and B share a sum of money in the ratio 2 : 3. If A's share is €40, calculate B's share.
2. A sum of money was divided in the ratio 3 : 4. If the larger share was €24, calculate
   (i) the sum of money and   (ii) the smaller share.
3. A prize fund was divided between two people in the ratio 2 : 3. If the larger prize was €120, calculate the total prize fund.
4. In a school, the ratio of girls to boys is 4 : 5. If there are 364 girls, calculate:
   (a) the total number of pupils in the school, and
   (b) the number of boys in the school.
5. The ratio of the speeds of two cars is 3 : 2. If the faster car is travelling at 96 km/h, calculate the speed of the slower car.
6. The ages of a father and daughter are in the ratio 8 : 3. If the father is 48 years old, how old is the daughter?
7. At a football match, the ratio of the home supporters to away supporters was 5 : 3. 15,000 away supporters attended the match. How many home supporters were at the match?
8. A piece of string was cut into two pieces in the ratio 5 : 9. The larger piece was 36 cm long.
   (i)   How long was the piece of string before it was cut?
   (ii) How long was the shorter piece?
9. Two lengths are in the ratio 8 : 5. If the larger length is 120 cm, find the other length.
10. Two lengths are in the ratio 7 : 5. If the shorter length is 45 cm, calculate the other length.
11. The lengths of the sides of a triangle are in the ratio 4 : 3 : 2. If the shortest side is of length 36 cm, calculate the perimeter of the triangle.
12. A, B and C share a sum of money in the ratio 2 : 3 : 4. If C's share is €48, find
    (a) the total sum of money shared and
    (b) the amount A and B received.
13. The first three money prizes in a draw are in the ratio 5 : 3 : 2. If the second-largest prize is €240, calculate the first and third prizes.
14. A sum of money was divided in the ratio 5 : 2. If the larger share was €39 more than the smaller share, calculate the sum.
15. A woman gave some money to her 4 children in the ratio 2 : 3 : 5 : 9. If the difference between the largest and the smallest share is €11.76 how much money did she give altogether?

Direct proportion

If two quantities increase, or decrease, in the same ratio they are said to be in '**direct proportion**'. Direct proportion problems, using the unitary method, are solved with the following steps:

> **1.** Write down the equation given in disguise.
>   (Put the quantity that we want to find on the right-hand side.)
> **2.** Divide both sides by the first quantity that is given.
>   (This gives the amount for one unit of the first quantity.)
> **3.** Multiply both sides by the first quantity required.

Note: Strictly speaking, these are not equations, but using equations makes the working easier.

Example ▼

(i) A woman earns €280 for working 40 hours. How much will she earn if she worked 33 hours for the same rate of pay?
(ii) A car can travel 75 km on 5 litres of petrol. How far will it travel on 8 litres of petrol, at the same rate of consumption?

Solution:

(i) 1. Given: 40 hours = €280 (answer required in euros, therefore euros on the right)
     2.   1 hour = €7   (divide both sides by 40)
     3.   33 hours = €231 (multiply both sides by 33)
(ii) 2. Given: 5 litres = 75 km (answer required in kilometres, therefore kilometres on the right)
     2.   1 litre = 15 km (divide both sides by 5)
     3.   8 litres = 120 km (multiply both sides by 8)

Exercise 13.5 ▼

1. If 5 chairs cost €400, find the cost of   (i) 1 chair and   (ii) 7 chairs.
2. 7 pens cost €1.75. Calculate the cost of   (i) 1 pen,   (ii) 3 pens,   (iii) 12 pens.
3. 8 apples cost €1.92. How much will 10 apples cost?
4. A machine produces 200 bolts every 5 minutes. How many bolts will the machine produce in   (i) one minute,   (ii) 8 minutes,   (iii) 30 seconds?
5. A woman earns €376 for working 40 hours. How much would she earn if she worked 32 hours at the same rate of pay?
6. 8 metres of cloth cost €11.60. What is the cost of 14 metres of the same cloth?
7. A laser printer can print 800 pages in 40 minutes. How many pages can it print in   (a) 1 minute,   (b) 70 minutes,   (c) 1 hour   (d) 55 minutes at the same rate of printing?

8. If 12 books weigh 2.4 kg, find the weight of **(a)** 1 book, **(b)** 3 books, **(c)** 40 books.

9. The train fare for a return journey for an adult from Galway to Dublin is €32. The child's fare is three-quarters of the adult fare. Calculate the cost of a return journey from Galway to Dublin for:
   (i) 3 adults   **(ii)** 1 child
   (iii) 2 adults and 3 children   **(iv)** 5 children and 1 adult.

10. Seven tubes of toothpaste have a weight of 840 g. Calculate the weight of 8 tubes of the same toothpaste.

11. A hotel charges €343 per person for seven days. Calculate the charge for 12 days, at the same rate.

12. A candle that is 24 cm tall will burn for 8 hours. What height remains when the candle has been burning for 3 hours 30 minutes?

13. If 450 people attend a concert, the takings amount to €5,625. How many people attended on the following evening, when the takings amounted to €6,000? (Assume that all seats were sold at the same price on both evenings.)

14. On a map 10 km is represented by 1 cm. What distances are represented on the map by
   (a) 2 cm,   **(b)** 8 cm,   **(c)** 0.5 cm,   **(d)** 1.5 cm,   **(e)** 0.35 cm?
   What distances on the map represent
   (f) 40 km,   **(g)** 60 km,   **(h)** 75 km,   **(i)** 150 km, **(j)** 12.5 km?

15. A model car is built 72 times smaller than the real car. What are the real measurements represented by   **(a)** 4 cm,   **(b)** $\frac{1}{2}$ cm and   **(c)** $3\frac{1}{4}$ cm on the model?
   A part on the real car is 2.16 m long. What size will this be on the model?

16. It costs €120 to carpet a rectangular room measuring 5 m by 4 m. How much would it cost to cover a room measuring $7\frac{1}{2}$ m by 6 m with the same carpet? (Hint: Calculate the cost of carpeting 1 m^2.)

17. 7 books costs €12 more than 5 books cost. How much would
   (a) one book and   **(b)** 30 books cost?

18. 9 cups cost €4.50 more than 6 cups. How much would 20 cups cost?

Currency conversion

Currency is another name for money. In the European Union the unit of currency is called the euro (€). If you travel to a country outside the European Union you will need the currency of that country. For example, if you travel to the United States you will need US dollars ($). The method of direct proportion is used to convert one currency into another currency.

Note: As before, write down the equation given in disguise, putting the currency we want to find on the right-hand side.

Example ▼

On a certain day, €1 = $1.40. Find the value of:

(i) €120 in dollars   **(ii)** $84 in euros.

Solution:

(i)   Given: €1 = $1.40   (dollars on the right, because we want our answer in dollars)

Therefore €120 = $1.4 × 120   (multiply both sides by 120)

€120 = $168

(ii) Given: $1.40 = €1   (euros on the right, because we want out answer in euros)

$$\$1 = €\frac{1}{1.4}$$ (divide both sides by 1.4)

$$\$84 = €\frac{1}{1.4} \times 84$$ (multiply both sides by 84)

$84 = €60   (simplify the right-hand side)

Exercise 13.6 ▼

1. If €1 = $1.50, find the value of   **(i)** €100 in dollars   **(ii)** $180 in euros.
2. A train ticket cost €40. How much would the ticket cost in Canadian dollars if €1 = $2.25?
3. A ticket to a football game costs €25. How much does the ticket cost in US dollars if €1 = $1.6?
4. An airline ticket costs $416. If €1 = $1.30, calculate the cost of the ticket in euros.
5. If €1 = ¥320 (Japanese yen), convert ¥27,200 to euros.
6. If €1 = $1.20 (US), €1 = $2.76 (Canadian), and €1 = ¥331.2,
    (i) how many US dollars would you get for €40?
    (ii) how many Canadian dollars would you get for €350?
    (iii) how many Japanese yen would you get for €180?
    (iv) how many euros would you get for 90 US dollars?
    (v) how many euros would you get for 1,380 Canadian dollars?
    (vi) how many euros would you get for 238,464 Japanese yen?
    (vii) calculate the value of p, q and r, given the following exchange rates:
        (a) $1 (US) = p (Canadian)   **(b)** $1 (US) = ¥$q$ **(c)** $1 (Canadian) = ¥$r$.
7. Calculate the exchange rate for €1 in each case, given the following transactions:
    (i) €80 for $112 (US)   **(ii)** €75 for $165 (Canadian)
8. A CD costs €28.50 in Ireland, and the same CD costs ¥9,600 in Japan.
    If €1 = ¥320, in which country is it cheaper, and by how much (in euros)?

9. A calculator costs $104 in the United States and $157.50 in Canada. If $1.3 (US) = €1 = $2.1 (Canadian), in which country is it cheaper, and by how much (in euros)?

10. A tourist changed €800 on board ship into South African rand, at a rate of €1 = R2.4. How many rand did she receive? When she came ashore she found that the rate was €1 = R2.48. How much did she lose, in rands, by not changing her money ashore?

Inverse proportion

If 8 men can build a wall in 24 hours, then 1 man could build the wall in $8 \times 24 = 192$ hours (8 times as long as 8 men), and 6 men could build the wall in $\frac{192}{6} = 32$ hours ($\frac{1}{6}$ of the time its takes 1 men).

Notice that as the number of men decreases the number of hours increases in the same ratio, and as the number of men increases the number of hours decreases in the same ratio. This is an example of '**inverse proportion**'.

> Two quantities are in inverse proportion if one increases at the rate at which the other decreases (or vice versa).

Inverse proportion problems are best solved with the unitary method. When writing down the equation given in disguise, always put the quantity required on the right-hand side.

Example ▼

10 men can paint a factory in 6 days.

(i) How long would it take 4 men to paint the same factory?
(ii) How many men are required to paint the factory in 2 days?

Solution:
(i) We are looking for the number of days, so days go on the right-hand side.

10 men = 6 days	(given)	
Therefore 1 man = 60 days	(1 man takes 10 times as long as 10 men)	
Therefore 4 men = 15 days	(4 men take $\frac{1}{4}$ of the time it takes 1 man)	

Therefore 4 men could paint the factory in 15 days.

(ii) We are looking for the number of men, so men go on the right-hand side.

6 days = 10 men	(given)	
1 day = 60 men	(1 day requires 6 times the number of men required by 6 days)	
2 days = 30 men	(2 days require $\frac{1}{2}$ the number of men required by 1 day)	

Note: Strictly speaking, these are not equations, but using equations makes the working easier.

1. If 8 men can build a wall in 3 days, how long would it take **(i)** 1 man, **(ii)** 4 men and **(iii)** 12 men to build the same wall?

2. It takes 4 women 10 days to build a boat. How long would it take
   (i) 1 woman, **(ii)** 8 women and **(iii)** 2 women to build the same boat?

3. 5 people can build an extension on a house in 20 days. How long would it take 4 people to build the same extension?

4. A bag of sweets is shared among 10 children, and each child gets 6 sweets. How many sweets would each get if the same bag of sweets were to be shared among 15 children?

5. 5 people can dig a hole in 40 minutes. How long would it take 8 men to dig the same hole?

6. 3 people take 6 hours to complete a job. How long would it take 2 people to do the same job?

7. Ten people can complete a job in 12 days. How many people are required to do the job in **(i)** 1 day, **(ii)** 40 days, **(iii)** 60 days?

8. 12 people escaped on a lifeboat with enough food for 9 days. If they picked up another 6 people, how long would the food last?

9. A farmer needs 18 people to pick her apples in 15 days. If she wanted her apples picked in 10 days, how many people would she need?

10. In a supermarket with 10 check-outs, the average length of time customers spend queuing is 8 minutes. How many check-outs are needed to reduce the queuing time to 5 minutes?

11. In a school with 45 classrooms there are 1,350 pupils. What is the average number of pupils per classroom? How many classrooms are needed to reduce the average number of pupils per classroom to 27?

12. A field of grass provides enough food for 25 animals for 6 days. For how long would the same field feed 10 animals?

13. A girls' camp has enough stores to support 28 girls for 21 days. If 42 girls attend the camp, how long will the stores last?

14. A ball of string may be cut into 30 pieces, each of length 24 cm. How many pieces 40 cm long could be cut from the same ball?

15. A factory requires 15 sewing machines to produce a given quantity of dresses in 12 days. How many machines would be required to produce the same number of dresses in 9 days?

Chapter test

1. A boy has 60 marbles some of which are red and some of which are blue. If there are 15 red marbles, what is the ratio of the number of red marbles to the number of blue marbles?

2. Divide 144 in the ratio **(i)** 2 : 1 **(ii)** 3 : 5 **(iii)** 7 : 2.

3. Divide €420 between A, B and C in the ratio 5 : 7 : 9.

4. A boy is 18 years old. His father is 54 years old. Calculate the ratio of the boy's age to the father's age   (a) now,   (b) 6 years ago,   (c) in 6 years' time.

5. 600 g of alloy is made up of copper, tin and lead in the ratio 3 : 4 : 3. How many grams of each metal are there in the alloy?

6. A prize was divided between two people in the ratio 4 : 3. If the smaller prize was €24, calculate the larger prize.

7. A man earns €8 for working 50 minutes. How much would he earn if he worked for   (a) one hour,   (b) 1 hr 15 mins and   (c) 40 mins at the same rate of pay?

8. A, B and C are to share €840 in such a way that A gets twice as much as B and B gets twice as much as C. How much does each receive?

9. A car uses $2\frac{1}{2}$ litres of petrol for a journey of 30 km. How many kilometres per litre is this?

10. $1\frac{1}{2}$ litres of oil cost €6. Find the cost of 1 litre.

11. 5 oranges cost the same as 4 apples. If 15 oranges cost €2.40, calculate the cost of one apple.

12. (a) A sum of money is divided between Jane and Sandra in the ratio 2 : 3. If Jane gets €4.50, find   (i) what Sandra receives and   (ii) the total sum of money.
    (b) If Jane spends $\frac{1}{3}$ of her money and Sandra spends $\frac{1}{5}$ of her money, how much will they have left between them?

13. When a prize is divided among 8 people, they receive €120 each. If the same prize were to be divided among 5 people, how much would each receive?

14. If $x = 8$, $y = 12$, and $z = 15$, express each of the following ratios in its simplest form:
    (i) $x : y$ (ii) $z : y$ (iii) $y : 2x$ (iv) $2z : 3y$ (v) $3x : 2y$.

15. A builder's plan is drawn to a scale of 1 cm to 10 m. How long, in kilometres, is a road that is 18 cm on the map?

16. 8 books cost €18 more than 5 books. Calculate the cost of (i) one book and (ii) 12 books.

17. An airline ticket costs €450. Calculate the cost of the ticket in Canadian dollars if €1 = \$2.70.

18. When he arrived in Ireland for a 10-day holiday, an American tourist changed \$672 into euros. He received €480. He spent an average of €27 per day on food and travel and a total of €140 on accommodation. Before leaving for home he converted the remaining euros back into dollars at the same exchange rate. How many dollars did he receive?

CHAPTER 14

STATISTICS

Statistics deals with sorting, presenting and drawing conclusions from information that has been collected. The collected information is often called 'data'.

Diagrams are used to display the data. On our course there are three ways of representing data in a diagram:

     1. Bar charts   **2.** Trend graphs   **3.** Pie charts

The word 'frequency' is used a lot in statistics. Its definition is as follows:

> **frequency** = the number of times that something occurs.

1. Bar charts

A bar chart displays information by means of bars of different lengths to represent the size or frequency of data in a category. The bars can be vertical or horizontal. A bar chart makes visual comparison easy.

When drawing bar charts, keep the following in mind:

> **1.** Draw each bar the correct height, or length, to represent the information it displays.
> **2.** Make sure all the bars are the same width.
> **3.** Leave equal narrow spaces between the bars. (However, the bars can be touching.)
> **4.** Label each axis.
> **5.** Label each bar clearly.
> **6.** Give the bar chart a title to describe the information.

The following table gives the rainfall, in centimetres, over a six-month period in a certain district:

Month	March	April	May	June	July	August
Rainfall	7 cm	8 cm	6 cm	5 cm	2 cm	4 cm

(i) Draw a bar chart to illustrate the data.
(ii) What percentage of the total rainfall in the six-month period fell in the wettest month.

Solution:
(i)

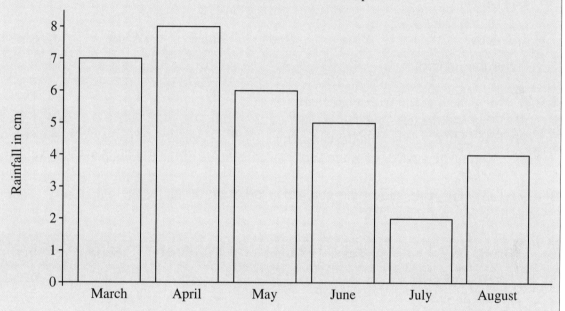

Rainfall over a six-month period

(ii) The wettest month was April, with 8 cm of rain.

The total rainfall = 7 + 8 + 6 + 5 + 2 + 4 = 32 cm.

Percentage of rain in April of the total rainfall

$$= \frac{\text{rainfall in April}}{\text{total rainfall}} \times \frac{100}{1} = \frac{8}{32} \times \frac{100}{1} = 25\%$$

1. The pupils in a certain class were asked how they travelled to school. The results are shown in the table below:

Mode of transport	Train	Bus	Bicycle	Walking
Number of pupils	4	6	5	9

    (i)   Show the data on a bar chart.
    (ii)   What was   (a) the least common and   (b) the most common mode of travel?
    (iii) How many pupils are there in the class?
    (iv)   Express the number of pupils who travelled by bus as a percentage of the total number of pupils.

2. A survey was carried out on the colours of cars in a car park. The results are shown in the table below:

Colour	Blue	Red	Black	White	Green
Number of cars	7	12	10	8	3

    (i)   Illustrate the data with a bar chart.
    (ii)   What was the least popular colour?
    (iii) How many cars were in the car park?
    (iv)   Express the number of white cars as a percentage of the total number of cars in the car park.

3. The following table shows the number of different drinks purchased from a vending machine on a particular day:

Drink	Tea	Coffee	Chocolate	Soup	Other
Number of drinks	11	12	10	8	9

    (i)   Represent the data with a bar chart.
    (ii)   What was the total number of drinks sold on the day?
    (iii) Express the most popular drink as a percentage of the total number of drinks sold on the day.

4. A sample of second-year pupils in a particular school were asked to vote for their favourite sport. The results are represented in the bar chart below

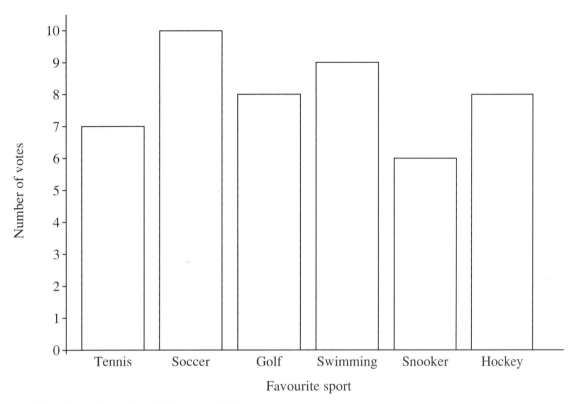

(i) Complete the following table.

Favourite Sport	Tennis	Soccer	Golf	Swimming	Snooker	Hockey
Number of votes				9		

(ii) What was the most popular sport among these second-year pupils?
(iii) How many pupils altogether were asked to vote?
(iv) What percentage of these pupils voted for snooker as their favourite sport?
(v) If there were 120 second-year pupils in this school, what percentage of the total number of second-year pupils were asked to vote?

5. The table gives the number of calories per 25 g for various fruits:

Type of fruit	Apple	Pear	Orange	Banana	Peach	Rhubarb
Number of calories	9	5	8	4	7	3

(i) Represent the information in a bar chart.
(ii) How many calories are there in 1 kg of apples?

6. A check on the cars crossing a bridge during a 15-minute period yielded the following record of the number of occupants per car:

$$1, 2, 3, 4, 2, 1, 3, 2, 1, 2, 3, 1, 4, 2, 1, 5$$
$$3, 5, 1, 1, 1, 4, 6, 4, 1, 5, 3, 4, 3, 6, 5, 2$$
$$4, 3, 2, 5, 3, 3, 2, 2, 3, 2, 4, 2, 3, 1, 2, 6$$

(i) Complete the following table:

Number of occupants	1	2	3	4	5	6
Number of cars						3

(ii) Represent the information on a bar chart.
(iii) How many cars had only one occupant?
(iv) How many cars crossed the bridge during this 15-minute period?
(v) Express the number of cars with two occupants as a percentage of the total number of cars that crossed the bridge during this 15-minute period.

7. A maths test consisted of 10 questions. 1 mark was given for a correct solution and 0 marks were given for an incorrect solution. The following bar chart represents the marks obtained by a class in the test:

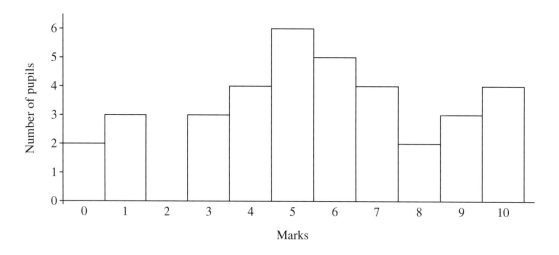

(i) Complete the following table:

Marks	0	1	2	3	4	5	6	7	8	9	10
Number of pupils	3								2		

(ii) How many pupils scored 2 marks?
(iii) How many pupils scored 8 marks or more?
(iv) How many pupils took the test?
(v) If the pass mark is 5, calculate the percentage of pupils that passed the test.

2. Trend graph

A trend graph, as the name suggests, is used to display quantities that change over time and are recorded at regular intervals (hours, days, years, etc.). As before, label the axes clearly and give the diagram a title to explain what it represents.

Note: The time is always marked on the horizontal axis.

Example ▼

The table below shows the temperature, in degrees Celsius, of a room over a period of seven hours:

Time	09:00	10:00	11:00	12:00	13:00	14:00	15:00
Temperature	4°C	5°C	9°C	10°C	8°C	3°C	5°C

(i) Represent the data on a trend graph.
(ii) What was the maximum recorded temperature, and at what time did this maximum occur?
(iii) Estimate the temperature at 11:15.

Solution:
(i) The points (time, temperature) are plotted and joined by **straight** lines.

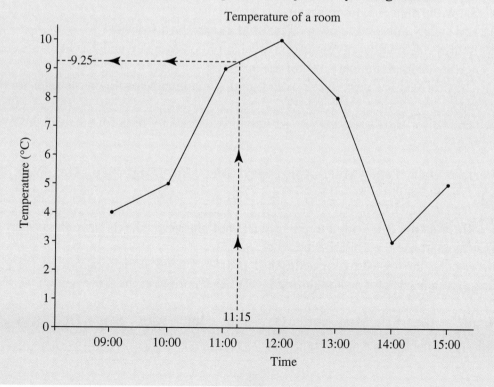

Temperature of a room

Exercise 14.2 ▼

1. The number of microwave ovens sold in a particular six-day period by a large electrical
   shop is shown in the table below:

Day	Monday	Tuesday	Wednesday	Thursday	Friday	Saturday
Sales	5	7	10	6	8	12

   (i)   Show the data on a trend graph.
   (ii) How many microwave ovens were sold during the six days?
   (iii) Express the number of microwave ovens sold on Monday and Tuesday as a percent-
         age of the total number sold for the six days.
   (iv) The profit on one microwave oven is €40. Calculate the profit on the sales for the six
         days.

2. The table below shows successive two-monthly electricity bills for a household over the
   course of a year:

Period	Jan.–Feb.	Mar.–Apr.	May–Jun.	Jul.–Aug.	Sep.–Oct.	Nov.–Dec.
Bill	€150	€110	€80	€60	€70	€130

   (i)   Illustrate the data with a trend graph. (Mark the vertical axis in units of €10.)
   (ii) Calculate the total bill for the whole year.
   (iii) Express the lowest two-monthly bill as a percentage of the total bill for the year.

3. The ice cream sales for a shop during a year are recorded in the table below:

Month	Jan	Feb	Mar	Apr	May	Jun	Jul	Aug	Sep	Oct	Nov	Dec
Sales (€)	4,000	6,000	7,000	8,000	10,000	15,000	18,000	20,000	19,000	12,000	10,000	15,000

(i) Show the data on a trend graph. Mark the vertical axis in units of €1,000.

(ii) Calculate the total sales for the whole year.

(iii) Express the sales in July as a percentage of the total sales for the year.

4. The table below shows the rainfall in an area over a six-month period:

Month	April	May	June	July	August	September
Rainfall	10 cm	8 cm	5 cm	3 cm	1 cm	3 cm

(i) Illustrate the data with a trend graph.

(ii) What was the total rainfall over the six-month period?

(iii) What percentage of the total rainfall in the six-month period fell in the wettest month?

5. The table below shows the temperature of an object over a six-hour period:

Time	11:00	12:00	13:00	14:00	15:00	16:00	17:00
Temperature	6°C	4°C	5°C	9°C	10°C	6°C	4°C

(i) Show the information on a trend graph.

(ii) What was the maximum recorded temperature, and at what time did this maximum occur?

(iii) Estimate the temperature at 15:45.

(iv) What are the two times when the temperature was 4°C?

6. The number of pupils studying in the school library was counted at hourly intervals and the results recorded on the trend graph below:

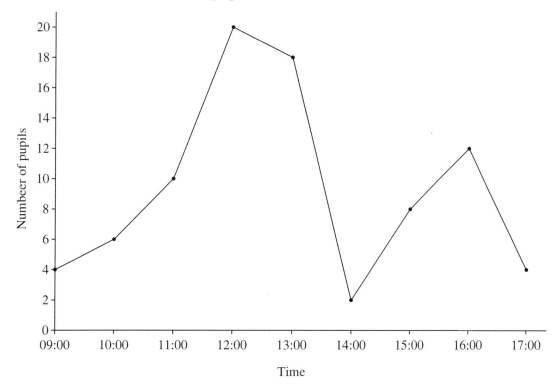

(i) How many pupils were in the library at 13:00?

(ii) How many pupils were in the library at 11:00?

(iii) At what time was the number of pupils in the library at a maximum?

(iv) Estimate the number of pupils in the library at 13:30.

7. A girl was born on 1 January 1984. On her eighth birthday her height was recorded as 120 cm. Her height was recorded on her birthday for the next eight years. The measurements are in the table below:

Year	1992	1993	1994	1995	1996	1997	1998	1999	2000
Height	120 cm	126 cm	133 cm	141 cm	145 cm	150 cm	159 cm	165 cm	168 cm

(i) Illustrate the information on a trend graph.
   (Start the vertical axis, height, at 100 cm.)

(ii) What was her height on her twelfth birthday?

(iii) During what year did she gain the least height?

(iv) Calculate the percentage increase in her height from
   (a) her eighth birthday to her sixteenth birthday
   (b) her thirteenth birthday to her fourteenth birthday.

3. Pie chart

A pie chart is a circle divided into sectors in proportion to the frequency of the information. It displays the proportions as angles measured from the centre of the circle.

Steps in drawing a pie chart:

> **1.** Add up all the frequencies.
> **2.** Divide this into 360°.
> **3.** Multiply the answer in step 2 by each individual frequency.
>   (This gives the size of the angle for each sector.)
> **4.** Draw the pie chart, label each sector, and give it a title.
>   (It is a good idea to write the size of each angle on the pie chart.)

Note: It is good practice to check that all your angles add up to 360° before drawing the pie chart.

The career guidance teacher asked a number of sixth-year pupils what sort of career they would like after leaving school. The results are in the table below:

Career	Office work	Professions	Industrial work	Agricultural work	Don't know
Number of pupils	17	12	21	14	8

Represent this information in a pie chart.

Solution:
$17 + 12 + 21 + 14 + 8 = 72$; therefore there are 72 pupils altogether.

In a circle there are 360°. The whole circle has to include all 72 pupils, so it is first necessary to find out how many degrees one pupil will represent on the pie chart. This is then multiplied by the number of pupils in each category.

So we have: 72 pupils = 360°
Therefore 1 pupil = 5° (divide both sides by 72)

In other words, one pupil will take up 5° on the pie chart. We make up a table to work out the angle for each sector.

Sector	Number of pupils	Angle
Office work	17	$17 \times 5° = 85°$
Professions	12	$12 \times 5° = 60°$
Industrial work	21	$21 \times 5° = 105°$
Agricultural work	14	$14 \times 5° = 70°$
Don't know	8	$8 \times 5° = 40°$
Total	72 pupils	360°

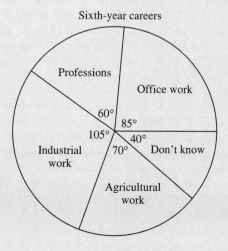

Sixth-year careers

1. A survey was carried out in a class of 36 primary-school pupils to see how they travelled to school. The results of the survey are shown in the following table:

walked	bus	bike	car	train
14	6	10	4	2

   Represent this information on a pie chart.

2. The ages of 40 boys in a local youth club were as follows:

Age	13	14	15	16	17	18
Number	5	4	8	9	12	2

   Represent this data with a pie chart.

3. 24 fifth-year pupils were asked to choose from an option of 4 subjects. The results are in the table below.

Accounting	Applied maths	Physics	French
5	8	4	7

   Illustrate the data with a pie chart. What percentage of the 24 pupils chose applied maths?

4. In a survey, 120 girls were asked for their shoe size. The results of the survey were as follows:

Shoe size	2	3	4	5	6	7
Number of girls	10	21	24	36	17	12

   (i) Show the information on a pie chart.
   (ii) Express the most popular shoe size as a percentage of the 120 girls in the survey.

5. A box of coloured balloons contains the following numbers of balloons of each colour:

Colour	Blue	White	Red	Green	Orange
Number of balloons	18	10	30	12	20

   (i) Illustrate the data with a pie chart.
   (ii) What percentage of the balloons are not blue?

6. An election for a leader is held between six people: A, B, C, D, E, and F. The person who receives most votes wins. The results are in the table below:

Person	A	B	C	D	E	F
Number of votes	15	20	40	54	26	25

(i) How many people voted in the election?

(ii) Who won the election? Calculate the percentage of the vote they received.

(iii) Illustrate the data on a pie chart.

7. A survey of occupations of women in a certain club gave the following table:

Occupation	Doctor	Teacher	Salesperson	Banker	Housewife	Accountant
Number of women	8	12	20	18	10	12

(i) Illustrate the information on a pie chart.

(ii) What percentage of the women are teachers?

8. In a certain district the percentages of land used for specific purposes were recorded in the following table:

Purpose	Industry	Farming	Housing	Parks	Hospital
Percentage	35	5	30	10	20

Represent the information with a pie chart.

Given the pie chart

In some questions we are given the pie chart, or the angles in a pie chart, and we have to work backwards to calculate the numbers in each category.

In each question we are given an equation in disguise, and from this we can work out the number represented by $1°$.

Example ▼

The pie chart below shows the sports 720 people were playing on a certain day. Find the number of people in each sector.

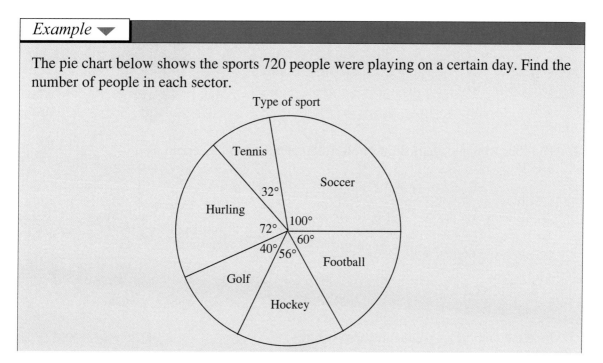

Type of sport

Solution:

In this example we work in reverse. So we have:

$$360° = 720 \text{ people} \qquad \text{(equation given in disguise)}$$
$$1° = 2 \text{ people} \qquad \text{(divide both sides by 360)}$$

In other words, 1° represents 2 people on the pie chart. Let us make out our table:

Sector	Angle	Number of people
Soccer	100°	$2 \times 100 = 200$
Tennis	32°	$2 \times 32 = 64$
Hurling	72°	$2 \times 72 = 144$
Golf	40°	$2 \times 40 = 80$
Hockey	56°	$2 \times 56 = 112$
Football	60°	$2 \times 60 = 120$
Total	360°	720

So we have:

(a) 200 play soccer;   (b) 64 play tennis;   (c) 144 play hurling;
(d) 80 play golf;   (e) 112 play hockey;   (f) 120 play football.

Exercise 14.4 ▼

1. The pie chart shown represents 720 people. How many people are represented by the shaded portion?

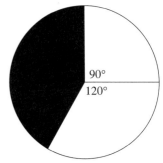

2. The following pie chart shows how 1,080 people spent a certain day.

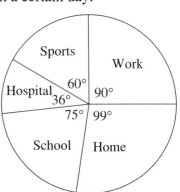

   Find the number of people in each sector.

3. The following pie chart shows where 1,440 pupils went on holidays.

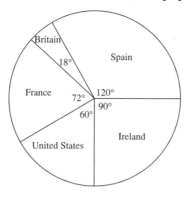

Complete the following table:

Country	Spain	Britain	France	United States	Ireland
Number of pupils					

4. An examination was taken by a number of pupils, and each obtained a grade of A, B, C, D, or E.
The pie chart illustrates the grades obtained.
(i) What is the angle representing grade E?
(ii) Complete the following table:

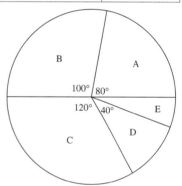

Grade	A	B	C	D	E
Number of pupils	40				

5. The pie chart on the right shows the means of transport used by all the pupils in a school.
(i) What angle represents the bicycle as a means of transport?
(ii) Complete the following table:

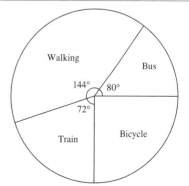

Mode of transport	Bus	Walking	Train	Bicycle
Number of pupils			108	

(iii) How many pupils are in the school?

6. The pie chart on the right shows the monthly expenses of a household.

  (a) Write down the angle in the pie chart representing the amount spent on bank repayments.

  (b) Find how much the family spent on each particular item if €135 was spent on power and fuel.

  (c) Express the amount spent on each item as a percentage of the total.

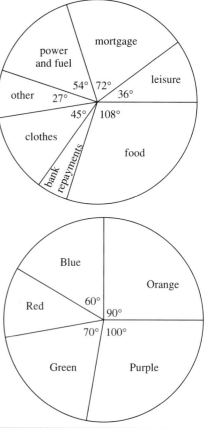

7. All the pupils in a school were asked to name their favourite colour. The results are in the pie chart on the right.

  (i) Write down the angle representing red.

  (ii) Complete the table below:

Colour	Orange	Blue	Red	Green	Purple
Number of pupils		84			

Averages

There are many types of averages. Two that we will meet are called the **mean** and the **mode**. They are also known as **measures of central tendency**.

Mean

The **mean** is the proper name for what most people call the average.

> The mean of a set of values is the sum of all the values divided by the number of values.

That is,

$$\text{mean} = \frac{\text{sum of all the values}}{\text{number of values}}$$

The formula is often written as:

$$\bar{x} = \frac{\Sigma x}{n}$$

where,

(i) $\bar{x}$ (read as 'x bar') is the symbol for the mean

(ii) Σ (the Greek capital letter *sigma*) means 'the sum of'
(i.e. Σx means 'add up all the x values')

(iii) n is the number of values of x.

Note: Strictly speaking, $\bar{x}$ should be called the '**arithmetic mean**'.

Mode

> The **mode** is the value that occurs most often.

In other words, the mode is the value with the highest frequency, or the most popular value.

Example ▼

Find **(i)** the mean and **(ii)** the mode of the array of numbers 3, 7, 8, 4, 2, 4, 3, 10, 4.

Solution:

3, 7, 8, 4, 2, 4, 3, 10, 4

(i) Mean $= \bar{x} = \dfrac{\Sigma x}{n} = \dfrac{3+7+8+4+2+4+3+10+4}{9} = \dfrac{45}{9} = 5$

(ii) The number which occurs most often is 4.
Therefore the mode is 4.

Example ▼

A boy took a typing speed test. He typed seven pages as fast as possible. The number of errors on the pages are as follows: 8, 2, 5, 0, 4, 6, 3. Calculate the mean number of errors per page.

Solution:

Mean number of errors per page $= \dfrac{\text{total number of errors}}{\text{number of pages}}$

$$= \frac{8+2+5+0+4+6+3}{7} = \frac{28}{7} = 4$$

Note: 0 is counted as a value.

Find the mean of each of the following arrays of numbers:

1. 3, 4, 5

2. 5, 4, 3, 6, 7

3. 1, 2, 3, 3, 2, 1

4. 2, 7, 3, 7, 3, 7, 8, 11

5. 20, 40, 60, 80, 100

6. 3, 4, 3, 7, 8, 6, 4, 5

7. 3, 0, 5, 0, 7, 9

8. 4, 0, 2, 6, 8, 2, 6, 4

9. 31, 47, 16, 23, 19, 86

10. 3.1, 4.5, 3.2, 7.4, 6.8

11. −2, 5, 0, 4, −1, −5, −1

12. 5.5, −2.3, −4.2, 2.1, 4.4

Find the mean and the mode of each of the following arrays of numbers:

13. 5, 4, 2, 2, 7

14. 3, 6, 10, 6, 11, 6

15. 2, 2, 3, 3, 3, 4, 4

16. 4, 3, 2, 3, 2, 2, 5

17. 6, 1, 0, 4, 0, 3, 2, 6, 0, 8

18. 10.2, 8.4, 7.3, 8.4, 6.5, 8.4

19. 2.3, 4.1, 6.7, 0.3, 4.1

20. $\frac{1}{3}, \frac{3}{4}, \frac{1}{3}, \frac{1}{2}, \frac{2}{3}, \frac{5}{12}$

21. $1\frac{1}{2}, 2\frac{3}{4}, 5\frac{2}{3}, 1\frac{1}{2}, \frac{7}{12}$

22. A waiter kept a record of the tips given to her each day for seven days. The record read: €3.68, €10.11, €2.93, €5.42, €1.94, €6.19, €5.15. Calculate the mean amount of tips given to her per day.

23. The six electricity bills over a year for a household were as follows: €106.48, €115.04, €88.93, €97.02, €123.49, €104.14. Calculate the average electricity bill for the year.

24. The price of the same maths book at seven different bookshops was as follows: €15.49, €16.49, €15.99, €15.79, €17.00, €15.49, €15.89. Calculate the mean price of the book for these seven bookshops.

25. The rainfall in a village in County Kerry was measured each day for one week. The results are in the table below:

Day	Monday	Tuesday	Wednesday	Thursday	Friday	Saturday	Sunday
Rainfall	7 mm	10 mm	16 mm	0	11 mm	0	12 mm

   (i)   Calculate the total rainfall for the week.

   (ii) Calculate the mean daily rainfall for this week.

26. The times taken by five boys to complete a training run were as follows: 11 min 15 sec; 10 min 43 sec; 13 min 12 sec; 12 min 42 sec; 14 min 18 sec. Find the mean time taken for the five boys to complete the training run.

27. A teacher records the marks of nine pupils who took a test. The results for the nine pupils were: 41, 32, 88, 64, 72, 19, 38, 63, 69. Calculate the mean mark in the test for the nine pupils.

One pupil was absent on the day the test was taken. When the tenth pupil took the test the following day he received a mark of 74. Calculate the mean mark for the ten pupils.

Given the mean

Often we are given the mean and we need to find one of the values. Essentially, we are given an equation in disguise. This equation is used to find the missing value.

Example ▼

The mean of the six numbers 2, 8, 6, 3, x and 7 is 5.
Calculate the value of x.

Solution:
Equation given in disguise: mean = 5

Therefore $\dfrac{2+8+6+3+x+7}{6} = 5$ (put in given values)

$\dfrac{x+26}{6} = 5$ (simplify the top)

$x + 26 = 30$ (multiply both sides by 6)

$x = 4$ (subtract 26 from both sides)

Alternatively, to avoid having a equation with a fraction, we can do the following:

The mean of the six numbers is 5.
Therefore the numbers must add up to 30.

(because $6 \times 5 = 30$, or $\dfrac{30}{6} = 5$)

Equation given in disguise:
Total of the numbers = 30

Therefore $2 + 8 + 6 + 3 + x + 7 = 30$ (put in given values)

$x + 26 = 30$ (simplify the right-hand side)

$x = 4$ (subtract 26 from both sides)

Example ▼

The mean of eight numbers is 9. When one of the numbers is taken away the mean is increased by 1. Find the number that was taken away.

Solution:

Old situation (8 numbers)
The mean of the 8 numbers is 9.
Therefore the numbers must add up to 72.

(because $8 \times 9 = 72$, or $\dfrac{72}{8} = 9$)

New situation (7 numbers)
The mean of the remaining 7 numbers is 10.
Therefore the numbers must add up to 70.

(because $7 \times 10 = 70$, or $\dfrac{70}{7} = 10$)

$$72 - 70 = 2$$
Therefore the number taken away was 2.

1. The mean of four numbers is 8. Find the sum of the numbers.
2. The mean of five numbers is 6. Find the sum of the numbers.
3. The mean of six numbers is 4. Find the sum of the numbers.
4. The mean of seven numbers is 3. Find the sum of the numbers.
5. The mean of the three numbers 3, 4 and x is 4. Calculate the value of x.
6. The mean of the four numbers x, 4, 6 and 7 is 5. Calculate the value of x.
7. The mean of the five numbers 8, 5, x, 4 and 6 is 6. Calculate the value of x.
8. The mean of the six numbers 4, 2, 1, x, 2 and 4 is 3. Calculate the value of x.
9. The mean of the seven numbers 5, 7, 3, 4, x, 8 and 6 is 7. Calculate the value of x.
10. The mean of the five numbers 7, 3, 2, x and 6 is 4. Calculate the value of x.
11. The mean of the four numbers 9, 8, x and 5 is 7. Calculate the value of x.
12. The mean of the six numbers 6, 10, x, 3, 5 and 2 is 5. Calculate the value of x.
13. The mean of the four numbers 5, 9, x and 7 is 6. Calculate the value of x.
14. The mean of the five numbers 7, x, 5, $2x$ and 4 is 5. Calculate the value of x.
15. The mean of the three numbers x, 3 and $2x$ is 3. Calculate the value of x.
16. The mean of the four numbers x, $2x$, 3 and $4x$ is 6. Calculate the value of x.
17. The mean of three numbers is 5. Find the sum of the numbers. When another number is added on, the mean of the four numbers is 6. Find the number that was added on.
18. The mean of four numbers is 5. When another number is added on, the mean is increased by 1. Find the number that was added on.
19. The mean of five numbers is 6. When one of the numbers is taken away, the mean is increased by 1. Find the number that was taken away.
20. The mean of six numbers is 3. When one of the numbers is taken away, the mean is decreased by 1. Find the number that was taken away.
21. The mean of 7 numbers is 4. When another number is added on, the mean is still 4. Find the eighth number.
22. The mean of 5 numbers is 3. When another number is added on, the mean is doubled. Find the sixth number.
23. The mean of the three numbers 8, 6 and x is the same as the mean of the five numbers 5, 7, 3, 9 and 6. Find x.

Frequency distribution

> If the values are arranged in ascending, or descending, size and show their corresponding frequency, the distribution is called a **frequency distribution**.

Note: If the values and frequencies are given in a table, it is called a **frequency distribution table**.

Mean and mode of a frequency distribution

Mean

To find the mean of a frequency distribution, do the following:

1. Multiply each value by its corresponding frequency.
2. Sum all these products.
3. Divide this sum by the total number of frequencies.

That is,
$$\bar{x} = \frac{\Sigma fx}{\Sigma f}$$

where

(i) x is the value of each measurement
(ii) f is the frequency of each measurement
(iii) Σfx is the sum of all the fx values
(iv) Σf is the sum of all the frequencies.

Mode

The mode can be read directly from the table. The mode is the value with the highest frequency (most common value).

Note: Remember that the mode is the value, **not** the frequency.

Example ▼

The result of a survey of the number of passengers carried by 30 taxis was recorded as follows:

$$3, 2, 1, 5, 4, 3, 2, 5, 1, 3$$
$$4, 3, 2, 4, 5, 3, 3, 2, 4, 2$$
$$3, 2, 3, 5, 4, 2, 3, 4, 1, 2$$

(i)   Represent the information with a frequency distribution table.
(ii) What was the modal number of passengers per taxi?
(iii) Calculate the mean number of passengers per taxi.

Solution:

(i)   (mode, 3 occurs most often)

Number of passengers	1	2	3	4	5
Number of taxis	3	8	9	6	4

(highest frequency)

(ii) From the table, we see that 3 occurs more than any other value.
Thterefore the modal number of passengers per taxi is 3.

(iii) Mean number of passengers per taxi = $\dfrac{\text{total number of passengers}}{\text{total number of taxis}}$

$$= \frac{3(1) + 8(2) + 9(3) + 6(4) + 4(5)}{3 + 8 + 9 + 6 + 4}$$

$$= \frac{3 + 16 + 27 + 24 + 20}{30} = \frac{90}{30} = 3$$

Therefore the mean number of passengers per taxi is 3.

Exercise 14.7 ▼

Find **(i)** the mode and **(ii)** the mean of each of the following frequency distributions:

1.

Number	1	2	3	4
Frequency	8	6	4	2

2.

Number	1	3	5	7
Frequency	12	9	6	3

3.

Number	1	2	3	4	5
Frequency	2	3	5	3	2

4.

Number	3	4	5	6
Frequency	2	2	5	6

5.

Number	0	1	2	3	4	5	6
Frequency	1	7	6	5	2	6	3

6.

Number	0	1	2	3	4	5	6	7
Frequency	9	4	8	14	15	6	0	4

7. 30 pupils were given a test containing 6 questions. The number of correct answers was recorded in the following table:

Number of correct answers	0	1	2	3	4	5	6
Number of pupils	3	3	5	7	6	4	2

(i) Find the mean and the modal mark.

(ii) If 3 out of 6 is accepted as a pass mark, how many pupils failed the test?

(iii) Represent the data with a pie chart.

8. 24 children were asked their age. The results are in the table below.

Age	4	5	6	7	8	9
Number of children	5	4	7	3	4	1

   (a) State the modal age.
   (b) Calculate the mean age.
   (c) Represent the information with a pie chart.

9. The table below shows the number of days on which pupils in a certain class were absent during the month of December.

Number of days absent	0	1	2	3	4	5
Number of pupils	8	6	4	5	4	3

   (a) How many pupils are in the class?
   (b) What is the modal number of days absent?
   (c) Calculate the mean number of absent days.
   (d) Were all the pupils absent on any day? Give a reason for your answer.
   (e) Represent the information with a bar chart.

10. The frequency table below shows the number of donations given by 34 people as they passed a collector outside a supermarket.

Amount	0	€1	€2	€3	€4	€5
Number of people	8	7	6	6	4	f

   (i) Write down the value of f (the number of people who donated €5).
   (ii) What is the mode of the distribution?
   (iii) Calculate the mean contribution.
   (iv) How many people gave €2 or more?
   (v) Represent the information with a bar chart.

11. Each child in a class of 30 pupils was asked to throw a dice once. The results were recorded as follows:

$$1, 4, 6, 3, 3, 2, 1, 6, 5, 4$$
$$1, 5, 3, 5, 4, 6, 5, 2, 6, 3$$
$$3, 4, 6, 6, 1, 5, 6, 3, 6, 5$$

   (a) Represent the information by a frequency distribution table.
   (b) Write down the modal result.
   (c) Calculate the mean result.
   (d) Evaluate $(\text{mode})^2 - (\text{mean})^2$
   (e) Illustrate the data with a bar chart

12. A road check on 40 cars yielded the following record of the number of occupants in each car:

$$3, 1, 4, 2, 3, 1, 1, 5, 2, 1, 6, 4, 2, 6, 3, 2, 3, 1, 5, 2$$
$$5, 2, 3, 1, 5, 6, 2, 3, 2, 1, 5, 4, 6, 1, 2, 5, 1, 2, 3, 4$$

 (i) Represent the data with a frequency distribution table.
 (ii) State the modal number of occupants per car.
 (iii) Calculate the mean number of occupants per car.
 (iv) In how many cars was the driver alone?
 (v) What percentage of the cars carried more than the mean number of people per car?

13. A test, consisting of 6 questions, was given to 30 pupils. One mark was awarded per question for a correct solution and no marks for an incorrect solution. The results obtained by each of the 30 pupils are as follows:

$$1, 3, 5, 2, 4, 1, 3, 5, 1, 2$$
$$2, 5, 1, 2, 0, 6, 5, 2, 6, 5$$
$$1, 4, 3, 3, 5, 3, 1, 2, 6, 1$$

 (i) Complete the following frequency distribution table:

Marks	0	1	2	3	4	5	6
Number of pupils	1						3

 (ii) Write down the modal mark.
 (iii) Calculate the mean mark.
 (iv) What percentage of the pupils received a mark greater than 4?
 (v) Represent the distribution of the marks on a pie chart.

Exercise 14.8 ▼

Chapter test

1. The rainfall in a town for six consecutive days was recorded as follows:

Day	Monday	Tuesday	Wednesday	Thursday	Friday	Saturday
Rainfall	4 mm	6 mm	3 mm	7 mm	12 mm	8 mm

Illustrate the information with **(a)** a bar chart, **(b)** a pie chart, and **(c)** a trend graph.

2. In a survey, 20 people were asked how much money they spent in a month on the National Lottery. The result (in euros) was:

$$6 \quad 6 \quad 4 \quad 6 \quad 7$$
$$6 \quad 6 \quad 5 \quad 4 \quad 6$$
$$7 \quad 5 \quad 6 \quad 7 \quad 6$$
$$5 \quad 6 \quad 6 \quad 5 \quad 5$$

Copy the following frequency distribution table into your copy book and complete it:

Amount	€4	€5	€6	€7
Number of people	2			

(i) Find the mode.
(ii) What percentage of the 20 people spent €6 or more?
(iii) Calculate the mean amount of money spent per person.
(iv) Draw a pie chart to represent this data, showing clearly the size of the angles at the centre.

3. (a) Write down the mode of the following array of numbers:
1, 2, 3, 4, 5, 4, 3, 2, 1, 2, 3, 4, 5, 4.

(b) The mass of 22 articles (in kilograms) was recorded as follows:

15, 15, 17, 16, 18, 15, 15, 15, 16, 16, 18,
16, 15, 15, 16, 15, 18, 18, 15, 16, 15, 17.

Express the recordings as a frequency distribution table.
What is the mode? Calculate the mean.
Evaluate $(mean)^2 - (mode)^2$.

4. The following table shows the number of hours of sunshine recorded each day for one week in May.

Day	Monday	Tuesday	Wednesday	Thursday	Friday	Saturday	Sunday
Number of hours of sunshine	8	7	9	6	6	7	5

(i) Draw a trend graph of the data, putting days on the horizontal axis.
(ii) How many hours of sunshine were recorded for the week?
(iii) The number of hours of sunshine recorded for the week represents 24% of the total number of hours of sunshine recorded for the month of May. Calculate the number of hours of sunshine recorded for the month of May.
(iv) Calculate the mean number of hours of sunshine recorded per day for the month of May, correct to one place of decimals.

5. A group of 40 pupils were given 5 projects each to complete. The results are shown in the table below. There were two pupils, for example, who did not complete any project.

Number of projects completed	0	1	2	3	4	5
Number of pupils	2	7	12	10	6	3

(i) Draw a bar chart of the data.
(ii) Calculate the mean number of projects completed per pupil.
(iii) One of the projects involved swimming a certain distance. Find the smallest number of pupils who could have completed this project.

Find the largest number of pupils who could have completed this project.

6. The table shows the number of newspapers sold per day in a shop from Monday to Saturday:

Day	Monday	Tuesday	Wednesday	Thursday	Friday	Saturday
Number of newspapers sold	50	25	20	35	50	60

(i) Show the data on a trend graph.
(ii) Calculate the mean daily sales.
(iii) The profit on a newspaper is 15c. Find the mean daily profit on newspaper sales.
(iv) If the mean daily sale of newspapers for the seven days was 47, calculate the number of newspapers sold on Sunday.

7. (i) Find the mean (average) of 1.1, 1.8, 2.3, 3.5, 4.1, and 5.2.

(i) On a certain morning, 24 pupils took a test. Their scores were:
4, 5, 5, 6, 8, 4, 6, 9, 6, 4, 7, 6, 7, 8, 6, 4, 6, 7, 5, 6, 4, 8, 5, 8.
Complete the following frequency distribution table:

Mark	4	6	8	
Frequency		7		

(a) State the modal mark per pupil.
(b) Calculate the mean mark per pupil.
(c) On a pie chart representing all 24 pupils, illustrate the number of pupils scoring (i) below the mean, (ii) the mean, and (iii) above the mean. Show clearly how you calculate the angle representing them.

8. (a) Calculate, correct to one decimal place, the mean of 1, 1.5, 2, 2.5, 3, 2.5, 2, 1.5, and 1.

(b) The table shows the number of cars bringing pupils to school on a certain morning and the number of pupils per car. There were 12 cars, for example, bringing one pupil each.

Number of pupils per car	1	2	3	4	5
Frequency (number of cars)	12	22	14	8	4

(i) How many pupils in total came to school by car that morning?
(ii) Calculate the mean number of pupils per car.
(iii) How many pupils altogether came to school on that morning if 30% of them had come by car?

In a pie chart contrasting the number who came by car with the number who came otherwise, what size of angle at the centre would represent the car travellers?

Draw an accurate pie chart to show the contrast.

9. (a) The mean of the numbers 3, 4, 5, 8 is the same as the mean of the numbers 2, 4, x. Calculate x.

(b) A class of 25 pupils were given the following grades in a test:

$$
\begin{array}{ccccc}
A & D & D & B & C \\
B & E & B & B & B \\
C & A & A & B & C \\
B & B & C & D & B \\
D & E & E & A & B
\end{array}
$$

(i) State the grade that is the mode.

(ii) Construct a frequency table:

Grade	A(93)	B(77)	C(62)	D(47)	E(32)
Number of pupils					

(iii) Calculate the mean mark per pupil if A is exactly 93 marks, B is exactly 77 marks etc., as shown.

10. In a survey, the number of people travelling in each car that crossed a certain bridge between 08:00 and 08:15 on a particular day was recorded. The results of the survey are contained in the following frequency distribution table:

Number of people per car	1	2	3	4	5
Number of cars	25	15	5	10	5

(i) Write down the modal number of people per car.

(ii) Draw a bar chart to illustrate the data given in the frequency distribution table. Put the number of people per car on the horizontal axis.

(iii) How many cars were involved in the survey?

(iv) Calculate the mean number of cars that crossed the bridge per minute while the survey was taking place.

(v) How many people travelled over the bridge by car while the survey was taking place?

(vi) Calculate the mean number of people per car.

11. (a) The mean of the six numbers 3, 4, 4, 5, x and 7 is 5. Calculate the value of x.

(b) The pie chart on the right shows how a boy spent €10.80 that he was given by his uncle. Find how much he spends on each item.

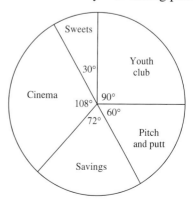

12. (a) The mean of the five numbers x, 6, 9, 7 and 8 is 8. Calculate the value of x.

(b) The pie chart on the right shows how a family spent their weekly income. If €45 was saved, how much did the family spend on each of the other items?

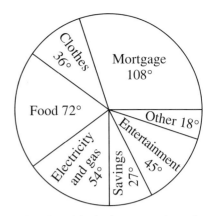

13. (a) The mean of four numbers is 8. When another number is added, the mean is reduced to 7. Find the number that was added on.

(b) In a class of 40, each pupil had a bicycle. Only 4 makes of bicycle, A, B, C, and D, had been bought. A pie chart was drawn to illustrate the information.
This table shows the data:

Make of bicycle	A	B	C	D
Number of bicycles			10	8
Angle of pie chart	90°	108°		

Complete the table and draw the pie chart.

14. The frequency distribution table below shows the number of goals scored by 50 teams in 25 matches, each team playing only once:

Number of goals scored	0	1	2	3	4	5	6
Number of teams	1	8	12	11	9	5	4

(a) What is the mode of the distribution?

(b) Calculate the mean number of goals scored **(i)** per team and **(ii)** per match.

(c) What percentage of the teams scored 4 goals or more?

(d) Find the greatest number of matches that could have ended in a draw.

(e) Find the least number of matches that could have ended in a victory for one team.

SETS

Introduction to sets

> A set is a well-defined collection of objects.

The different objects that make up a set are called **elements** or **members** of that set. The elements in a set usually have something in common and are often linked by some rule or condition. Capital letters are used to name or denote sets. The individual elements in a set can be **listed** within braces { } and separated by commas. A set can also be shown with a **Venn** diagram (set diagram). A Venn diagram uses a closed curve (loop) for each set, with the elements as labelled points inside this curve.

Notes:

1. When listing the elements of a set or showing a set with a Venn diagram, **an element is never repeated**.
2. The **order** in which the elements are listed or shown is **not** important.
3. The condition, or rule, describing the elements of a set is often put inside braces. For example, $M = \{$months of the year$\}$.

Example ▼

(i) If $A = \{$letters of the word MISSISSIPPI$\}$, list the elements of A.
(ii) If $F = \{$factors of 6$\}$, list the elements of F and represent F with a Venn diagram.

Solution:
(i) M I S S I S S I P P I
There are 11 letters in the word M I S S I S S I P P I, but only 4 different letters are used. These 4 different letters are M, I, S, P.

Therefore $A = \{$M, I, S, P$\}$

(ii) The factors of 6 are 1, 2, 3, and 6.

Therefore $F = \{1, 2, 3, 6\}$

Venn diagram

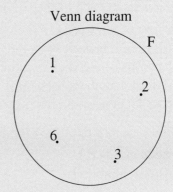

> $\in$ means 'is an element of'
> $\notin$ means 'is not an element of'

Example ▼

If $A = \{$the first five letters in the alphabet$\}$, insert $\in$ or $\notin$ in each of the following state-ments: **(i)** $d \_ A$ **(ii)** $g \_ A$

Solution:

$\qquad A = \{$first five letters in the alphabet$\}$

Therefore $A = \{a, b, c, d, e\}$

(i) d is an element of A,   therefore $d \in A$.
(ii) g is not an element of A,   therefore $g \notin A$.

Exercise 15.1 ▼

List the elements of each of the following sets, and in each case represent the set with a Venn diagram:

1. $A = \{$even numbers between 1 and 9$\}$
2. $B = \{$odd numbers between 0 and 10$\}$
3. $C = \{$factors of 12$\}$
4. $D = \{$letters of the word S U C C E S S E S$\}$
5. $E = \{$prime numbers less than 14$\}$
6. $F = \{$letters of the word A R R A N G E M E N T$\}$
7. $G = \{$vowels in the alphabet$\}$
8. $H = \{$vowels in the word M A T H E M A T I C S$\}$
9. $I = \{$numbers between 2 and 22 that can be divided evenly by 3$\}$
10. $J = \{$numbers between 4 and 31 that can be divided evenly by 5$\}$

List the elements of each of the following sets:

11. $X = \{$days of the week$\}$
12. $Y = \{$days of the week beginning with the letter S$\}$
13. $Z = \{$months of the year beginning with the letter J$\}$
14. $M = \{$whole numbers between 1 and 9, including 1 and 9$\}$
15. $S = \{$the squares of the first six natural numbers$\}$

State whether each of the following is true or false:

16. $7 \in \{$odd numbers$\}$
17. $8 \notin \{$even numbers$\}$

18. Monday $\in$ {days of the week}

19. Friday $\notin$ {months of the year}

If $X = \{a, b, c, d, e\}$, $Y = \{0, 2, 4, 6, 8\}$, and $Z = \{1, 4, 9, 16, 25, 36\}$,
insert $\in$ or $\notin$ in each of the following statements:

20. $d \_ X$

21. $5 \_ Y$

22. $a \_ Y$

23. $5 \_ Z$

24. $b \_ Y$

25. $c \_ Y$

26. $49 \_ Z$

27. $b \_ X$

28. $25 \_ Y$

29. $\sqrt{16} \_ Y$

30. $\sqrt{16} \_ Z$

31. $\sqrt{64} \_ X$

32. $4 \_ Y$ and $4 \_ Z$

Terminology

Number of elements in a set

The number of elements in the set A is denoted by $\#(A)$.

> $\#(A)$ = the number of elements in set A.

For example,

If $A = \{a, b, c, d, e\}$, then $\#(A) = 5$.

If $X = \{2, 4, 6, 8\}$, then $\#(X) = 4$.

Equality of sets

> Sets are said to be **equal** if they contain exactly the same elements.

The **order** in which the elements are listed is **not** important. For example,
if $A = \{a, b, c, d\}$ and $B = \{b, c, d, a\}$, then $A = B$, as they contain exactly the same elements.

The null set

The set that contains **no** elements is called the **null** or **empty** set.
The null set is denoted by $\varnothing$ or $\{\ \}$.

> The null set, $\varnothing$ or $\{\ \}$, is the set that contains no elements.

Examples of the null set:

$\varnothing = \{$months of the year that have more than 31 days$\}$

$\{\ \} = \{$odd numbers that can be divided evenly by 2$\}$

Note: $\{0\}$ is **not** the null set.
$\{0\}$ is a set that contains one element, 0, and so it is **not** empty.

1. Which of the following sets are equal?
   $P = \{2, 4, 6, 8\}, \quad Q = \{3, 5, 7\}, \quad R = \{5, 7, 3\}, \quad S = \{8, 2, 4, 6\}.$
   Evaluate **(i)** $\#(P) + \#(Q)$ **(ii)** $[\#(S)]^2$

2. If $A = \{p, q, r\}$ and $B = \{p, q, s\}$, explain why $A \neq B$.

3. $A = \{2, 4, 6, 8\}$ and $B = \{\text{even numbers between 1 and 9}\}$.
   (i) Is $A = B$? **(ii)** Evaluate $\#(A) + \#(B)$.

4. $C = \{\text{days of the week containing nine letters}\}$
   $D = \{\text{days the week beginning with the letter W}\}$
   Is $C = D$?

5. $P = \{\text{vowels in the word 'median'}\}$, $Q = \{\text{vowels in the word 'mean'}\}$
   (i) List the elements in (*a*) P, (*b*) Q. **(ii)** Is $P = Q$?
   (iii) Evaluate $\#(P) - \#(Q)$.

6. $A = \{p, q\}$, $B = \{1, 2, 3\}$ and $C = \{m, i, s, t\}$.
   Evaluate each of the following:
   (i) $\#(A) + \#(B) + \#(C)$ **(ii)** $5[\#(A)] + 4[\#(B)] + 3[\#(C)]$
   (iii) $[\#(A)]^2 + [\#(B)]^2 + [\#(C)]^2$ **(iv)** $[\#(A) + \#(B)]^2$

7. $A = \{\text{even numbers between 6.7 and 7.9}\}$.
   (i) Describe the set A. **(ii)** Evaluate $\#(A)$.

8. $A = \{\text{letters in the word 'rearrange'}\}$, $B = \{\text{letters in the word 'ranger'}\}$.
   (i) List the elements (*a*) of A, (*b*) of B. **(ii)** Is $A = B$? **(iii)** Evaluate $\#(A) - \#(B)$

Membership of a set defined by a rule

A set can also be described by using a rule.
Consider the set $P = \{\text{prime numbers less than 8}\}$. This set can also be written as:

$P = \{x \mid x \text{ is a prime number less than 8}\}$

This is read as:

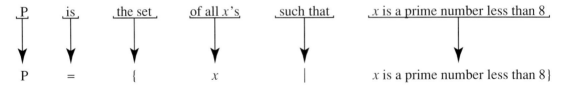

P	is	the set	of all x's	such that	x is a prime number less than 8
P	=	$\{$	x	$\mid$	x is a prime number less than 8$\}$

This is the '**rule method**' of describing a set.

$A = \{x \mid x$ is an even number between 3 and 11$\}$. List the elements of A.

Solution:
Using the rule, $x = 4, 6, 8, 10$

Therefore $A = \{4, 6, 8, 10\}$

Exercise 15.3 ▼

List the elements of each of the following sets:
1. $A = \{x \mid x$ is an even number between 5 and 15$\}$
2. $B = \{x \mid x$ is an odd number between 2 and 12$\}$
3. $C = \{x \mid x$ is a letter of the word 'T E N N E S S E E'$\}$
4. $D = \{x \mid x$ is a letter of the word 'T O M O R R O W'$\}$
5. $E = \{x \mid x$ is a factor of 28$\}$
6. $F = \{x \mid x$ is a factor of 36$\}$
7. $G = \{x \mid x$ is a whole number between 3 and 25 and divisible by 4$\}$
8. $P = \{x \mid x$ is a prime number less than 20$\}$
9. $V = \{x \mid x$ is a vowel$\}$
10. $M = \{x \mid x$ is a vowel in the word 'N O T O R I O U S'$\}$
11. $W = \{x \mid x$ is a day of the week beginning with T$\}$
12. $R = \{x \mid x$ is a whole number between $2\frac{1}{4}$ and $2\frac{1}{2}\}$
13. $T = \{x \mid x$ is a vowel in the word 'D R Y'$\}$
14. $S = \{x \mid x$ is an even number between $4\frac{1}{2}$ and $5\frac{1}{2}\}$

Subsets (sets within sets)

If every element of a set B is also an element of a set A, then B is said to be a subset of A.
This is written $B \subset A$.

$\subset$ means 'is a subset of'
$\not\subset$ means 'is not a subset of'

Example ▼

$A = \{1, 3, 5, 7, 9\}$, $B = \{3, 5\}$, $C = \{3, 6\}$

(i) Say why B is a subset of A **(ii)** Is $B \subset C$?
(iii) Represent A and B with a Venn diagram.

(i) Every element in B is also in A, therefore B is a subset of A.
i.e. $B \subset A$

(ii) The element 5 is in B and not in C,
therefore B is not a subset of C.
i.e. $B \not\subset C$

(iii)

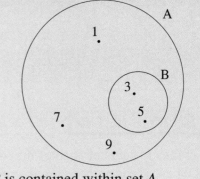

Set B is contained within set A

Notes:
1. Every set is a subset of itself.   **2.** The null set is a subset of every set.

Example ▼

$A = \{p, q\}$. Write out all the subsets of A.

Solution:
The subsets of A are: $\{\ \}, \{p\}, \{q\}, \{p, q\}$.

Exercise 15.4 ▼

1. $A = \{1, 2, 3, 4, 5, 6, 7, 8\}$, $B = \{4, 5, 6, 7\}$, $C = \{\ \}$, $D = \{3, 4, 8, 9\}$, $E = \{2\}$, $F = \{4, 6\}$.
State whether each of the following is true or false:
(a) $B \subset A$ **(b)** $E \subset B$ **(c)** $C \subseteq E$ **(d)** $D \subset D$
(e) $F \not\subset B$ **(f)** $E \subset A$ **(g)** $A \subset D$ **(h)** $F \not\subset C$
(i) $D \subset C$ **(j)** $F \subset B \subset A$

2. $H = \{1, 2, 3, 4, 5, 6, 7, 8, 9, 10\}$. List the following subsets of H:
(i) {even numbers}   **(ii)** {odd numbers}   **(iii)** {numbers divisible by 3}
(iv) {prime numbers}   **(v)** {multiples of 5}   **(vi)** {factors of 24}
(vii) {perfect squares}   **(viii)** {perfect cubes}   **(ix)** {numbers divisible by 17}

3. Represent each of the following with Venn diagrams:
(a) $A = \{1, 3, 5, 7, 9\}$ and $B = \{1, 3\}$
(b) $P = \{6, 9\}$ and $Q = \{2, 5, 6, 7, 9, 12\}$
(c) $C = \{x \mid x$ is an even number between 1 and 19$\}$ and

$D = \{x \mid x$ is a number between 3 and 17 that is divisible by 4$\}$

4. If $A = \{231, 43, 141, 600, 501, 430, 610, 35\}$, write down a subset of A in which the sum of the digits in each number is 6.
5. $A = \{p, q, r\}, B = \{1, 2, 3, 4\}$
   Write out all the subsets of **(i)** A and   **(ii)** B.
6. $C = \{a, b, c, d\}$. List all the subsets of C that contain exactly three elements.

Universal set

The **universal set** is the set containing all the elements used in a given question. It is denoted by U. In a Venn diagram the universal set is represented by a rectangle.

Intersection

> The intersection of two sets, A and B, is the set of elements that are in both A and B.

It is written as $A \cap B$, pronounced 'A intersection B'.

Union

> The union of two sets, A and B, is the set of elements formed by joining together all the elements of A and B.

It is written as $A \cup B$, pronounced 'A union B'.

Example ▼

$U = \{1, 2, 3, 4, 5, 6, 7, 8, 9, 10\}$, $A = \{1, 3, 4, 7\}$, and $B = \{3, 6, 7, 8, 9\}$.

(i) Represent U, A and B with a Venn diagram.
(ii) List the elements of $A \cap B$ and $A \cup B$.
(iii) Evaluate $\#(A \cup B) - \#(A \cap B)$.

Solution:
(i)

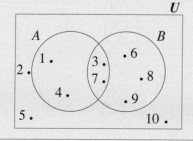

(ii) $(A \cap B) = \{3, 7\}$
$(A \cup B) = \{1, 3, 4, 6, 7, 8, 9\}$

(iii) $\#(A \cup B) - \#(A \cap B)$
$= 7 - 2 = 5$

Note: U need not be included if it is not relevant to the question.

1. $A = \{1, 2, 3, 4, 5\}$ and $B = \{4, 5, 6, 7\}$.
   (i)   Represent A and B with a Venn diagram.
   (ii) List the elements of $A \cap B$ and $A \cup B$.
   (iii) Evaluate $\#(A \cup B) - \#(A \cap B)$.
   (iv) Is $(A \cap B) \subset A$? Explain your answer.
2. $C = \{a, b, c, d\}$ and $D = \{b, d, e, f, g, h\}$.
   (i)   Represent C and D with a Venn diagram.
   (ii) List the elements of $C \cap D$ and $C \cup D$.
   (iii) Evaluate $\#(D) - \#(C \cap D)$.
3. $U = \{a, b, c, d, e, f, g, h, i, j\}$, $A = \{c, d, e, f\}$, and $B = \{e, f, g, h\}$.
   (i)   Represent U, A and B with a Venn diagram.
   (ii) List the elements of $A \cap B$ and $A \cup B$.
   (iii) Evaluate $\#(A \cup B) - \#(A \cap B)$.
4. $U = \{2, 3, 4, 5, 6, 7, 8, 9\}$, $A = \{2, 4, 5\}$, and $B = \{2, 5, 6, 8\}$.
   (i)   Represent U, A and B with a Venn diagram.
   (ii) List the elements of $A \cup B$ and $A \cap B$.
   (iii) Explain why $(A \cup B) \subset U$.
   (iv) Evaluate $\#(U) - \#(A \cup B)$.
5. From the Venn diagram shown here, say whether each of the following statements is true
   or false:

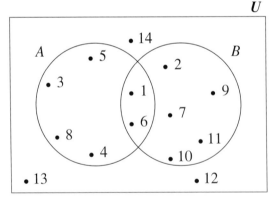

   (i) $6 \in A$
   (ii) $6 \in B$
   (iii) $(A \cap B) = \varnothing$
   (iv) $13 \in U$
   (v) $1 \in (A \cap B)$
   (vi) $12 \in (A \cup B)$
   (vii) $\#(A) = 4$
   (viii) $\#(A \cap B) = 2$
   (ix) $\#(A) > \#(B)$
   (x) $\#(U) - \#(B) = 6$
   List the elements of U that are not in $A \cup B$.
6. $A = \{1, 2, 6\}$, $B = \{1, 2, 3, 4, 5\}$, and $U = \{1, 2, 3, 4, 5, 6, 7, 8\}$.
   (i)   Explain why $A \not\subset B$ and $B \subset U$.
   (ii) Represent A, B and U with a Venn diagram.
   (iii) Evaluate $\#(U) - \#(A \cup B)$.
   (iv) List the elements of U that are not in A or B.

7. Link each of the following with $\in, \notin, =, \neq, \subset, \cup$ or $\cap$:

(a) $5 \quad \{2, 3, 4, 5, 6\}$ **(b)** $\{t, r\} \quad \{r, t\}$ **(c)** $\{a, b\} \quad \{a, b, c\}$ **(d)** $\{4\} \quad \{3, 4, 5\}$

(e) $\{p, q, r\} \quad \{r, p, q\}$ **(f)** $q \quad \{m, n, o\}$ **(g)** $\{a, b, c\} \quad \{c, d, e\} \quad \{a, b, c, d, e\}$

(h) $\{1, 2, 3, 4, 5\} \quad \{4, 5, 6, 7, 8\} \quad \{4, 5\}$ **(i)** $\{1, 3\} \quad \{1, 3, 5, 9\} \quad \{1, 3, 5, 7, 9\}$

8. $U = \{1, 4, 9, 12, 15, 18, 19, 20\}$.

$A = \{$numbers in U divisible by $2\}$.

$B = \{$numbers in U divisible by $3\}$.

Copy and complete the Venn diagram.

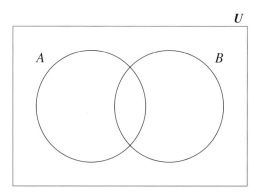

Set difference

$A \backslash B$ is the set of elements that are in A but **not** in B.

$A\backslash B$ is pronounced 'A less B' or 'A not B'.

In some ways it is like the subtraction of one set from another.

Example ▼

$A = \{a, b, c, d, e, f\}$ and $B = \{e, f, g, h\}$.

Represent A and B with a Venn diagram.

List the elements of **(i)** $A\backslash B$ **(ii)** $B\backslash A$

Solution:

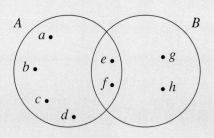

(i) $A\backslash B$

$= \{a, b, c, d, e, f\} \backslash \{e, f, g, h\}$

$= \{a, b, c, d\}$

(all the elements in A that are not in B)

(ii) $B\backslash A$

$= \{e, f, g, h\} \backslash \{a, b, c, d, e, f\}$

$= \{g, h\}$

(all the elements of B that are not in A)

If brackets are involved, the operation inside the brackets must be done first.

$P = \{a, b, c\}$, $Q = \{c, d, e\}$, $R = \{a, c, e, f\}$.
List the elements of **(i)** $(P \cup Q)\backslash R$ **(ii)** $Q\backslash(P \cap R)$

Solution:

(i) $(P \cup Q)\backslash R$
  $P \cup Q$ (brackets first)
  $= \{a, b, c\} \cup \{c, d, e\}$
  $= \{a, b, c, d, e\}$
  Therefore $(P \cup Q)\backslash R$
  $= \{a, b, c, d, e\}\backslash\{a, c, e, f\}$
  $= \{b, d\}$

(ii) $Q\backslash(P \cap R)$
  $P \cap R$ (brackets first)
  $= \{a, b, c\} \cap \{a, c, e, f\}$
  $= \{a, c\}$
  Therefore $Q\backslash(P \cap R)$
  $= \{c, d, e\}\backslash\{a, c\}$
  $= \{d, e\}$

Exercise 15.6 ▼

1. $A = \{1, 2, 3, 4, 5, 6\}$ and $B = \{4, 5, 6, 7, 8\}$. Represent A and B with a Venn diagram.
    List the elements of **(i)** $A\backslash B$ **(ii)** $B\backslash A$.
2. $P = \{a, b, c, d\}$ and $Q = \{a, c, e, f, g\}$. Represent P and Q with a Venn diagram.
    List the elements of **(i)** $P\backslash Q$ **(ii)** $Q\backslash P$.
    Evaluate $\#(Q\backslash P) - \#(P\backslash Q)$.
3. $X = \{p, q, r, s\}$, and $Y = \{p, q, u, v, w\}$. List the elements of:
    (i) $X\backslash Y$ **(ii)** $Y\backslash X$ **(iii)** $(X\backslash Y) \cup (Y\backslash X)$ **(iv)** $(X\backslash Y) \cap (Y\backslash X)$
4. From the Venn diagram shown, answer true or false to each of the following statements:
    (i) $\#(U) = 10$ **(ii)** $P \cap Q = \{3, 4\}$ **(iii)** $Q\backslash P = \{9, 10\}$
    (iv) $\#(P\backslash Q) = 2$ **(v)** $(P \cup Q)\backslash(P \cap Q) = \{1, 6, 7, 9, 10\}$

5. $A = \{1, 2, 3, 4, 5\}$, $B\{1, 2, 6, 7, 8\}$, and $C = \{2, 5, 7, 9\}$. List the elements of:
    (i) $A\backslash B$ **(ii)** $A\backslash C$ **(iii)** $B\backslash A$ **(iv)** $B\backslash C$
    (v) $A \cup B$ **(vi)** $(A \cup B)\backslash C$ **(vii)** $B \cap C$ **(viii)** $A\backslash(B \cap C)$
    (ix) $B \cup C$ **(x)** $(B \cup C)\backslash(B \cap C)$ **(xi)** $(B \cap C)\backslash A$

Complement of a set

The **complement** of a set A is the set of elements in the universal set, U, that are **not** elements of A.

The complement of a set A is written A' (pronounced 'A complement' or 'A dashed').

$$A' = U \backslash A$$
Every element in the universal set U except those in A.

It is an extension of set difference.

$$(A \cup B)' = U \backslash (A \cup B) \qquad \text{and} \qquad (A \cap B)' = U \backslash (A \cap B)$$

The four regions for the three sets U, A, and B

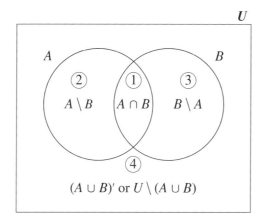

Note: If the universal set, U, is not involved, there are only three regions.
When drawing a Venn diagram, always work from the centre outwards.

Example ▼

$U = \{1, 2, 3, 4, 5, 6, 7, 8, 9\}, \qquad A = \{1, 3, 4, 7\}, \qquad B = \{2, 3, 5, 7, 9\}.$
Represent U, A and B with a Venn diagram.
List the elements of **(i)** A' **(ii)** B' **(iii)** $A' \cup B'$ **(iv)** $(A \cup B)'$

Solution:

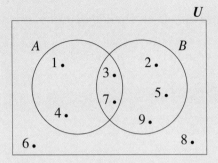

(i) $A' = U \backslash A$
$= \{1, 2, 3, 4, 5, 6, 7, 8, 9\} \backslash \{1, 3, 4, 7\}$
$= \{2, 5, 6, 8, 9\}$

(ii) $B' = U \backslash B$
$= \{1, 2, 3, 4, 5, 6, 7, 8, 9\} \backslash \{2, 3, 5, 7, 9\}$
$= \{1, 4, 6, 8\}$

(iii) $A' \cup B' = \{2, 5, 6, 8, 9\} \cup \{1, 4, 6, 8\} = \{1, 2, 4, 5, 6, 8, 9\}$

(iv)
$(A \cup B)'$
$= U \backslash (A \cup B)$
$= \{1, 2, 3, 4, 5, 6, 7, 8, 9\} \backslash \{1, 2, 3, 4, 5, 7, 9\} \longleftarrow$
$= \{6, 8\}$

$(A \cup B)$
$= \{1, 3, 4, 7\} \cup \{2, 3, 5, 7, 9\}$
$= \{1, 2, 3, 4, 5, 7, 9\}$

Exercise 15.7 ▼

1. $U = \{a, b, c, d, e\}$ and $A = \{c, d, e\}$. List the elements of A'.
2. $U = \{3, 4, 5, 6, 7, 8\}$ and $P = \{3, 5, 7\}$. List the elements of P'.
3. $U = \{1, 2, 3, 4, 5, 6, 7, 8\}$, $A = \{1, 5, 6, 8\}$, and $B = \{1, 4, 5\}$.
   Represent U, A and B with a Venn diagram.
   List the elements of **(i)** A' **(ii)** B'.
   Verify that $A' \cap B' = (A \cup B)'$.
4. $U = \{a, b, c, d, e, f, g\}$, $P = \{a, d, f, g\}$, and $Q = \{a, b, g\}$.
   Represent U, P and Q with a Venn diagram.
   List the elements of **(i)** P' **(ii)** Q' **(iii)** $P' \cap Q'$ **(iv)** $(P \cup Q)'$.
   Evaluate $\#(P') + \#(Q') - \#(P' \cap Q')$.
5. Given the Venn diagram on the right, list the elements of the following sets:

   (i) U **(ii)** A **(iii)** B
   (iv) $A \cap B$ **(v)** $A \cup B$ **(vi)** $A \backslash B$
   (vii) $B \backslash A$ **(viii)** A' **(ix)** B'
   (x) $A' \cap B'$ **(xi)** $(A \cup B)'$ **(xii)** $A' \cap B$
   (xiii) $A \cap B'$ **(xiv)** $(B \backslash A)'$

Set operations with three sets

*The eight regions for the four sets **U**, **A**, **B**, and **C***

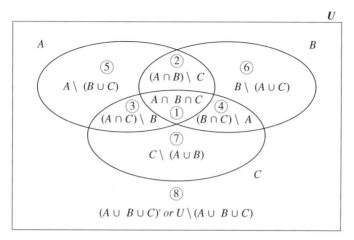

When drawing a Venn diagram representing the four sets **U**, **A**, **B**, and **C**, do the following:

Draw three intersecting curves, *A*, *B*, and *C*, then draw a rectangle, *U*, around the curves. Fill in the elements in the following order, working from the centre outwards:

1. $A \cap B \cap C$ ①
2. $(A \cap B)\backslash C$ ②, $(A \cap C)\backslash B$ ③, $(B \cap C)\backslash A$ ④
3. $A\backslash(B \cup C)$ ⑤, $B\backslash(A \cup C)$ ⑥, $C\backslash(A \cup B)$ ⑦
4. $(A \cup B \cup C)'$ or $U\backslash(A \cup B \cup C)$ ⑧

Note: If the universal set, **U**, is not involved, there are only seven regions.

Example ▼

$U = \{1, 2, 3, 4, 5, 6, 7, 8, 9, 10\}$, $A = \{2, 3, 4, 8\}$, $B = \{1, 3, 4, 5, 9\}$, and $\{C = \{4, 5, 7, 9\}$. Represent *U*, *A*, *B* and *C* with a Venn diagram.

Solution:

1. $A \cap B \cap C = \{4\}$
2. $(A \cap B)\backslash C = \{3\}$
   $(A \cap C)\backslash B = \{\ \}$
   $(B \cap C)\backslash A = \{5, 9\}$
3. $A\backslash(B \cup C) = \{2, 8\}$
   $B\backslash(A \cup C) = \{1\}$
   $C\backslash(A \cup B) = \{7\}$
4. $U\backslash(A \cup B \cup C) = \{6, 10\}$

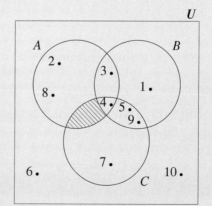

Note: On a Venn diagram, empty sets are usually indicated by shading with straight lines.

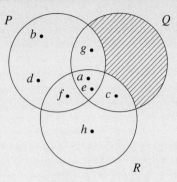

Example ▼

Given the Venn diagram on the right, list the elements of the following sets:

(i) $P \cap Q \cap R$ (ii) Q
(iii) $P \backslash Q$ (iv) $(P \cap Q) \backslash R$

Solution:

(i) $P \cap Q \cap R = \{a, e\}$ (ii) $Q = \{a, c, e, g\}$
(iii) $P \backslash Q = \{a, b, d, e, f, g\} \backslash \{a, c, e, g\} = \{b, d, f\}$

(iv) $(P \cap Q) \backslash R$
$= \{a, e, g\} \backslash \{a, c, e, f, h\}$ ←
$= \{g\}$

$P \cap Q$ (brackets first)
$= \{a, b, d, e, f, g\} \cap \{a, c, e, g\}$
$= \{a, e, g\}$

Exercise 15.8 ▼

1. $U = \{1, 2, 3, 4, 5, 6, 7, 8, 9\}$
   $A = \{6, 8, 9\}$
   $B = \{1, 2, 3, 8, 9\}$
   $C = \{2, 5, 9\}$
   Copy the Venn diagram and complete it.

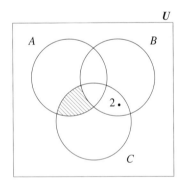

2. $P = \{a, b, d, e\}$
   $Q = \{b, c, d, f\}$
   $R = \{a, d, g, h\}$
   Copy the Venn diagram and complete it.

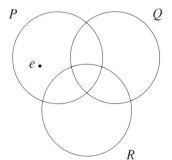

In each of the following four questions, represent the sets with a Venn diagram:

3. $U = \{1, 2, 3, 4, 5, 6, 7, 8\}$, $A = \{2, 4, 7, 8\}$,
   $B = \{4, 5, 6, 8\}$, and $C = \{1, 6, 7, 8\}$.
4. $U = \{a, b, c, d, e, f, g, h\}$, $P = \{a, b, c, g\}$, $Q = \{b, d, g, h\}$ and $R = \{c, d, f, g\}$.
5. $X = \{1, 2, 4, 5\}$, $Y = \{2, 3, 5, 8\}$ and $Z = \{4, 5, 6, 7\}$.
6. $A = \{p, q, r, s, x\}$, $B = \{p, q, t, u, v, w\}$ and $C = \{p, r, u, v\}$.

7. From the Venn diagram shown, list the elements of the following sets:

(i) P (ii) Q (iii) R
(iv) $P\backslash Q$ (v) $P \cup Q$ (vi) $P \cap Q$
(vii) $(P \cup Q)\backslash R$ (viii) $(P \cap Q)\backslash R$
(ix) $(P \cup Q) \cap R$ (x) $(R \cap Q) \cup P$

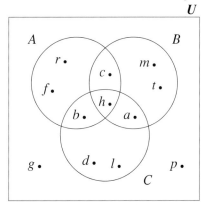

8. $U = \{1, 2, 3, 4, 5, 6, 7\}$, $P = \{1, 2, 3\}$, $Q = \{3, 4, 5\}$, and $R = \{1, 3, 5, 6\}$.
Represent U, P, Q and R with a Venn diagram.
List the elements of:

(i) $P \cap Q \cap R$ (ii) $P\backslash Q$ (iii) $P \cup Q$ (iv) $(P \cup Q)\backslash R$
(v) $P \cap Q$ (vi) $(P \cap Q)\backslash R$ (vii) R' (viii) $(P \cup Q \cup R)'$
(ix) $P\backslash(Q \cup R)$ (x) $(Q \cup R)'$ (xi) $(P \cup Q)'$ (xii) $(P \cup Q) \cap R$
Evaluate $\#(R')$.

9. From the Venn diagram shown, answer true or false to each of the following statements:

(i) $A \cap B = \{c\}$
(ii) $(A \cap C)\backslash B = \{b\}$
(iii) $A \cap B \cap C = \{h\}$
(iv) $A\backslash(B \cup C) = \{r, f, g\}$
(v) $p \in U\backslash(A \cup B \cup C)$
(vi) $U = A \cup B \cup C$
(vii) $(A \cup C) \cap B = \{c, h, a\}$
(viii) $(B \cap C) \subset A$
(ix) $\#[(A \cup B)\backslash C] = 5$
(x) $\#[(A \cup B \cup C)'] = 3$

10. $A = \{1, 2, 3, 4, 5\}$, $B = \{3, 4, 5, 6\}$, and $C = \{1, 4, 5, 6, 7\}$.

(a) List the elements of:
     (i) $A \cap B$ (ii) $C\backslash B$ (iii) $(B \cap C)\backslash A$ (iv) $A\backslash(B \cup C)$
(b) Evaluate: (i) $(A \cup B)$ (ii) $\#[(A \cap B)\backslash C]$ (iii) $\#[C\backslash(A \cup B)]$
(c) Substitute one of the signs $\cup, \cap$ or $\backslash$ for $*$ so that
     (i) $(A * B) * C = \{2, 3\}$ (ii) $\#[B * (A * C)] = 0$
Note: It may help to represent A, B and C with a Venn diagram.

Numerical problems on two sets

When using Venn diagrams to solve numerical problems we put the **actual number** of elements in a region on the diagram. It is important at this stage that the meanings of the symbols used are considered.

Set notation	Meaning
$\cup$	or
$\cap$	and, both
$A \cup B$	in A or B
$A \cap B$	in A and B
$A \backslash B$	in A but not in B (A only)
$B \backslash A$	in B but not in A (B only)
U	universal set
A'	in U but not in A
$(A \cup B)'$ or $U \backslash (A \cup B)$	in U but not in A or B
$(A \cap B)'$ or $U \backslash (A \cap B)$	in U but not in A and B

When putting the values into a Venn diagram, always work from the centre outwards.

Example ▼

In a class of 34 pupils, 22 study music, 18 study science, and 8 study both. Draw a Venn diagram to illustrate the information and use it to find the number of pupils in the class who study **(i)** music only, **(ii)** science only, and **(iii)** neither music nor science.

Solution:
Draw a Venn diagram showing U for the class, M for music, and S for science.
Given: $\#(U) = 34$, $\#(M) = 22$, $\#(S) = 18$ and $\#(M \cap S) = 8$.

(i) Number who study music only
   $= \#(M \backslash S) = 22 - 8 = 14$
(ii) Number who study science only
   $= \#(S \backslash M) = 18 - 8 = 10$
(iii) Number who study neither music nor science
   $= \#[U \backslash (M \cup S)] = 34 - (14 + 8 + 10)$
   $= 34 - 32 = 2$

(Check: $14 + 8 + 10 + 2 = 34$.)

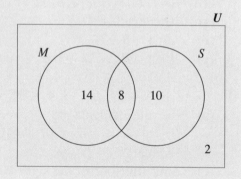

In some questions the number of elements in the intersection of the two sets is not given, and this leads to the problem of **double counting**.

In a survey of 32 people, 20 said they liked rock music, 13 said they liked classical music, and 4 said they like neither.

(i) How may liked both rock and classical music?
(ii) Represent the survey with a Venn diagram.
(iii) How many only like rock music?
(iv) How many liked only one of these types of music?

Solution:

On the Venn diagram, let U represent the number of people in the survey, R the number who liked rock music, and C the number who liked classical music.

(i) The number of people in the survey who liked rock music, classical music or neither
$= 20 + 13 + 4 = 37$
The number of people in the survey $= 32$
Therefore the number of people counted twice $= 37 - 32 = 5$
Thus, 5 people liked both rock and classical music.

(ii)

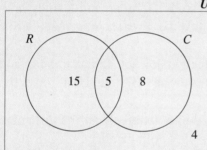

$\#(R \cap C) = 5$
$\#(R \backslash C) = 20 - 5 = 15$
$\#(C \backslash R) = 13 - 5 = 8$

(Check: $15 + 5 + 8 + 4 = 32$.)
(iii) Number of people who only liked rock music $= \#(R \backslash C) = 15$
(iv) Number of people who liked only one of these types of music
$= \#(R \backslash C) + \#(C \backslash R) = 15 + 8 = 23$

1. 66 pupils were asked in a survey if they liked rock music, R, or classical music, C, or neither. The results are shown in the Venn diagram. How many said they liked:
    (i) both   **(ii)** rock music
    (iii) classical music   **(iv)** neither
    (v) only one of these types of music?

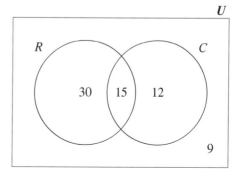

2. Each of the 50 members of a club were asked if they played chess (*C*), hockey (*H*), or neither. The results are shown in the Venn diagram. How many said they played
  (i)   both   (ii) chess
  (iii) hockey   (iv) neither
  (v)   only one of these games?

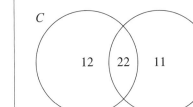

3. In a class of 30 pupils, 18 play basketball (*B*), 14 play football (*F*), and 2 play neither.
  Copy the Venn diagram and complete it.
  How many pupils in the class play
  (i)   both games   (ii) only one of these games
  (iii) at least one of these games?

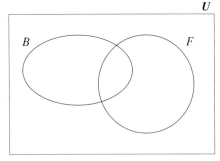

4. In a class of 30 pupils, 16 study French, 17 study German, and 5 study both French and German. How many pupils in the class study **(i)** French only, **(ii)** German only, and **(iii)** neither?

5. In a survey of 80 people, 58 said they had a television set, 45 had a radio, and 30 said that they had both. How many people in the survey had **(i)** television only, **(ii)** radio only, and **(iii)** neither?

6. In a class of 32 girls, 19 play hockey and 22 play tennis. If all the girls play at least one of these games, how many girls in the class play both games?

7. In a survey, 100 people were asked if they liked oranges or grapefruit. 75 people said they liked oranges, 50 said they liked grapefruit, and 10 said they liked neither. How many people in the survey said they liked both?

8. In a survey of 300 houses, 250 had television sets, 180 had a phone, and 20 had neither a television nor a phone. How many households in the survey had both?

9. The Venn diagram shows the number of elements in the sets *U*, *A*, and *B*. Evaluate each of the following:
  (i)   #(*U*)   (ii) #(*A* ∩ *B*)   (iii) #(*A**B*)
  (iv) #(*B**A*)   (v)   #(*A* ∪ *B*)   (vi) #(*A* ∪ *B*)′
  (vii) #(*A*′)   (viii) #(*B*′)   (ix) #[*U*\\(*A* ∩ *B*)]

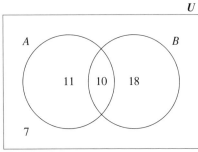

10. If #(*A*) = 20, #(*B*) = 15, and #(*A* ∩ *B*) = 8,
  find #(*A* ∪ *B*).

11. If #(*X*) = 16, #(*Y*) = 18, and #(*X* ∪ *Y*) = 24, find #(*X* ∩ *Y*).

12. If #(*A*) = 22, #(*A* ∪ *B*) = 35, and #(*A* ∩ *B*) = 12, find #(*B*).

13. If #(*X*) = 15, #(*Y*) = 13, and #(*X* ∪ *Y*) = 23, find **(i)** #(*X**Y*) and **(ii)** #(*Y**X*).

14. If #(*U*) = 35, #(*X*) = 19, #(*Y*) = 17, and #(*X* ∩ *Y*) = 7, find #[*U*\\(*X* ∪ *Y*)].

15. The Venn diagram shows the number of girls in a class of 30 who study maths (M), economics (E), or both. If each girl must study one of these subjects, how many girls in the class study **(i)** both subjects, **(ii)** maths only, and **(iii)** economics only?

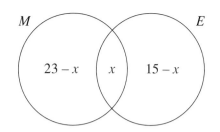

16. All 22 pupils in a class took part in the long (L) or the high (H) jump in a sports day. 16 took part in the long jump and 12 took part in the high jump. If $\#(L \cap H) = x$, write an equation in x and find the value of x.

Numerical problems on three sets

Numerical problems on three sets are solved in exactly the same way as those using two sets. However, there are more regions to deal with.

Again, let us consider the meanings of the symbols used.

Set notation	Meaning
$A \cup B \cup C$	In A or B or C
$A \cap B \cap C$	In A and B and C
$(A \cup B)\backslash C$	In A or B but not in C
$(A \cap B)\backslash C$	In A and B but not in C
$A\backslash(B \cup C)$	in A but not in B or C (A only)
$(A \cup B \cup C)'$ or $U\backslash(A \cup B \cup C)$	in U but not in A or B or C

As before, when putting values into a Venn diagram always work from the centre outwards.

Example ▼

100 fifth-year pupils were asked to choose from three subjects: accounting, biology, and chemistry. 41 chose accounting, 48 chose biology, and 44 chose chemistry. 16 chose accounting and biology; 15 chose accounting and chemistry, and 17 chose biology and chemistry. 5 chose all three subjects. Draw a Venn diagram to illustrate the information, and use the diagram to find the number of pupils who do not take any of these subjects.

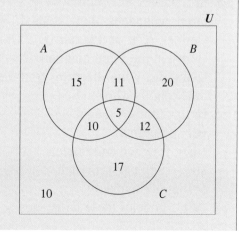

Solution:

Draw a Venn diagram showing U for all 100 pupils, A for accounting, B for biology, and C for chemistry.

$\#(A \cap B \cap C) = 5$

Therefore $\#[(A \cap B)\backslash C] = 16 - 5 = 11$ | $\#[A\backslash(B \cup C)] = 41 - (10 + 11 + 5) = 15$

and $\#[(A \cap C)\backslash B] = 15 - 5 = 10$ | $\#[B\backslash(A \cup C)] = 48 - (12 + 11 + 5) = 20$

and $\#[(B \cap C)\backslash A] = 17 - 5 = 12$ | $\#[C\backslash(A \cup B)] = 44 - (10 + 5 + 12) = 17$

Therefore $\#(A \cup B \cup C) = 5 + 11 + 12 + 10 + 15 + 20 + 17 = 90$

Therefore $\#[U\backslash(A \cup B \cup C)] = 100 - 90 = 10$

Therefore 10 pupils did not take accounting, biology, or chemistry.

Exercise 15.10 ▼

1. All 73 members in a youth club were asked in a survey if they played football, F, snooker, S, or tennis, T. The results are shown in the Venn diagram. Using the Venn diagram, find the number of members of the youth club who play

   (i) all three sports

   (ii) football and snooker

   (iii) football or snooker

   (iv) none of these sports

   (v) snooker and tennis but not football

   (vi) snooker or tennis but not football

   (vii) football

   (viii) tennis only

   (ix) only one of these sports

   (x) only two of these sports.

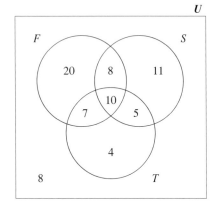

2. In a survey, 57 pupils were asked which of three languages they studied: English (E), German (G), or French (F). The results are shown in the Venn diagram.

   Using the Venn diagram, find the number of those pupils who studied

   (i) all three languages

   (ii) English

   (iii) English and French

   (iv) English or French

   (v) German only

   (vi) none of these languages

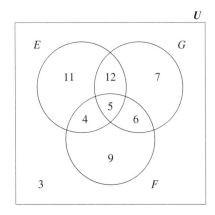

   (vii) German and French but not English
   (viii) German or French but not English
   (ix) only one of these languages
   (x) exactly two of these languages
   (xi) at least one of these languages.

3. In a school of 162 pupils, 115 study mathematics, 105 study English, 115 study Irish, 80 study mathematics and English, 90 study mathematics and Irish, 75 study English and Irish, and 60 study all three. How many study none of the three subjects?

4. 50 pupils in Cork were asked how they had spent a particular evening at home. 34 watched television, 24 played CDs, 20 listened to the radio, 10 played CDs and listened to the radio, 11 watched television and listened to the radio, 13 watched television and played CDs. 4 did all three. How many did none of the three?

5. 24 pupils in Galway were asked which of the following types of programme they watched on television: news, sport, or drama. They answered as follows: 13 watched news, 16 watched sport, 12 watched drama, 8 watched news and sport, 6 watched news and drama, 8 watched sport and drama, and 3 watched all three. How many watched **(a)** none of the programmes, **(b)** sport only, and **(c)** news and sport only?

6. 45 people were asked which countries they had visited last year. They answered as follows: 14 visited Canada, 16 visited France, 14 visited Russia, 4 visited Canada and France, 5 visited Canada and Russia, 6 visited France and Russia, and 3 visited all three countries. How many people visited **(i)** none of the three countries, **(ii)** Russia only, **(iii)** only one of the three countries, **(iv)** at least one country, **(v)** Canada or Russia, and **(vi)** Canada and France but not Russia?

7. The Venn diagram shows the number of elements in the different subsets of U, A, B, and C. Evaluate each of the following:

   (i) $\#(U)$ **(ii)** $\#(A)$
   (iii) $\#(B)$ **(iv)** $\#(C)$
   (v) $\#(A \cap B \cap C)$ **(vi)** $\#(B \cup C)$
   (vii) $\#(A \cup B \cup C)$ **(viii)** $\#[(A \cup B \cup C)']$
   (ix) $\#[(A \cap B)\backslash C]$ **(x)** $\#[(B \cup C)\backslash A]$
   (xi) $\#[B\backslash(A \cup C)]$ **(xii)** $\#(A \cup B) - \#(A \cap B)$

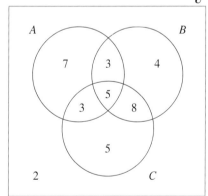

8. U is the set of all 29 pupils in a class; B is the set of pupils who play basketball; C is the set who play chess; and T is the set who play tennis.
$\#(B) = 14$, $\#(C) = 13$, $\#(T) = 11$, $\#(B \cap T) = 7$, $\#(C \cap T) = 4$, $\#(B \cap C) = 5$,   and $\#(B \cap C \cap T) = 3$.
How many pupils in the class play
(i) none of these games, **(ii)** only one of the three games, **(iii)** only two of the three games, **(iv)** at least two of the three games?

9. *U* is the set of all 30 pupils in a class. *A*, *B* and *C* represent the number of pupils in the class who study accounting, biology, and chemistry, respectively.
$\#(A) = 18$, $\#(B) = 15$, $\#(C) = 16$, $\#(A \cap B) = 7$, $\#[(B \cap C)\backslash A] = 6$, $\#[C\backslash(A \cup B)] = 0$, $\#(A \cap B \cap C) = 2$.
How many pupils study: **(a)** accounting only, **(b)** accounting and chemistry but not biology, **(c)** none of the three subjects, **(d)** only two of the three subjects, **(e)** at least one of the three subjects, **(f)** biology or chemistry but not accounting?

10. *X*, *Y* and *Z* are subsets of the universal set.
$\#(X \cap Y \cap Z) = 4$, $\#[(X \cap Y)\backslash Z] = 5$, $\#[X\backslash(Y \cup Z)] = 6$, $\#[Y\backslash(X \cup Z)] = 2$, $\#[(X \cap Z)\backslash Y] = 3$, $\#[(Y \cap Z)\backslash X] = 2$, $\#[Z\backslash(X \cup Y)] = 5$ and $\#[U\backslash(X \cup Y \cup Z)] = 3$.   Find $\#(U)$.

11. There are three shops in a village: the post office, the butcher's, and the grocer's. *P*, *B* and *G* represent the number of customers who went into each shop. Represent the following situation with a Venn diagram:
$\#(P) = 25$, $\#(B) = 29$, $\#(G) = 26$, $\#(P \cap B) = 15$, $\#(B \cap G) = 16$, $\#[G\backslash(P \cup B] = 4$ and $\#(P \cap B \cap G) = 10$.

   (a) Find the number of people who went to **(i)** the post office only, **(ii)** the post office and the grocer's but not the butcher's, **(iii)** the butcher's or the grocer's but not the post office.

   (b) Describe the people in the set **(i)** $(P \cap B)\backslash G$ **(ii)** $(G \cup B)\backslash P$

Regions on a Venn diagram

In some questions we have to shade or name a region on a Venn diagram.

Example ▼

(i) Name the shaded region in the Venn diagram.
(ii) On a Venn diagram, shade in the region $(A \cup B)\backslash C$.

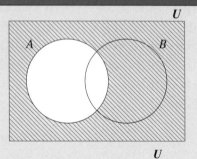

Solution:
(i) The elements in the shaded region are all the elements that are **not** in *A*. Therefore the shaded region is A' or $U\backslash A$.
(ii) In this type of question draw a Venn diagram and label each region with a number. Then use your knowledge of sets to find the regions required. Then shade in these regions.

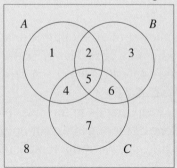

$A \cup B = \{1, 2, 4, 5\} \cup \{2, 3, 5, 6\}$
$\qquad = \{1, 2, 3, 4, 5, 6\}$
$C = \{4, 5, 6, 7\}$
Therefore $(A \cup B)\backslash C$
$\qquad = \{1, 2, 3, 4, 5, 6\}\backslash\{4, 5, 6, 7\}$
$\qquad = \{1, 2, 3\}$
Therefore we shade in the regions, 1, 2, and 3.

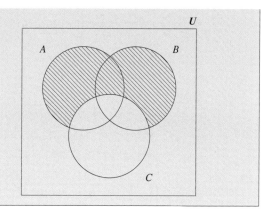

Exercise 15.11 ▼

For each of the following questions, copy the Venn diagram and shade in the required region:

1. $A \cup B$
2. $(A \cup C)'$
3. $(B \cup C)\backslash A$
4. $(A \cup B \cup C)'$
5. B'
6. $U\backslash(A \cup C)$
7. $(A \cup C) \cap B$
8. $(B \cap C)\backslash A$
9. $(A \cap B) \cap (B \cap C)$
10. $(A \cup B)\backslash(A \cap B)$
11. $(A\backslash B)\backslash C$
12. $A' \cap B'$

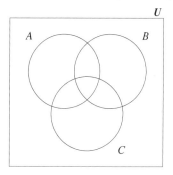

Name the shaded region in each of the following Venn diagrams:

13.

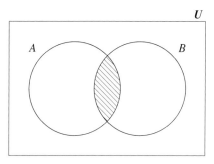

14.

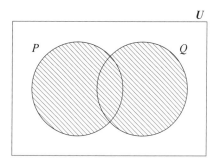

15.

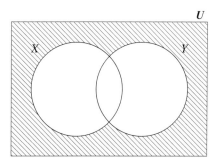

16.

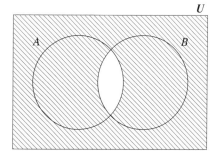

17.

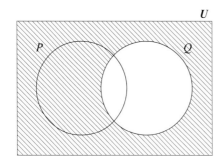

18.

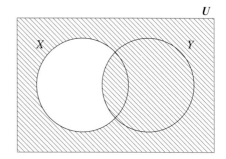

19.

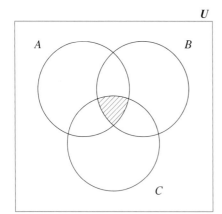

20.

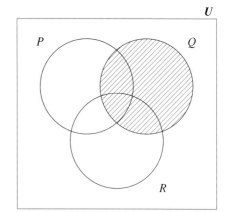

21.

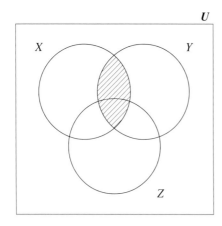

22.

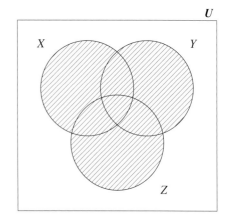

23.

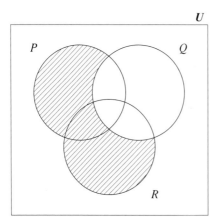

24.

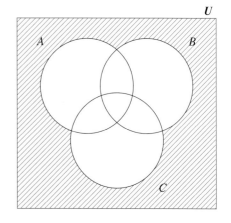

25.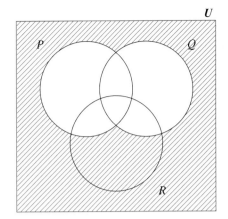

26.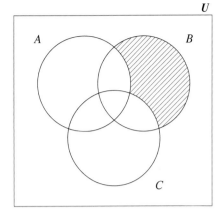

27.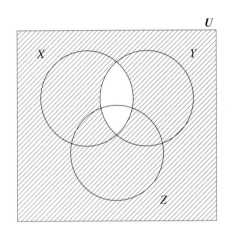

28.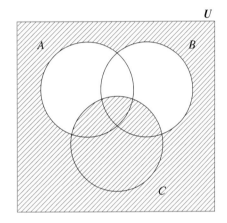

Exercise 15.12 ▼

Chapter test

1. List the elements of the set of letters in each of the following words:
   (i)   BANANA
   (ii) BOOKKEEPER
   (iii) TENNESSEE
   (iv) THIRTIETH.

2. The Venn diagram shows the sets *U*, *A*, and *B*.
   List the elements of the following sets:
   (i)   *A*   **(ii)** *B*
   (iii) *U*   **(iv)** $A \cap B$
   (v)   *A'*   **(vi)** $A \cup B$
   (vii) $(A \cup B)'$ **(viii)** $(A \cap B)'$

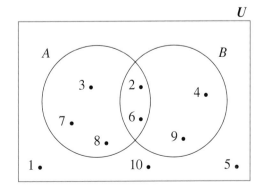

3. The Venn diagram shows the sets U, A, and B.

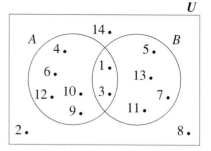

(a) State whether each of the following statements is true or false:

(i) $3 \in A$ (ii) $3 \notin B$

(iii) $A \cap B = \{1\}$ (iv) $16 \notin U$

(v) $8 \in (A \cup B)$ (vi) $(A \cap B) \subset B$

(vii) $\#(A \backslash B) = 5$ (viii) $\#(B) > \#(A)$

(ix) $\#[(A \cup B)'] = 2$

4. The Venn diagram shows the sets U, P, Q, and R.

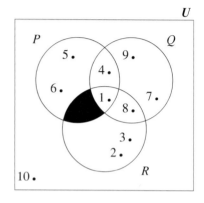

List the elements of each of the following sets:

(i) Q (ii) $P \cap Q$

(iii) $R \backslash P$ (iv) $(P \cup Q) \backslash R$

(v) $P \cup Q \cup R$ (vi) $(P \cup Q \cup R)'$

(vii) $P \cap R$ (viii) $(P \cap Q) \backslash R$

(ix) $(P \cup Q) \cap R$

Replace each $*$ with one of the signs $\cup$, $\cap$ or $\backslash$ in the statement $(P * R) * Q = \varnothing$.

5. Use a Venn diagram to solve each of the following:

(a) If $\#(A) = 25$, $\#(B) = 12$ and $\#(A \cap B) = 7$, find   (i) $\#(A \cup B)$ and   (ii) $\#(B \backslash A)$.

(b) If $\#(P) = 9$, $\#(Q) = 11$ and $\#(P \cup Q) = 15$, find   (i) $\#(P \cap Q)$ and   (ii) $\#(P \backslash Q)$.

(c) If $\#(U) = 20$, $\#(X) = 9$, $\#(Y) = 10$, and $\#(X \cup Y) = 16$, find   (i) $\#[U \backslash (X \cup Y)]$ and (ii) $\#[U \backslash (X \cap Y)]$.

6. $U = \{1, 2, 3, 4, 5, 6, 7, 8, 9\}$, $A = \{1, 3, 6, 7\}$, $B = \{1, 2, 4, 6, 9\}$, and $C = \{4, 6, 7, 8\}$.

Represent U, A, B and C with a Venn diagram.

List the elements of the following sets:

(i) $A \backslash B$ (ii) $A \cap B \cap C$ (iii) $(A \cup B) \backslash C$ (iv) $A \backslash (B \cup C)$ (v) $(B \cup C)'$

7. 37 people were asked which of 3 newspapers, P, Q, and R, they read. 2 people did not read any of these newspapers. 10 read P and Q, 13 read Q and R. Nobody read Q only, 28 read R, and 23 read P. 6 read all three newspapers. Represent the data with a Venn diagram.

Calculate how many people read:

(iv) P and R only   (ii) P only

(iii) R only   (iv) only one newspaper

(v) at least two newspapers.

8. 33 pupils were asked whether they had visited France, Spain, or England. 5 had been to all three countries, 7 to both France and Spain, 13 to both Spain and England, and 9 to both France and England.

If 12 had been to France, 18 to Spain, and 23 to England, represent the information on a Venn diagram.

Find how many had visited (i) one country only, (ii) at least one country, (iii) more than one country, (iv) France or Spain, and (v) none of these countries.

9. Illustrate the following problem with a Venn diagram. In a class of 29 pupils, U is the set of all pupils in the class. A is the set of pupils over 16 years of age; B is the set of pupils who wear glasses; C is the set of pupils who live more than 2 km from the school.

$\#(A \cap B \cap C) = 2$, $\#(A \cap B) = 5$, $\#(B \cap C) = 7$, $\#[(A \cap C)\backslash B] = 5$,
$\#(A) = 13$, $\#(B) = 14$, $\#(C) = 16$.

   (i) Calculate $\#[A\backslash(B \cup C)]$.
   (iii) How many pupils under 16 do not wear glasses?
   (iii) Describe in words the pupils in the sets **(a)** $C\backslash(A \cup B)$ **(b)** $U\backslash(A \cup B \cup C)$.

10. The Venn diagram given here shows the elements in the sets A, B, and C.
State the value of

   (i) $\#(A \cup B \cup C)$.
   (ii) $\#[(A \cap B) \cup C]$.
   (iii) $\#[C\backslash(A \cup B)]$.
   (iv) $\#[(A\backslash B\backslash C]$.

Substitute one of the signs $\cup$, $\cap$ or $\backslash$
for each question mark so that
$\#[B?C)?A] = 0$.

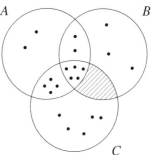

11. A and B are two sets. $\#(A) = 5$ and $\#(B) = 4$.
Copy the Venn diagram five times, and use
the diagrams to illustrate each of the
following:

   (i) $\#(A \cap B) = 3$
   (ii) $\#(A\backslash B) = 3$
   (iii) $\#(A \cup B) = 8$
   (iv) $\#(A \cup B)$ is a maximum
   (v) $\#(A \cup B)$ is a minimum.

12. A and B are two sets such that $\#(A \cup B) = 15$ and $\#(A \cap B) = 3$. There are twice as many elements in $A\backslash B$ as there are in $B\backslash A$. Find $\#(A)$.

13. A shop in a school sold only three items:
crisps (A), sweets (B), and soft drinks (C).
40 pupils spent money in the shop one morning;
10 bought crisps and sweets,
12 bought crisps and soft drinks,
8 bought crisps only, and 3 bought sweets only.
No-one bought all three items.
Twice as many bought crisps as bought sweets.
Enter this data in a Venn diagram.
How many

   (i) bought soft drinks only?
   (ii) bought two items only?

Show in detail how you arrive at the last two answers.

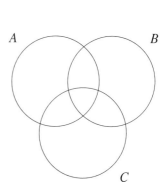

CHAPTER
16

FACTORS

Factorising

> **Factorising is the reverse procedure to removing brackets.**

Expanding removes brackets.
Factorising does the opposite by putting in brackets.

For example:

Expanding:	$5(2a + 3b) = 10a + 15b$	Remove brackets.
Factorising:	$10a + 15b = 5(2a + 3b)$	Put in brackets.

The process of finding the factors of an expression is called **factorisation**.

There are four types of factors that we will meet on our course:

	Type	Example	Factors
1.	Take out the HCF	$6pq + 3pr$	$3p(2q + r)$
2.	Factors by grouping	$ax + bx + ay + by$	$(a + b)(x + y)$
3.	Quadratic trinomials	$x^2 - 4x - 12$	$(x - 6)(x + 2)$
4.	Difference of two squares	$4a^2 - 9b^2$	$(2a - 3b)(2a + 3b)$

Note: It is good practice to check your answer by removing the brackets to make sure that the factors give the original expression you were asked to factorise.

1. Taking out the highest common factor (HCF)

> 1. Find the HCF of all the terms making up the expression.
> 2. Put the HCF outside the brackets.
> 3. Divide each term by the HCF to find the factor inside the brackets.

Factorise: **(i)** $5ab + 10ac$ **(ii)** $6xy - 3y^2$ **(iii)** $pq - pr + p$

Solution:

(i) $5ab + 10ac$
The HCF is $5a$
Therefore $5ab + 10ac$ (put $5a$ outside the bracket,
$= 5a(b + 2c)$ then divide each term by $5a$)

$$\frac{5ab}{5a} = b$$

$$\frac{10ac}{5a} = 2c$$

(ii) $6xy - 3y^2$
The HCF is $3y$
Therefore $6xy - 3y^2$ (put $3y$ outside the bracket,
$= 3y(2x - y)$ then divide each term by $3y$)

$$\frac{6xy}{3y} = 2x$$

$$\frac{-3y^2}{3y} = -y$$

(iii) $pq - pr + p$
The HCF is p
Therefore $pq - pr + p$ (put p outside the bracket,
$= p(q - r + 1)$ then divide each term by p)
        ↑
(There must be a 1 here)
Notice that the HCF is the same as one of the terms.

$$\frac{pq}{p} = q$$

$$\frac{-pr}{p} = -r$$

$$\frac{p}{p} = 1$$

Exercise 16.1 ▼

Simplify each of the following:

1. $\dfrac{8a}{2}$ **2.** $\dfrac{6p}{3}$ **3.** $\dfrac{4xy}{2x}$ **4.** $\dfrac{2q}{2q}$ **5.** $\dfrac{9ab}{3b}$

6. $\dfrac{-4p}{2}$ **7.** $\dfrac{3xy}{3y}$ **8.** $\dfrac{-20pq}{10q}$ **9.** $\dfrac{6x^2y}{2xy}$ **10.** $\dfrac{12pqr}{4pq}$

11. $\dfrac{5ab}{5a}$ **12.** $\dfrac{6ab}{3ab}$ **13.** $\dfrac{2x^2y}{2x^2y}$ **14.** $\dfrac{8ab}{2b}$ **15.** $\dfrac{6a^2b}{3ab}$

Copy each of the following, and fill in the missing terms in the brackets:

16. $2x + 4y = 2($ $)$ **17.** $5a + 15 = 5($ $)$

18. $x^2 + 3x = x($ $)$ **19.** $ac + ad = a($ $)$

20. $2pq - 6pr = 2p($ $)$ **21.** $4x^2 - 2xy = 2x($ $)$

22. $a^2 - a = a($ $)$ **23.** $5x - 10xy = 5x($ $)$

Factorise each of the following:

24. $4x + 8$ **25.** $ab + ac$ **26.** $3a + 3b$

27. $2p + pq$ **28.** $12a + 8b$ **29.** $3m + 6n$

30. $x^2 + x$ **31.** $x^2 - 3x$ **32.** $2x + 4x^2$

33. $a^2 + 5a$ **34.** $4p + 2p^2$ **35.** $5x^2 + 10x$

36. $3ax + 6bx$ **37.** $4ab - 8a$ **38.** $2pq - 6pr$

39. $6xp - 6xq$ **40.** $5ab + 10ac$ **41.** $7x - 28xy$

42. $2a - 4a^2$ **43.** $3a + 6ab + 9ac$ **44.** $4a^2 - 20ab$

45. $pq + pr - p$ **46.** $6xy - 9xz$ **47.** $qr - 2qs$

48. $4ab - 3b^2$ **49.** $3x^2 - 9xy$ **50.** $18p^2q - 6pq$

51. $4x^2y + 8xy^2$ **52.** $2a^2b + 6ab^2$ **53.** $10abc - 15abd$

54. Simplify $3(a^2 + a - 2) + 2(3 - a^2)$ and then factorise your answer.

55. Factorise   **(i)** $8ab + 12a$ **(ii)** $4b + 6$

Hence, simplify $\dfrac{8ab + 12a}{4b + 6}$

2. Factors by grouping

An expression consisting of four terms with no common factor can be factorised with the following steps:

> 1. Group into pairs with a common factor.
> 2. Take out the common factor in each pair separately.
> 3. Take out the new common factor.

Factorise: **(i)** $ax + bx + ay + by$ **(ii)** $3ac - 3ad + bc - bd$ **(iii)** $pq + pr - q - r$

Solution:

(i)

$$ax + bx + ay + by$$
$$= (ax + bx) + (ay + by) \qquad \text{(group into pairs with a common factor)}$$
$$= x(a + b) + y(a + b) \qquad \text{(take out common factor in each pair)}$$
$$= (a + b)(x + y) \qquad \text{(take out common factor } (a + b))$$

(ii)

$$3ac - 3ad + bc - bd$$
$$= (3ac - 3ad) + (bc - bd) \qquad \text{(group into pairs with a common factor)}$$
$$= 3a(c - d) + b(c - d) \qquad \text{(take out common factor in each pair)}$$
$$= (c - d)(3a + b) \qquad \text{(take out common factor } (c - d))$$

(iii) $pq + pr - q - r$

Method 1:

$$pq + pr - q - r$$
$$= (pq + pr) - (q + r) \qquad \text{(group into pairs with a common factor)}$$
$$= p(q + r) - 1(q + r) \qquad \text{(take out common factor in each pair)}$$
$$= (q + r)(p - 1) \qquad \text{(take out common factor } (q + r))$$

Note: 1 or −1 is always a common factor.

Method 2:

$$pq + pr - q - r$$
$$= pq - q + pr - r \qquad \text{(rearrange order of the terms)}$$
$$= (pq - q) + (pr - r) \qquad \text{(group into pairs with a common factor)}$$
$$= q(p - 1) + r(p - 1) \qquad \text{(take out common factor in each pair)}$$
$$= (p - 1)(q + r) \qquad \text{(take out common factor } (p - 1))$$

Exercise 16.2 ▼

Factorise each of the following:

1. $c(a + b) + d(a + b)$
2. $r(p + q) + s(p + q)$
3. $p(x + a) + q(x + a)$
4. $m(x - y) + m(x - y)$
5. $2x(y - 3) + 5(y - 3)$
6. $2a(c - 3d) - b(c - 3d)$
7. $ax + bx + ay + by$
8. $pq + pr + xq + xr$
9. $mx + nx + my + ny$
10. $5a + 5b + xa + xb$
11. $4x + 4y + zx + zy$
12. $ab + ac + bd + cd$
13. $3p + 3q + pr + qr$
14. $ax + 4a + px + 4p$
15. $5x + 5y + ax + ay$
16. $ap + aq + bp + bq$
17. $ax - ay + 2x - 2y$
18. $3p - 3q + rp - rq$
19. $am - an + 4m - 4n$
20. $ac - bc + ad - bd$

21. $3a + 3b - ac - bc$

22. $pq + pr - 5q - 5r$

23. $px + qx - py - qy$

24. $pr + qr - 2ps - 2qs$

25. $a^2 + ab + 2a + 2b$

26. $x^2 - xy + xz - yz$

27. $x^2 + 2px + qx + 2pq$

28. $2x - x^2 + 2y - xy$

29. $m^2 + mn + 4m + 4n$

30. $p^2 - 3p + pq - 3q$

31. $ab + ac + b + c$

32. $pq + pr + q + r$

33. $ax + bx - a - b$

34. $xy + xz - y - z$

More difficult 'factors by grouping'

Sometimes rearranging is necessary, and often we have to take out a **negative** common factor from the second grouped pair.

For example: $-3a - 3b = -3(a + b)$ (take out common factor -3)

$-5ax + 5ay = -5a(x - y)$ (take out common factor $-5a$)

(notice that this sign changes to a $-$)

Example ▼

Factorise   **(i)** $pq - 4r + pr - 4q$ **(ii)** $6xy + ab - 2by - 3ax$

Solution:

(i) $pq - 4r + pr - 4q$

No common factors in the first two terms or in the last two terms, therefore rearrange.

$= pq + pr - 4q - 4r$ (rearrange)

$= (pq + pr) - (4q + 4r)$ (group into pairs with a common factor)

$= p(q + r) - 4(q + r)$ (take out common factor in each pair)

$= (q + r)(p - 4)$ (take out common factor $(q + r)$)

(ii) $6xy + ab - 2by - 3ax$

No common factors in the first two terms or in the last two terms, therefore rearrange.

$= 6xy - 2by - 3ax + ab$ (rearrange)

$= (6xy - 2by) - (3ax - ab)$ (group into pairs with a common factor)

$= 2y(3x - b) - a(3x - b)$ (take out common factor in each pair)

$= (3x - b)(2y - a)$ (take out common factor $(3x - b)$)

Exercise 16.3 ▼

Copy each of the following, and fill in the missing terms in the brackets:

1. $-5a - 5b = -5(\quad\quad)$

2. $-3ab - 3ac = -3a(\quad\quad)$

3. $-2pq - 2pr = -2p(\quad\quad)$

4. $-4ax - 4bx = -4x(\quad\quad)$

5. $-3a + 3b = -3(\quad\quad)$

6. $-qr + 3qs = -q(\quad\quad)$

7. $-5pq + 5pr = -5p(\quad\quad)$

8. $-x^2 + 2x = -x(\quad\quad)$

Factorise each of the following:

9. $ac + bd + ad + bc$
10. $pq + 3r + pr + 3q$
11. $ax + 2b + 2a + bx$
12. $3x + yz + 3y + xz$
13. $px - qy - qx + py$
14. $2ab - 5c - 5b + 2ac$
15. $ab - cd + bd - ac$
16. $2ap + bq - 2aq - bp$
17. $ax + 4p - 4a - px$
18. $3a + bq - 3b - aq$
19. $pq + rs - pr - qs$
20. $pa + bq - pb - aq$
21. $x(a + b) - a - b$
22. $p - q - 3ap + 3aq$
23. $p(a - b) - a + b$
24. $a - c(b - a) - b$

Quadratic trinomials

An expression of the form $x^2 + bx + c$, where b and c are numbers, is called a '**quadratic trinomial**', since in the expression the highest power of x is 2 (quadratic) and it contains three terms (trinomial).

Factorising quadratic trinomials

Quadratic trinomials can be broken up into **two** types:

1. **Final term positive**
   When the final term is positive, the signs inside the middle of the brackets will be the **same**, either two pluses or two minuses. Keep the sign of the middle term given in the question.

Middle term plus:	$(x + \text{number})(x + \text{number})$	(two pluses)
Middle term minus:	$(x - \text{number})(x - \text{number})$	(two minuses)

2. **Final term negative**
   When the final term is negative, the signs inside the middle of the brackets will be **different**.

   $(x + \text{number})(x - \text{number})$ or $(x - \text{number})(x + \text{number})$

In both cases the factors can be found by trial and improvement. The test is to multiply the inside terms, multiply the outside terms, and add the results to see if you get the middle term of the original quadratic trinomial.

Factorise: (i) $x^2 + 8x + 15$ (ii) $x^2 - 7x + 10$ (iii) $x^2 + x - 12$ (iv) $x^2 - 2x - 8$

Solution:

(i) $x^2 + 8x + 15$

Final term is + and middle term is +,
therefore the factors are $(x + \text{number})(x + \text{number})$.

Factors of 15
1×15
3×5

$(x + 1)(x + 15)$ $x + 15x = 16x$ (no)

$(x + 3)(x + 5)$ $3x + 5x = 8x$ (yes, this is the middle term)

Therefore $x^2 + 8x + 15 = (x + 3)(x + 5)$

(ii) $x^2 - 7x + 10$

Final term is + and middle term is –,
therefore factors are $(x - \text{number})(x - \text{number})$.

Factors of 10
1×10
2×5

$(x - 1)(x - 10)$ $-x - 10x = -11x$ (no)

$(x - 2)(x - 5)$ $-2x - 5x = -7x$ (yes, this is the middle term)

Therefore $x^2 - 7x + 10 = (x - 2)(x - 5)$

(iii) $x^2 + x - 12$

Final term is –,
therefore the factors are $(x + \text{number})(x - \text{number})$
or
$(x - \text{number})(x + \text{number})$.

Factors of 12
1×12
2×6
3×4

Note: It is good practice to begin the trial and improvement with $(x + \text{number})(x - \text{number})$.

$(x + 2)(x - 6)$ $2x - 6x = -4x$ (no)

$(x + 3)(x - 4)$ $3x - 4x = -x$ (no, wrong sign)

On our second trial we have the correct number in front of x but of the wrong sign.
So we just swap the signs:

$(x - 3)(x + 4)$ $-3x + 4x = x$ (yes, this is the middle term)

Therefore $x^2 + x - 12 = (x - 3)(x + 4)$

(iv) $x^2 - 2x - 8$

Final term is –,
therefore the factors are $(x + \text{number})(x - \text{number})$
or
$(x - \text{number})(x + \text{number})$.

Factors of 8
1×8
2×4

$(x + 1)(x - 8)$ $x - 8x = -7x$ (no)

$(x + 2)(x - 4)$ $2x - 4x = -2x$ (yes, this is the middle term)

Therefore $x^2 - 2x - 8 = (x + 2)(x - 4)$

Factorise each of the following:

1. $x^2 + 3x + 2$ 2. $x^2 + 4x + 3$ 3. $x^2 + 6x + 5$
4. $x^2 + 8x + 7$ 5. $x^2 + 12x + 11$ 6. $x^2 + 6x + 8$
7. $x^2 + 5x + 4$ 8. $x^2 + 7x + 12$ 9. $x^2 + 7x + 10$
10. $x^2 + 11x + 10$ 11. $x^2 + 8x + 12$ 12. $x^2 + 13x + 12$
13. $x^2 - 9x + 14$ 14. $x^2 - 10x + 21$ 15. $x^2 - 8x + 12$
16. $x^2 - 2x - 8$ 17. $x^2 + 8x - 20$ 18. $x^2 - 4x - 12$
19. $x^2 + 2x - 15$ 20. $x^2 - x - 12$ 21. $x^2 + x - 30$
22. $x^2 + 6x + 9$ 23. $x^2 + 4x + 4$ 24. $x^2 + 10x + 24$
25. $x^2 + x - 2$ 26. $x^2 - x - 6$ 27. $x^2 - 5x - 24$
28. $x^2 - 2x - 3$ 29. $x^2 + 5x - 6$ 30. $x^2 - 29x + 100$
31. $x^2 + 19x + 48$ 32. $x^2 + 3x - 4$ 33. $x^2 + x - 20$
34. $x^2 - 2x - 24$ 35. $x^2 - 3x - 10$ 36. $x^2 + 17x - 60$
37. $x^2 - 2x - 35$ 38. $x^2 - 9x + 20$ 39. $x^2 - x - 42$
40. $x^2 + 3x - 18$ 41. $x^2 + 14x + 45$ 42. $x^2 - 3x - 28$
43. $x^2 - 5x - 14$ 44. $x^2 + 3x - 40$ 45. $x^2 - 6x - 27$
46. $x^2 - 14x - 72$ 47. $x^2 + 28x - 60$ 48. $x^2 - 11x - 80$

49. Simplify $5(x^2 - 3x + 4) - 4(x^2 - 6x)$ and then factorise your answer.
50. Simplify $2(2x - x^2) - 3(5 + 2x - x^2)$ and then factorise your answer.

Difference of two squares

An expression such as $a^2 - b^2$ is called the '**difference of two squares**'.

The product $(a - b)(a + b) = a^2 - b^2$.

In reverse, $a^2 - b^2 = (a - b)(a + b)$.

We use this to factorise any expression that can be written as the difference of two squares.

We factorise the difference of two squares with the following steps:

1. Write each term as a perfect square with brackets.
2. Use the rule $a^2 - b^2 = (a - b)(a + b)$.
   In words: $(\text{first})^2 - (\text{second})^2 = (\text{first} - \text{second})(\text{first} + \text{second})$.

Factorise   **(i)** $4x^2 - 9y^2$ **(ii)** $1 - 16a^2$

Solution:
(i) $4x^2 - 9y^2$
   $= (2x)^2 - (3y)^2$ (write as perfect squares in brackets)
   $= (2x - 3y)(2x + 3y)$ (apply the rule, (first − second)(first + second))
(ii) $1 - 16a^2$
   $= (1)^2 - (4a)^2$ (write as perfect squares in brackets)
   $= (1 - 4a)(1 + 4a)$ (apply the rule, (first − second)(first + second))

Note: $1 = 1^2$, i.e. 1 is a perfect square.

The factorisation of the difference of two squares can also be used to simplify some calculations.

By resolving into factors, evaluate the following:
(i) $101^2 - 99^2$ **(ii)** $(1.02)^2 - (0.98)^2$

Solution:

(i) $101^2 - 99^2$
   $= (101 - 99)(101 + 99)$
   $= (2)(200)$
   $= 400$

(ii) $(1.02)^2 - (0.98)^2$
   $= (1.02 - 0.98)(1.02 + 0.98)$
   $= (0.04)(2)$
   $= 0.08$

Copy each of the following, and fill in the missing terms in the brackets:

1. $4x^2 = ($ $)^2$ **2.** $9a^2 = ($ $)^2$ **3.** $36b^2 = ($ $)^2$
4. $25a^2 = ($ $)^2$ **5.** $1 = ($ $)^2$ **6.** $49y^2 = ($ $)^2$
7. $81b^2 = ($ $)^2$ **8.** $100p^2 = ($ $)^2$ **9.** $144q^2 = ($ $)^2$

Factorise each of the following:

10. $9a^2 - 4b^2$ **11.** $16x^2 - 25y^2$ **12.** $36p^2 - 25$
13. $4 - 9y^2$ **14.** $25 - 4b^2$ **15.** $16 - 9a^2$
16. $4 - x^2$ **17.** $x^2 - 25$ **18.** $x^2 - 36$
19. $x^2 - y^2$ **20.** $a^2 - b^2$ **21.** $p^2 - 16$
22. $q^2 - 9$ **23.** $49p^2 - 81q^2$ **24.** $25x^2 - 4$
25. $100 - a^2$ **26.** $4a^2 - 25$ **27.** $9 - 4a^2$
28. $64p^2 - 1$ **29.** $1 - 9x^2$ **30.** $16x^2 - 1$

31. $a^2 - 25b^2$ **32.** $16a^2 - b^2$ **33.** $100 - 9p^2$
34. $1 - 121a^2$ **35.** $36 - 25x^2$ **36.** $25p^2 - 49$
37. $121 - 9x^2$ **38.** $25a^2 - 64$ **39.** $64a^2 - 1$
40. $16p^2 - 81q^2$ **41.** $100a^2 - 49b^2$ **42.** $144x^2 - 121y^2$

Factorise and hence evaluate each of the following:

43. $5^2 - 3^2$ **44.** $8^2 - 4^2$ **45.** $10^2 - 7^2$
46. $11^2 - 10^2$ **47.** $15^2 - 5^2$ **48.** $9^2 - 8^2$
49. $103^2 - 97^2$ **50.** $1001^2 - 1$ **51.** $(5.2)^2 - (4.8)^2$
52. $(2.75)^2 - (1.25)^2$ **53.** $(5.5)^2 - (4.5)^2$ **54.** $(10.01)^2 - (9.99)^2$

55. Simplify $3(2x^2 - 5) - 2(x^2 - 3)$ and then factorise your answer.
56. Simplify $5(a^2 - 1) - 4(a^2 + 1)$ and then factorise your answer.

Exercise 16.6 ▼

Chapter test

Factorise each of the following by taking out the highest common factor:

1. $5x + 20$ **2.** $ab + ac$ **3.** $3p + 6pq$
4. $pq - 2p$ **5.** $p^2 - 3p$ **6.** $4a^2 - 2a$

Factorise each of the following by grouping the terms:

7. $ac + bc + ad + bd$ **8.** $pq - pr + qs - sr$ **9.** $3x + 3y - ax - ay$
10. $x^2 + x + xy + y$ **11.** $p^2 + pq + 3p + 3q$ **12.** $2pq - 5r - 5q + 2pr$

Factorise each of the following quadratic trinomials:

13. $x^2 + 7x + 6$ **14.** $x^2 - 8x + 15$ **15.** $x^2 + 5x + 6$
16. $x^2 + 2x - 8$ **17.** $x^2 + x - 6$ **18.** $x^2 + x - 12$
19. $x^2 + 3x - 28$ **20.** $x^2 + 5x - 14$ **21.** $x^2 + 2x - 80$

Factorise each of the following using the difference of two squares:

22. $16 - a^2$ **23.** $x^2 - 9$ **24.** $9x^2 - 25$
25. $1 - 25p^2$ **26.** $36a^2 - 1$ **27.** $25a^2 - 16b^2$

Factorise each of the following using the difference of two squares and hence evaluate:

28. $6^2 - 5^2$ **29.** $9^2 - 7^2$ **30.** $10^2 - 9^2$
31. $(6.2)^2 - (3.8)^2$ **32.** $(8.5)^2 - (1.5)^2$ **33.** $(10.1)^2 - (9.9)^2$

In the following problems first look for a highest common factor and take that out. If there is no highest common factor, look for the following:

(i)   factors by grouping (four terms)
(ii) quadratic trinomials (three terms)
(iii) difference of two squares (two terms)

Factorise each of the following:

34. $8a + 12b$

35. $ap + aq + 3p + 3q$

36. $x^2 + 9x + 18$

37. $4a^2 - 25b^2$

38. $ax - ay + bx - by$

39. $x^2 - 2x - 15$

40. $p^2 - 36$

41. $a^2 - 5a$

42. $x^2 + 7x - 8$

43. $4 - 9a^2$

44. $6pq + 6pr$

45. $a^2 + ac + ab + bc$

46. $ax + 4a + px + 4p$

47. $x^2 - 9$

48. $3x^2 - 12x$

49. $x^2 - 12x + 27$

50. $x^2 + 2px + qx + 2pq$

51. $8a^2b + 12ab + 4ab^2$

52. $x^2 - 7x - 30$

53. $5ap + px - 5aq - qx$

54. $6xy + 9y^2$

55. $x^2 + 3x - 40$

56. $16a^2 - 81b^2$

57. $qr - 2ps - 2qs + pr$

ALGEBRA 2

Simultaneous linear equations

An equation such as $2x + 3y = 19$ is called a linear equation in two unknowns, x and y. Simultaneous linear equations are a pair of such equations. Two equations are necessary if we are to be able to find the values of x and y that satisfy both equations.

For example, consider the following pair of simultaneous linear equations:

$$5x + 2y = 20 \quad ①$$

$$4x + 3y = 23 \quad ②$$

The solution of this pair of simultaneous linear equations is $x = 2$ and $y = 5$.

This pair of values satisfies both equations simultaneously (at the same time).

We can check this by substituting $x = 2$ and $y = 5$ in both equations and showing that the left-hand side is equal to the right-hand side in each equation.

Check:

$$5x + 2y = 20 \qquad ①$$
$$\downarrow \quad \downarrow$$
$$5(2) + 2(5) = 20$$
$$10 + 10 = 20$$
$$20 = 20 \qquad \text{True}$$

$$4x + 3y = 23 \qquad ②$$
$$\downarrow \quad \downarrow$$
$$4(2) + 3(5) = 23$$
$$8 + 15 = 23$$
$$23 = 23 \qquad \text{True}$$

Therefore, our solution $x = 2$ and $y = 5$ is correct.

Equations that are solved together are called simultaneous equations.

Solving a pair of simultaneous linear equations means finding the values of x and y that make both equations true at the same time.

Simultaneous linear equations are solved with the following steps:

1. Write both equations in the form $ax + by = k$ and number the equations ① and ②.
2. Multiply one or both of the equations by a number in order to make the coefficients of x or y the same (ignoring signs).
3. Add or subtract (depending on signs) to remove the variable with equal coefficients.
   (a) When the equal terms have the same sign **subtract** the equations.
   (b) When the equal terms have different signs **add** the equations.
4. Solve the resultant equation to find the value of the remaining unknown (x or y).
5. Substitute this value in equation ① or ② to find the value of the other unknown.

Example ▼

Solve for x and y:
$$3x + 2y = 5$$
$$4x + 5y = 2$$

Solution:

1. Both equations are in the form $ax + by = k$.
   Number the equations ① and ②.

   $$3x + 2y = 5 \qquad ①$$
   $$4x + 5y = 2 \qquad ②$$

2. Make coefficients of y the same.
   Multiply ① by 5 and ② by 2.

   $$15x + 10y = 25 \qquad ① \times 5$$
   $$8x + 10y = 4 \qquad ② \times 2$$

3. Subtract the second equation from the first.

   $$7x = 21$$

4. Divide both sides by 7.

   $$x = 3$$

5. Put $x = 3$ into equation ① or ②.

   $$3x + 2y = 5 \qquad ①$$
   $$\downarrow$$
   $$3(3) + 2y = 5$$
   $$9 + 2y = 5$$

(subtract 9 from both sides) $\qquad 2y = -4$

(divide both sides by 2) $\qquad y = -2$

Therefore, the solution is $x = 3$ and $y = -2$.

Solve for x and y: $\quad 5x + 6y = 19$
$\qquad\qquad\qquad\qquad x - 2y = -9$

Solution:

1. Both equations are in the form $ax + by = k$. $\qquad 5x + 6y = 19 \quad$ ①
   Number the equations ① and ②. $\qquad\qquad\quad\underline{x - 2y = -9} \quad$ ②

2. Make coefficients of y the same. $\qquad\qquad 5x + 6y = 19 \quad$ ①
   Multiply ② by 3. $\qquad\qquad\qquad\qquad\quad\underline{3x - 6y = -27} \quad$ ② × 3

3. Add these new equations. $\qquad\qquad\qquad\qquad 8x = -8$

4. Divide both sides by 8. $\qquad\qquad\qquad\qquad\quad x = -1$

5. Put $x = -1$ into ① or ②. $\qquad\qquad\qquad x - 2y = -9 \quad$ ②
   $\qquad\qquad\qquad\qquad\qquad\qquad\qquad\qquad\downarrow$
   $\qquad\qquad\qquad\qquad\qquad\qquad\quad -1 - 2y = -9$
   (add 1 to both sides) $\qquad\qquad\qquad\qquad -2y = -8$
   (multiply both sides by −1) $\qquad\qquad\qquad 2y = 8$
   (divide both sides by 2) $\qquad\qquad\qquad\quad y = 4$
   Therefore, the solution is $x = -1$ and $y = 4$.

Exercise 17.1 ▼

Solve the following pairs of simultaneous equations:

1. $2x + 3y = 7$
  $x + 4y = 6$

2. $3x + 2y = 13$
  $4x - 3y = 6$

3. $5x + 2y = 13$
  $4x + 5y = 24$

4. $3x + 4y = 23$
  $2x - 3y = 4$

5. $4x + 3y = 15$
  $2x - 5y = 1$

6. $x - 5y = -18$
  $3x + 2y = 14$

7. $3x + y = 13$
  $x - 2y = -5$

8. $3x + 5y = 13$
  $x + 2y = 5$

9. $3x + 2y = 19$
  $x + y = 7$

10. $4x + 2y = 20$
  $3x - 4y = 4$

11. $x - 2y = -2$
  $3x + 7y = 20$

12. $2x + 5y = 9$
  $3x + 2y = 8$

13. $3x + 4y = 15$
  $2x + y = 5$

14. $3x - 2y = 19$
  $2x + 3y = 30$

15. $x + 3y = 6$
  $x + y = 4$

16. $x + y = 11$
  $x - y = 7$

17. $2x + 3y = 7$
  $5x - 3y = -14$

18. $7x - 4y = -2$
  $3x + 4y = -18$

19. $3x - 2y = -12$
  $x - y = -5$

20. $5x - 2y = 3$
  $3x - 3y = 9$

21. $2x - 2y = 0$
  $3x - 5y = -2$

22. $5x + 2y = 26$
$\quad\;\; 2x - 5y = -7$

23. $4x - 3y = 1$
$\quad\;\; 3x + 5y = -21$

24. $3x + 2y = -6$
$\quad\;\; x - 4y = -2$

25. $3x - 2y = -6$
$\quad\;\; 7x + y = 3$

26. $x + 2y = 12$
$\quad\;\; 3x - 5y = 3$

27. $x + y = 3$
$\quad\;\; 5x - 7y = 3$

28. $4x + 3y = 0$
$\quad\;\; x + 2y = -5$

29. $5x + 3y = -8$
$\quad\;\; 2x + y = -3$

30. $3x + 4y = -14$
$\quad\;\; 5x - 2y = -6$

31. $5x = 10$
$\quad\;\; 3x + 2y = 12$

32. $3y = -12$
$\quad\;\; 5x - 2y = 13$

33. $3x + 5y = 19$
$\quad\;\; 7x = -14$

In the next six problems write both equations in the form $ax + by = k$ before trying to solve them.

34. $x + y - 10 = 0$
$\quad\;\; x - y - 4 = 0$

35. $3x + 2y - 7 = 0$
$\quad\;\; x - 3y + 5 = 0$

36. $2x = 5 - 3y$
$\quad\;\; x + 14 = 4y$

37. $3x + 5y = 26$
$\quad\;\; x = 3y - 10$

38. $3x = y + 2$
$\quad\;\; 2y + 4 = x$

39. $5x - 4 = 3y$
$\quad\;\; x = 6 - 2y$

Quadratic equations

An equation such as $x^2 - 3x - 10 = 0$ is called a quadratic equation in x.

A quadratic equation has x^2 (x squared) as its highest power. In general, a quadratic equation has two different solutions (often called roots), but with some quadratic equations the two solutions are the same.

For example, consider the quadratic equation $x^2 - 5x - 14 = 0$.

The two solutions of the equation $x^2 - 5x - 14 = 0$ are $x = 7$ and $x = -2$.

We can check this by substituting $x = 7$ or $x = -2$ in the equation and showing that in each case the left-hand side is equal to the right-hand side.

Check $x = 7$:
$$x^2 - 5x - 14 = 0$$
$$(7)^2 - 5(7) - 14 = 0$$
$$49 - 35 - 14 = 0$$
$$49 - 49 = 0$$
$$0 = 0 \quad \text{True}$$

Check $x = -2$:
$$x^2 - 5x - 14 = 0$$
$$(-2)^2 - 5(-2) - 14 = 0$$
$$4 + 10 - 14 = 0$$
$$14 - 14 = 0$$
$$0 = 0 \quad \text{True}$$

Therefore our solutions $x = 7$ or $x = -2$ are correct.

There are three types of quadratic equations we will meet on our course:

1. $x^2 - 2x - 15 = 0$
2. $x^2 - 3x = 0$ (no constant)
3. $x^2 - 9 = 0$ (no x term)

Solving a quadratic equation means finding the values of x that make the equation true.

Quadratic equations are solved with the following steps:

1. Bring every term to the left-hand side.
   (If necessary multiply both sides by −1 to make the coefficient of x^2 positive.)
2. Factorise the left-hand side.
3. Let each factor = 0.
4. Solve each simple equation.

Type 1

Example ▼

Solve for x: $x^2 - 4x - 21 = 0$

Solution:
1. $x^2 - 4x - 21 = 0$ (every term is on the left-hand side)
2. $(x + 3)(x - 7) = 0$ (factorise the left-hand side)
3. $x + 3 = 0$ or $x - 7 = 0$ (let each factor = 0)
4. $x = -3$ or $x = 7$ (solve each simple equation)
Threfore, $x = -3$ or $x = 7$

Type 2

Example ▼

Solve for x: $3x = x^2$

Solution:
1. $3x^2 = x^2$
   $-x^2 + 3x = 0$ (every term on the left-hand side)
   $x^2 - 3x = 0$ (multiply each term by −1)
2. $x(x - 3) = 0$ (factorise the left-hand side)
3. $x = 0$ or $x - 3 = 0$ (let each factor = 0)
4. $x = 0$ or $x = 3$ (solve each simple equation)
Therefore, $x = 0$ or $x = 3$.
Note: It is important not to divide both sides by x, otherwise the root $x = 0$ is lost.

Type 3

Example ▼

Solve for x: $x^2 - 25 = 0$

Solution:
We will use two methods to solve this quadratic equation.

Method 1:

1. $x^2 - 25 = 0$ (every term is on the left-hand side)

2. $(x)^2 - (5)^2 = 0$ (difference of two squares)

$(x - 5)(x + 5) = 0$ (factorise the left-hand side)

3. $x - 5 = 0$ or $x + 5 = 0$ (let each factor = 0)

4. $x = 5$ or $x = -5$ (solve each simple equation)

Therefore, $x = 5$ or $x = -5$

Method 2:

$x^2 - 25 = 0$

$x^2 = 25$ (add 25 to both sides)

$x = \pm\sqrt{25}$ (take square root of both sides)

$x = \pm 5$ $(\sqrt{25} = 5)$

Therefore, $x = 5$ or $x = -5$.

Exercise 17.2 ▼

Solve each of the following equations:

1. $(x - 1)(x + 3) = 0$
2. $(x - 8)(x - 3) = 0$
3. $(x + 5)(x + 4) = 0$

4. $x(x - 1) = 0$
5. $x(x + 4) = 0$
6. $x(x - 2) = 0$

7. $(x - 4)(x + 4) = 0$
8. $(x - 2)(x + 2) = 0$
9. $(x - 12)(x + 12) = 0$

10. $x^2 - 5x + 4 = 0$
11. $x^2 + 6x + 8 = 0$
12. $x^2 - 8x + 15 = 0$

13. $x^2 + 2x - 8 = 0$
14. $x^2 + x - 2 = 0$
15. $x^2 - 2x - 15 = 0$

16. $x^2 + 12x + 35 = 0$
17. $x^2 - x - 20 = 0$
18. $x^2 - 5x + 6 = 0$

19. $x^2 - 5x = 0$
20. $x^2 + 2x = 0$
21. $x^2 = 4x$

22. $x^2 - 9 = 0$
23. $x^2 - 64 = 0$
24. $x^2 = 100$

25. $x^2 - 1 = 0$
26. $x^2 - 81 = 0$
27. $x^2 - 49 = 0$

28. $x^2 - 7x = 0$
29. $x^2 - 7x - 8 = 0$
30. $x^2 - 121 = 0$

31. $x^2 - 9x + 20 = 0$
32. $x^2 - 3x - 4 = 0$
33. $x^2 + 8x = 0$

34. $x^2 - 8x = 9$
35. $x^2 - 36 = 0$
36. $x^2 - 10x + 21 = 0$

37. $x^2 - 12x + 35 = 15$
38. $x^2 = 4x + 12$
39. $x^2 + 12 = 7x$

40. $5x^2 + 2x = 4x^2 + 15$
41. $3x^2 - 8x + 4 = 2x^2 - 8$
42. $x(x - 6) - 16 = 0$

43. $x(x - 4) = 21$
44. $3(x^2 - 2x) = 2(x^2 - 3x + 8)$
45. $(x + 3)(x - 5) = 9$.

Linear inequalities in one variable

The four inequality symbols

> $>$ means 'greater than'
> $\geqslant$ means 'greater than or equal to'
> $<$ means 'less than'
> $\leqslant$ means 'less than or equal to'

Algebraic expressions that are linked by one of the four inequality symbols are called '**inequalities**'.

For example, $2x + 1 \geqslant 11$ is an inequality.

Solving inequalities is exactly the same as solving equations, with the following exception:

> Multiplying or dividing both sides of an inequality by a **negative** number **reverses** the direction of the inequality.
> That is:
> $>$ changes to $<$ $\geqslant$ changes to $\leqslant$
> $<$ changes to $>$ $\leqslant$ changes to $\geqslant$

For example, $5 > -7$ is true.

Multiplying both sides by -1 and reversing the direction of the inequality gives $-5 < 7$, which is also true.

Note: Inequalities can be turned around. For example:

$$8 > 5 \text{ means the same as } 5 < 8$$

$$3 \leqslant x \text{ means the same as } x \geqslant 3$$

Solving an inequality means finding the values of x that make the inequality true.

Linear inequalities in one variable, x, are solved with the following steps:

1. Remove the brackets.
2. x's to the left, numbers to the right.
3. Simplify both sides.
   (If the coefficient (number) of x is negative, multiply both sides by -1 and reverse the direction of the inequality.)
4. Divide both sides by the coefficient of x.
5. Graph your solution on the number line (if asked).

The following rules apply to graphing inequalities on a number line.

> Number line for $x \in \mathbf{N}$ or $x \in \mathbf{Z}$, use dots.
> Number line for $x \in \mathbf{R}$, use a 'full' heavy line.

Example ▼

Solve $3x + 4 \geqslant 1,$ $x \in Z.$
Graph your solution on the number line.

Solution:

$3x + 4 \geqslant 1$

$\quad 3x \geqslant 1 - 4$ (letters to the left, numbers to the right)

$\quad 3x \geqslant -3$ (simplify right-hand side)

$\quad\quad x \geqslant -1$ (divide both sides by 3)

This is the set of integers (whole numbers) greater than −1, including −1.

Number line:

Example ▼

Solve the inequality $3(x - 4) > 5(2x - 3) + 17$, $x \in \mathbf{R}.$

Graph your solution on the number line.

Solution:

$3(x - 4) > 5(2x - 3) + 17$

$3x - 12 > 10x - 15 + 17$ (remove the brackets)

$3x - 10x > -15 + 17 + 12$ (letters to the left, numbers to the right)

$\quad -7x > 14$ (simplify both sides)

$\quad\quad 7x < -14$ (multiply both sides by −1 and reverse the inequality)

$\quad\quad\quad x < -2$ (divide both sides by 7)

This is the set of real numbers less than −2 but not including −2.

Number line:

A circle is put around −2 to indicate that −2 is not included.

Find the values of x for which $\quad 3x - 11 < x - 1, \qquad x \in N.$
Graph your solution on the number line.

Solution:

$3x - 11 < x - 1$

$\quad 3x - x < -1 + 11 \qquad$ (letters to the left, numbers to the right)

$\qquad 2x < 10 \qquad\qquad$ (simplify both sides)

$\qquad\quad x < 5 \qquad\qquad$ (divide both sides by 2)

This is the set of natural numbers less than 5 but not including 5.
Therefore, the values are 0, 1, 2, 3, and 4.

Number line:

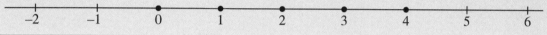

Solve each of the following inequalities, and in each case graph the solution set on the number line.

1. $x + 3 \geqslant 7, \quad x \in N$ **2.** $x - 2 \leqslant 1, \quad x \in Z$ **3.** $5x - 7 > 3, \quad x \in N$

4. $2x + 5 < 11, \quad x \in Z$ **5.** $3x - 1 \geqslant -4, \quad x \in Z$ **6.** $4x + 2 \leqslant -6, \quad x \in Z$

7. $2x + 3 \geqslant x + 1, \quad x \in R$ **8.** $5x + 4 \leqslant 2x + 10, \quad x \in R$

9. $6x + 1 \geqslant 4x + 7, \quad x \in R$ **10.** $4x - 6 \leqslant x + 9, \quad x \in Z$

11. $5x - 1 \leqslant 3x + 5, \quad x \in Z$ **12.** $7x - 20 \geqslant 2x + 5, \quad x \in N$

13. $8x + 2 \geqslant 5x + 8, \quad x \in N$ **14.** $9x - 1 \leqslant 5x + 3, \quad x \in Z$

15. $7x < 3x + 8, \quad x \in R$ **16.** $10x + 2 > 3x - 19, \quad x \in Z$

17. $2x - 5 > 4 - x, \quad x \in R$ **18.** $9x - 6 > 5x - 2, \quad x \in R$

19. $3x - 1 \leqslant 5x + 7, \quad x \in R$ **20.** $7x + 8 \geqslant 10x - 4, \quad x \in R$

21. $2x + 1 < 6x + 9, \quad x \in R$ **22.** $8x - 3 \geqslant 13x - 18, \quad x \in R$

23. $3 - 2x < 5x + 24, \quad x \in R$ **24.** $4 - x > 2x - 2, \quad x \in R$

25. $4(x - 3) \geqslant 3(x - 5), \quad x \in R$ **26.** $5(x + 3) \leqslant 2(2x + 6), \quad x \in Z$

27. $5(2x - 1) \leqslant 3(2x + 1), \quad x \in Z$ **28.** $5(x - 2) \geqslant 2(2 - x), \quad x \in Z$

29. $2(4x + 1) \leqslant 3(2x + 4), \quad x \in Z$ **30.** $5(1 - 2x) \geqslant 15, \quad x \in Z$

31. $3(x + 4) \leqslant -4(x - 10), \quad x \in Z$ **32.** $5(x - 2) + 8 \geqslant 3(x + 2), \quad x \in N$

33. $2(x - 1) < 5(x + 2), \quad x \in R$ **34.** $3(x - 2) - 2(x - 1) \geqslant 0, \quad x \in R$

35. Find the values of x for which $4x - 9 \leqslant 2x - 3, \quad x \in N.$

36. Write out all the values of x for which $x - 6 < 9 - 2x, \quad x \in N.$

37. Find the values of x for which $2x - 3 \leqslant 7, \quad x \in N.$

38. For what values of x is $5 - 2x \geqslant 1, \quad x \in N$?

39. Write out all the natural numbers such that:

     (i) $2x - 1 \leqslant 7$ **(ii)** $3 - 2x \geqslant 1$ **(iii)** $4 \geqslant 2x$

40. Find the smallest natural number that satisfies $x - 3 > 2.$

Chapter test

1. **(a)** Solve for x and y:

$$2x - y = 8$$
$$5x + y = 6$$

   (b) Solve for x:

$$x^2 - 7x + 12 = 0$$

   (c) Write out all the values of x for which $4x - 5 < x + 10$, $\quad x \in \mathbf{N}$.

2. **(a)** Solve for x:

$$x^2 + 6x = 27$$

   (b) Solve for x, $\quad 3x + 2 \geqslant -1$, $\quad x \in \mathbf{R}$, and graph your solution on the number line.

   (c) Solve for x and y:

$$2x - 3y = -7$$
$$2x + y = 5$$

3. **(a)** Solve for x, $\quad 2x - 5 \leqslant 3$, $\quad x \in \mathbf{Z}$, and graph your solution on the number line.

   (b) Solve for x and y:

$$3x + 2y = 7$$
$$x - 3y = -5$$

   (c) Solve for x:

$$x^2 - 2(3x + 8) = 0$$

4. **(a)** Solve for x and y:

$$3x - 4y = 18$$
$$x + y = -1$$

   (b) Solve for x:

$$x(x + 4) - 21 = 0$$

   (c) Write out all the values for x for which $3x - 5 \leqslant 2x + 1$, $\quad x \in \mathbf{N}$.

5. (a) Solve for x and y:

$$3x - y = 7$$
$$2x + y = -2$$

(b) Solve for x:

$$x^2 - 5x = 0$$

(c) Solve for x, $\quad 3(x - 1) + 5(x + 1) \geqslant 18$, $x \in N$, and graph your solution on the number line.

6. (a) Solve for x:

$$x^2 - 100 = 0$$

(b) Solve for x and y:

$$3x - 4y = 1$$
$$x - 3y = 2$$

(c) Solve for x, $\quad 3(x - 1) + 2(x - 3) > 1$, $\quad x \in R$, and graph your solution on the number line.

18

INDICES AND INDEX NOTATION

Repeated multiplication

We use a shorthand called '**index notation**' to indicate repeated multiplication.
For example, $(\text{number})^3 = (\text{number}) \times (\text{number}) \times (\text{number})$

$$\text{Thus, } 4^3 = 4 \times 4 \times 4 = 64$$

$$4^3 \leftarrow \text{power or index}$$

The power or index simply tells you how many times a number is multiplied by itself.
For example, 3^5 means 3 is to be multiplied by itself five times.

$$3^5 = 3 \times 3 \times 3 \times 3 \times 3 = 243$$

$2 \times 2 = 2^2$	read as '2 squared'
$2 \times 2 \times 2 = 2^3$	read as '2 cubed'
$2 \times 2 \times 2 \times 2 = 2^4$	read as '2 to the power of 4'
$2 \times 2 \times 2 \times 2 \times 2 = 2^5$	read as '2 to the power of 5,' and so on.

Note: The first power, or 'to the power of one', of a number is the number itself.
For example, $2^1 = 2, \quad 3^1 = 3, \quad 4^1 = 4$

$$a^{1/2} = \sqrt{a}; \text{ for example, } (16)^{1/2} = \sqrt{16} = 4$$

Powers with a calculator
You can find the value of a number in index form with a calculator by using repeated multiplication or by using the power key, $\boxed{y^x}$ or $\boxed{x^y}$.

To find 5^4 on your calculator use either of the two ways:
1. 5 $\boxed{\times}$ 5 $\boxed{\times}$ 5 $\boxed{\times}$ 5 $\boxed{=}$

power key
↓
2. 5 $\boxed{y^x}$ 4 $\boxed{=}$
↑
index

Exercise 18.1 ▼

Write each of the following in index form (index notation), i.e. x^y:

1. $2 \times 2 \times 2$ **2.** $3 \times 3 \times 3 \times 3$ **3.** $4 \times 4 \times 4 \times 4 \times 4 \times 4$
4. $6 \times 6 \times 6 \times 6 \times 6 \times 6 \times 6$ **5.** $10 \times 10 \times 10 \times 10 \times 10$

Using your calculator, or otherwise, calculate:

6. 2^4 **7.** 3^4 **8.** 5^3 **9.** 10^5 **10.** 8^5 **11.** 2^{10} **12.** 9^6

Rules for powers or indices

Multiplication

Consider the following:

$3^3 \times 3^2 = (3 \times 3 \times 3) \times (3 \times 3) = 3 \times 3 \times 3 \times 3 \times 3 = 3^5$

or

$3^3 \times 3^2 = 3^{3+2} = 3^5$ (add the indices)

Similarly,

$2^4 . 2^3 = (2 \times 2 \times 2 \times 2) \times (2 \times 2 \times 2) = 2 \times 2 \times 2 \times 2 \times 2 \times 2 \times 2 = 2^7$

or

$2^4 . 2^3 = 2^{4+3} = 2^7$ (add the indices)

When **multiplying** powers of the same number, **add** the indices.
$$a^m . a^n = a^{m+n}$$

Division

Consider the following:

$$\frac{5^6}{5^4} = \frac{\cancel{5} \times \cancel{5} \times \cancel{5} \times \cancel{5} \times 5 \times 5}{\cancel{5} \times \cancel{5} \times \cancel{5} \times \cancel{5}} = 5 \times 5 = 5^2$$

or

$\dfrac{5^6}{5^4} = 5^{6-4} = 5^2$ (subtract the index on the bottom from the index on the top)

Similarly,

$$\frac{4^7}{4^2} = \frac{\cancel{4} \times \cancel{4} \times 4 \times 4 \times 4 \times 4 \times 4}{\cancel{4} \times \cancel{4}} = 4 \times 4 \times 4 \times 4 \times 4 = 4^5$$

or

$\dfrac{4^7}{4^2} = 4^{7-2} = 4^5$ (subtract the index on the bottom from the index on the top)

When **dividing** powers of the same number,
subtract the index on the bottom from the index on the top.
$$\frac{a^m}{a^n} = a^{m-n}$$

Power of a power

Consider the following:

$(4^2)^3 = 4^2 \times 4^2 \times 4^2 = 4^{2+2+2} = 4^6$

or

$(4^2)^3 = 4^{2 \times 3} = 4^6$ (multiply the indices)

Similarly,
$$(3^4)^2 = 3^4 \times 3^4 = 3^{4+4} = 3^8$$
or
$$(3^4)^2 = 3^{4 \times 2} = 3^8 \qquad \text{(multiply the indices)}$$

> When a power of a number is raised to a power, **multiply** the indices.
> $$(a^m)^n = a^{mn}$$

Remember: $mn = m \times n$

Example ▼

Express each of the following as a single power:

(i) $5^3 \times 5^4 \times 5$ (ii) $\dfrac{4^7}{4^5}$ (iii) $(3^5)^2$

Solution:

(i) $\quad 5^3 \times 5^4 \times 5$
$\quad = 5^3 \times 5^4 \times 5^1$
$\quad = 5^{3+4+1}$
$\quad = 5^8$

(ii) $\quad \dfrac{4^7}{4^5}$
$\quad = 4^{7-5}$
$\quad = 4^2$

(iii) $\quad (3^5)^2$
$\quad = 3^{5 \times 2}$
$\quad = 3^{10}$

Exercise 18.2 ▼

Express each of the following as a single power:

1. $2^3 \times 2^4$ 2. $3^2 \times 3^6$ 3. $4^3 \times 4^2$ 4. $5^3 \times 5^3$

5. $6^4 \times 6^5$ 6. $5^3 \times 5^4$ 7. 3×3^5 8. $2 \times 2^2 \times 2^4$

9. $\dfrac{3^5}{3^2}$ 10. $\dfrac{4^7}{4^3}$ 11. $\dfrac{2^8}{2^5}$ 12. $\dfrac{10^5}{10^3}$

13. $\dfrac{9^6}{9^4}$ 14. $\dfrac{5^{10}}{5^6}$ 15. $\dfrac{6^9}{6^5}$ 16. $\dfrac{7^{10}}{7^8}$

17. $(2^2)^3$ 18. $(3^3)^4$ 19. $(5^4)^2$ 20. $(8^2)^5$

21. $(7^3)^5$ 22. $(6^4)^5$ 23. $(4^7)^2$ 24. $(9^3)^6$

In each of the following calculate the value of a:

25. $2^4 \times 2^2 = 2^a$ **26.** $3^5 \times 3^2 = 3^a$ **27.** $4^3 \times 4^2 = 4^a$

28. $\dfrac{5^7}{5^4} = 5^a$ **29.** $\dfrac{6^8}{6^6} = 6^a$ **30.** $\dfrac{7^6}{7^2} = 7^a$

31. $(3^2)^5 = 3^a$ **32.** $(5^2)^3 = 5^a$ **33.** $(2^5)^4 = 2^a$

34. Simplify $\dfrac{4^6 \times 4^3}{4^2 \times 4^5}$, giving your answer in the form 4^n.

35. Simplify $\dfrac{3^5 \times 3^3}{3^2 \times 3^2}$, giving your answer in the form 3^n.

36. Simplify $\dfrac{2 \times 2^3 \times 2^7}{(2^2)^4}$, giving your answer in the form 2^n.

37. Simplify $\dfrac{9^{1/2} \times 3^7}{3^4 \times 3^2}$, giving your answer in the form 3^n.

Index notation

Very large numbers are difficult to use, and many cannot be shown on your calculator display. For example, try this multiplication on your calculator: $4{,}000{,}000 \times 8{,}000{,}000$.
The answer is $32{,}000{,}000{,}000{,}000$. It has fourteen digits, which is too many digits to show on most calculator displays.
Your calculator will display your answer as $\boxed{3.2^{13}}$ or $\boxed{3.2 \quad 13}$ or $\boxed{3.2 \text{ E } 13}$.
This tells you that the 3.2 is multiplied by 10^{13}.

This is written: 3.2×10^{13}

This part is
a number between
1 and 10
(but not including 10)

This part
is written as
a power of 10
(the power is always a whole number)

This way of writing a number is called **exponential notation** or **index notation**, or sometimes **standard form**. (It was formerly called '**scientific notation**'.) Index notation gives a number in two parts:

Number between 1 and 10 (but not 10)	$\times$	power of 10

This is often written as $a \times 10^n$, where $1 \leqslant a < 10$ and $n \in \mathbf{N}$.

Express the numbers **(i)** 8,000,000 and **(ii)** 25,800 in the form $a \times 10^n$, where $1 \leqslant a < 10$ and $n \in \mathbf{N}$.

Solution:
To express a number in index notation, the value of a must be a number between 1 and 10.

(i)   8 000 000.   (put in the decimal point)

8.000 000   (move the decimal point six places to give a number between 1 and 10)

Therefore $8,000,000 = 8 \times 10^6$ ← (number of decimal places moved)

Alternatively, $8,000,000 = 8 \times 1,000,000 = 8 \times 10^6$

(ii)   25 800.   (put in the decimal point)

2.5800   (move the decimal point 4 places to give a number between 1 and 10)

Therefore $25,800 = 2.58 \times 10^4$

Alternatively, $25,800 = 2.5800 \times 10,000 = 2.58 \times 10^4$

Divide 1,506 by 0.3.
Express your answer in the form $a \times 10^n$, where $1 \leqslant a < 10$, and $n \in \mathbf{N}$.

Solution:
   $1506 \div 0{\cdot}3 = 5020$

5020.   (put in the decimal point)

5.020   (move the decimal point three places to give a number between 1 and 10)

Therefore $5,020 = 5.02 \times 10^3$
Alternatively, $5,020 = 5.020 \times 1,000 = 5.02 \times 10^3$

Express each of the numbers in the form $a \times 10^n$, where $1 \leqslant a < 10$ and $n \in \mathbf{N}$:

1. 4,000	**2.** 50,000	**3.** 200,000	**4.** 3,000,000
5. 300	**6.** 7,500	**7.** 36,000	**8.** 650,000
9. 2,300,000	**10.** 2,080	**11.** 6,070	**12.** 30,500
13. 1,580,000	**14.** 20,400	**15.** 503,000	**16.** 8,532,000

In each of the following calculations, write your answer in the form $a \times 10^n$, where $1 \leqslant a < 10$ and $n \in \mathbf{N}$:

17. $2,800 \times 0.5$ **18.** $48,000 \times 0.3$ **19.** $3,500 \times 1.2$

20. $58,000 \times 2.5$ **21.** $4.8 \times 25,000$ **22.** $1.4 \times 25,000$

23. $3,000 \div 1.2$ **24.** $7,200 \div 1.6$ **25.** $172,800 \div 5.4$

26. $67,500 \div 1.25$ **27.** $866,400 \div 3.8$ **28.** $1,118,000 \div 0.43$

29. $476,000 \div 2.8$ **30.** $12,000 \times (1.5)^2$ **31.** $61,920 \div (1.2)^2$

32. $45,000 \times 0.8 = a \times 10^n$, where $1 \leqslant a < 10$ and $n \in \mathbf{N}$. Write down the value of a and n.

33. $551,000 \times 2.9 = a \times 10^n$, where $1 \leqslant a < 10$ and $n \in \mathbf{N}$. Write down the value of a and n.

Addition and subtraction

Numbers given in index notation can be keyed into your calculator by using the 'exponent key'. It is marked $\boxed{\text{EXP}}$ or $\boxed{\text{EE}}$ or $\boxed{\text{E}}$.

To key in a number in index notation do the following:

> **1.** Key in 'a', the 'number part', first.
> **2.** Press the exponent key next.
> **3.** Key in the index of the power of 10.

To enter 3.4×10^6, for example, you key in 3.4 $\boxed{\text{EXP}}$ 6.

Note: If you press $\boxed{=}$ at the end, the calculator will write the number as a natural number, provided the index of the power of 10 is not too large.

To add or subtract two numbers in index notation, do the following:

> **1.** Write each number as a natural number.
> **2.** Add or subtract these numbers.
> **3.** Write your answer in index notation.
> Alternatively, you can use your calculator by keying in the numbers in index notation.

Example ▼

Calculate   **(i)** $2.32 \times 10^4 + 3.8 \times 10^3$ **(ii)** $8.72 \times 10^3 - 5.2 \times 10^2$.

Write your answers in the form $a \times 10^n$, where $1 \leqslant a < 10$ and $n \in \mathbf{N}$.

Solution:

(i)
$$\begin{array}{r} 2.32 \times 10^4 = 23200 \\ 3.8 \times 10^3 = \underline{3800} \\ 27000 \quad \text{(add)} \\ = 2.7 \times 10^4 \end{array}$$

(ii)
$$\begin{array}{r} 8.72 \times 10^3 = 8720 \\ 5.2 \times 10^2 = \underline{520} \\ 8200 \quad \text{(subtract)} \\ = 8.2 \times 10^3 \end{array}$$

▦ 2.32 $\boxed{\text{EXP}}$ 4 $\boxed{+}$ 3.8 $\boxed{\text{EXP}}$ 3 $\boxed{=}$
27000 (on the display)
$= 2.7 \times 10^4$

▦ 8.72 $\boxed{\text{EXP}}$ 3 $\boxed{-}$ 5.2 $\boxed{\text{EXP}}$ 2 $\boxed{=}$
8200 (on the display)
$= 8.2 \times 10^3$

Calculate each of the following and write your answer in the form $a \times 10^n$, where $1 \leqslant a < 10$ and $n \in \mathbf{N}$.

1. $5.6 \times 10^3 + 6 \times 10^2$

2. $5.8 \times 10^4 + 2 \times 10^3$

3. $4.36 \times 10^5 + 2.4 \times 10^4$

4. $3.53 \times 10^6 + 2.7 \times 10^5$

5. $6.57 \times 10^6 + 4.3 \times 10^5$

6. $6.468 \times 10^5 + 3.2 \times 10^3$

7. $7.569 \times 10^4 + 3.1 \times 10^2$

8. $4.276 \times 10^5 + 7.24 \times 10^4$

9. $6.4 \times 10^3 - 4 \times 10^2$

10. $7.2 \times 10^4 - 2 \times 10^3$

11. $2.84 \times 10^5 - 5.4 \times 10^4$

12. $5.49 \times 10^4 - 2.9 \times 10^3$

13. $6.4 \times 10^4 - 3.6 \times 10^4$

14. $2.58 \times 10^4 - 1.8 \times 10^3$

15. $3.74 \times 10^6 - 5.4 \times 10^5$

16. $2.348 \times 10^6 - 4.8 \times 10^4$

17. $2.43 \times 10^4 + 1.5 \times 10^3 + 2 \times 10^2$

18. $5.47 \times 10^5 + 3.8 \times 10^4 - 2.85 \times 10^5$

19. Calculate the value of a and n where $1 \leqslant a < 10$ and $n \in \mathbf{N}$:

   (i) $5.24 \times 10^4 + 3.6 \times 10^3 = a \times 10^n$ **(ii)** $6.45 \times 10^5 - 2.5 \times 10^4 = a \times 10^n$

Multiplication and division

To multiply or divide two numbers in index notation, do the following:

> **1.** Multiply or divide the 'a' parts (the number parts).
> **2.** Multiply or divide the powers of 10 (add or subtract the indices).
> **3.** Write your answer in index notation.
> Alternatively, you can use your calculator by keying in the numbers in index notation.

Example ▼

Express **(i)** $(2.25 \times 10^4) \times (1.6 \times 10^3)$ **(ii)** $(3.91 \times 10^5) \div (1.7 \times 10^2)$
in the form $a \times 10^n$, where $1 \leqslant a < 10$ and $n \in \mathbf{N}$.

Solution:

(i) $(2.25 \times 10^4) \times (1.6 \times 10^3)$
$= 2.25 \times 10^4 \times 1.6 \times 10^3$
$= 2.25 \times 1.6 \times 10^4 \times 10^3$
$= 3.6 \times 10^{4+3}$ (add the indices)
$= 3.6 \times 10^7$

2.25 $\boxed{\text{EXP}}$ 4 $\boxed{\times}$ 1.6 $\boxed{\text{EXP}}$ 3 $\boxed{=}$
36000000   (on the display)
$= 3.6 \times 10^7$

(ii) $(3.91 \times 10^5) \div (1.7 \times 10^2)$
$= \dfrac{3.91 \times 10^5}{1.7 \times 10^2}$
$= \dfrac{3.91}{1.7} \times \dfrac{10^5}{10^2}$
$= 2.3 \times 10^{5-2}$ (subtract the indices)
$= 2.3 \times 10^3$

3.91 $\boxed{\text{EXP}}$ 5 $\boxed{\div}$ 1.7 $\boxed{\text{EXP}}$ 2 $\boxed{=}$
2300   (on the display)
$= 2.3 \times 10^3$

Calculate each of the following and write your answer in the form $a \times 10^n$, where $1 \leqslant a < 10$ and $n \in \mathbf{N}$:

1. $(3 \times 10^4) \times (2 \times 10^2)$ **2.** $(4 \times 10^5) \times (2 \times 10^3)$ **3.** $(4 \times 10^3) \times (1.3 \times 10^2)$
4. $(6 \times 10^3) \times (1.4 \times 10^3)$ **5.** $(1.2 \times 10^2) \times (1.5 \times 10^4)$ **6.** $(2.5 \times 10^4) \times (1.8 \times 10^3)$
7. $(1.6 \times 10^5) \times (4.8 \times 10^3)$ **8.** $(4.5 \times 10^4) \times (2.1 \times 10^2)$ **9.** $(8 \times 10^5) \div (2 \times 10^3)$
10. $(6 \times 10^7) \div (3 \times 10^5)$ **11.** $(8.4 \times 10^6) \div (2.1 \times 10^2)$ **12.** $(8 \times 10^8) \div (3.2 \times 10^5)$
13. $(5.04 \times 10^7) \div (3.6 \times 10^2)$ **14.** $(8.64 \times 10^5) \div (3.6 \times 10^2)$
15. $(9.86 \times 10^5) \div (1.7 \times 10^2)$ **16.** $(6.72 \times 10^7) \div (5.6 \times 10^5)$
17. $(2.4 \times 10^4) \times (1.5 \times 10^2) \div (1.2 \times 10^3)$
18. Calculate the value of a and n where $1 \leqslant a < 10$ and $n \in \mathbf{N}$:
  (i) $(3.8 \times 10^4) \times (2.5 \times 10^2) = a \times 10^n$ **(ii)** $(9.28 \times 10^8) \div (5.8 \times 10^5) = a \times 10^n$

Chapter test

1. (a) $2^3 \times 2^5 = 2^a$. Write down the value of a.
  (b) Write 1.25×10^4 as a natural number.
  (c) Multiply 3,700 by 0.2 and express your answer in the form $a \times 10^n$, where $1 \leqslant a < 10$ and $n \in \mathbf{N}$.
  (d) $2.5 \times 10^3 + 1.5 \times 10^3 = a \times 10^n$. Write down the value of a and n, where $1 \leqslant a < 10$ and $n \in \mathbf{N}$.

2. (a) $\dfrac{5^7}{5^3} = 5^a$. Write down the value of a.
  (b) Write 2.8×10^3 as a natural number.
  (c) Multiply 480 by 0.3 and express your answer in the form $a \times 10^n$, where $1 \leqslant a < 10$ and $n \in \mathbf{N}$.
  (d) Express $(2.4 \times 10^5) \times (1.5 \times 10^3)$ in the form $a \times 10^n$, where $1 \leqslant a < 10$ and $n \in \mathbf{N}$.

3. (a) $(4^2)^3 = 4^a$. Write down the value of a.
  (b) Express $(1.5 \times 10^3) + (2.4 \times 10^2)$ as a natural number.
  (c) Divide 420 by 0.028. Express your answer in the form $a \times 10^n$, where $1 \leqslant a < 10$ and $n \in \mathbf{N}$.
  (d) Express $(4.25 \times 10^6) \div (1.7 \times 10^2)$ in the form $a \times 10^n$, where $1 \leqslant a < 10$ and $n \in \mathbf{N}$.

4. (a) Simplify $\dfrac{5^3 \times 5^7}{5^2 \times 5^6}$, giving your answer in the form 5^n.

  (b) (i) Divide 1,242 by 0.023 **(ii)** Calculate $\dfrac{1296 \div 0.24}{2 \times 0.45}$

    Express your answers in the form $a \times 10^n$, where $1 \leqslant a < 10$ and $n \in \mathbf{N}$.
  (c) Express $(1.2 \times 10^4) \times (5.4 \times 10^5) \div (2.16 \times 10^6)$, in the form $a \times 10^n$, where $1 \leqslant a < 10$ and $n \in \mathbf{N}$.

PERIMETER, AREA, AND VOLUME

Perimeter and area

> The perimeter, P, of a figure is 'the distance around its edges'.

The perimeter is found by adding together the lengths of all the sides. It is measured in length units such as metres (m) or centimetres (cm).

> The area, A, of a figure is 'the amount of flat surface' it contains.

Area is measured in square units such as square metres (m^2) or square centimetres (cm^2).

> When calculating perimeters or areas, make sure that all distances are in the same unit.

Rectangle, square, and triangle

Formulas required (A = area, l = length, b = breadth):

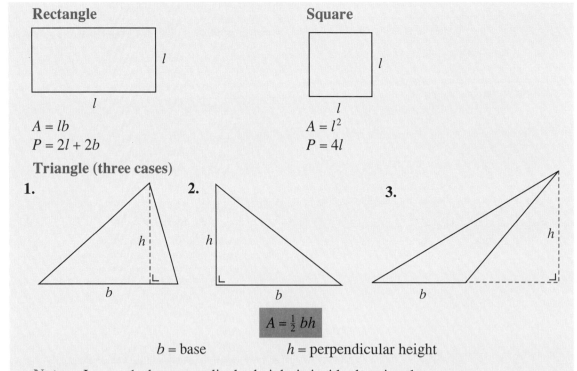

Rectangle

$A = lb$
$P = 2l + 2b$

Square

$A = l^2$
$P = 4l$

Triangle (three cases)

1.   2.   3.

$$A = \tfrac{1}{2}bh$$

b = base h = perpendicular height

Notes: In case 1, the perpendicular height is inside the triangle.
In case 2, a right-angled triangle, the perpendicular height is one of the sides.
In case 3, the perpendicular height is outside the triangle.

It is good practice to draw a diagram when doing questions on perimeter, area, and volume.

Example ▼

Find **(i)** the perimeter and **(ii)** the area
of the figure shown.

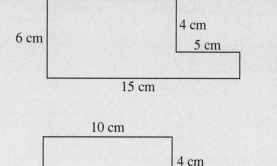

Solution:

(i) Put in the length of the sides that are
not given:
Perimeter
= distance around the edges
= $15 + 2 + 5 + 4 + 10 + 6$
= 42 cm

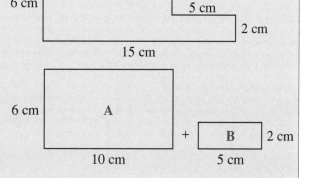

(ii) Break the figure up into two
rectangles, A and B (as shown):
Area of figure
= area of rectangle A + area of
rectangle B
= $10 \times 6 + 5 \times 2 = 60 + 10 = 70$ cm^2

Example ▼

Find the area of each of the following triangles (all dimensions are in centimetres):

(i)

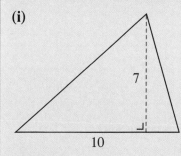

(ii)

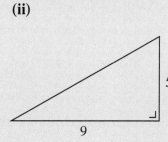

(iii)

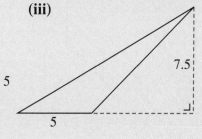

Solution:

(i) $A = \frac{1}{2} bh$
$= \frac{1}{2} (10)(7)$
$= 35$ cm^2

(ii) $A = \frac{1}{2} bh$
$= \frac{1}{2} (9)(5)$
$= 22.5$ cm^2

(iii) $A = \frac{1}{2} bh$
$A = \frac{1}{2} (5)(7.5)$
$= 18.75$ cm^2

Complete the following table, which gives certain information for various rectangles:

	Length	Breadth	Area	Perimeter
1.	8 cm	4 cm		
2.	10 m	6 m		
3.	12 cm	8 cm		
4.	20 m	15 m		
5.	30 cm	20 cm		
6.	18 m	12 m		

Find **(i)** the area and **(ii)** the perimeter of the squares whose sides are of the following length:

7. 5 cm   **8.** 8 m   **9.** 10 cm   **10.** 12 m   **11.** 2.5 cm   **12.** 4.5 m

Find **(i)** the perimeter and **(ii)** the area of each of the following figures (all dimensions are in centimetres):

13. 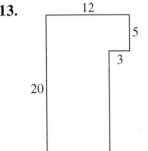   **14.** 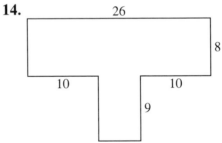   **15.**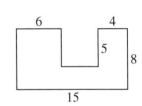

16. 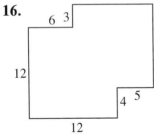   **17.** 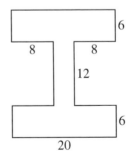   **18.**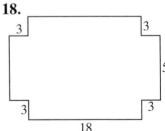

Calculate the area of each of the following (all dimensions are in centimetres):

19. 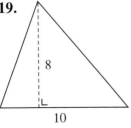   **20.** 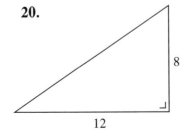   **21.**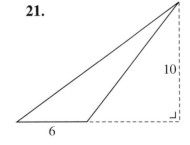

22.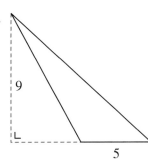

9

5

23.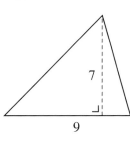

7

9

24.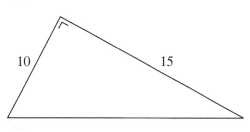

10

15

25.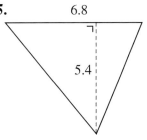

6.8

5.4

26.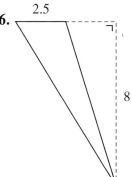

2.5

8

27.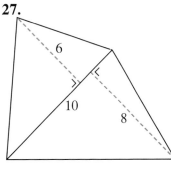

6

10

8

28. Calculate:

(i) the perimeter and
(ii) the area of the figure shown.
(All dimensions are in centimetres.)

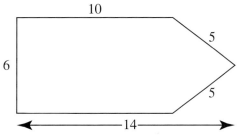

10

5

6

5

14

Calculate the area of the shaded regions (all dimensions are in metres)

29.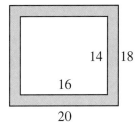

14 | 18

16

20

30.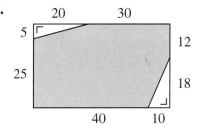

20   30

5

12

25

18

40   10

31.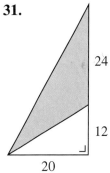

24

12

20

Given the perimeter of an area, to find the missing lengths

In some questions we are given the perimeter or area and asked to find the missing lengths. When solving this type of problem, do the following:

> 1. Draw a diagram.
> 2. Label the unknown length.
> 3. Write down the equation given in disguise.
> 4. Solve this equation.

Example ▼

(i) The area of a rectangle is 75 cm². If its length is 15 cm, calculate its breadth.
(ii) The perimeter of a square is 80 cm. Calculate its area.

Solution:

(i) Draw a diagram, and let b = the breadth.

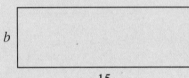

Equation given in disguise:

$$A = 75$$
$$\Rightarrow \quad lb = 75$$
$$\Rightarrow \quad (15)b = 75$$
$$\Rightarrow \quad 15b = 75$$
$$\Rightarrow \quad b = 5$$

Therefore the breadth of the rectangle is 5 cm

(ii) Draw a diagram, and let l = the length.

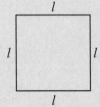

Equation given in disguise:

$$P = 80$$
$$\Rightarrow \quad 4l = 80$$
$$\Rightarrow \quad l = 20$$
$$A = l^2$$
$$= 20^2 = 400$$

Therefore the area of the square is 400 cm²

Example ▼

The area of a triangle is 44 cm².
If the base is 11 cm,
calculate its perpendicular height, h.

Solution:

Equation given in disguise:

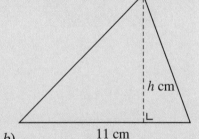

$$A = 44$$
$$\tfrac{1}{2}\,bh = 44$$
$$\tfrac{1}{2}(11)h = 44 \qquad \text{(put in 11 for } b\text{)}$$
$$11h = 88 \qquad \text{(multiply both sides by 2)}$$
$$h = 8 \qquad \text{(divide both sides by 11)}$$

The table shows certain information on rectangles. In each case write down the equation given in disguise and use the equation to find the missing dimensions and complete the table:

	Length	Breadth	Area	Perimeter
1.		4 m	20 m^2	
2.		6 m	48 m^2	
3.	5 m		35 m^2	
4.	10 m		80 m^2	
5.		3 m		14 m
6.	10 m			32 m

7. The area of a rectangle is 96 cm^2. If its breadth is 8 cm, calculate **(i)** its length and **(ii)** its perimeter.
8. The area of a rectangle is 110 m^2. If its length is 11 m, calculate **(i)** its breadth and **(ii)** its perimeter.
9. The perimeter of a rectangle is 28 cm. If its length is 9 cm, calculate its area.
10. The perimeter of a square is 20 cm. Calculate **(i)** its length and **(ii)** its area.
11. The area of a square is 36 m^2. Calculate **(i)** its length and **(ii)** its perimeter.
12. The area of a square is 64 mm^2. Calculate its perimeter.
    Find the perpendicular height in each case where the base and area are given (all dimensions in centimetres):

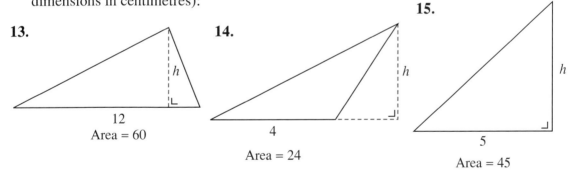

13.

12
Area = 60

14.

4
Area = 24

15.

5
Area = 45

16. The area of a triangle with base 8 cm is 24 cm^2. Find its perpendicular height.
17. The area of a triangle with perpendicular height 3 cm is 18 cm^2. Find the length of its base.
18. The rectangle and the triangle have equal area. Find h.

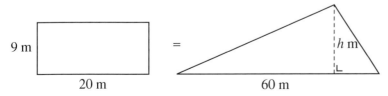

9 m

20 m

=

60 m

h m

Practical problems

Example ▼

A rectangular patio is 8 m long and 5 m wide. The patio is covered with square paving slabs with sides of length 25 cm. Calculate the number of slabs required to cover the patio.

Solution:
Change all dimensions to the smaller unit, centimetres.
Area of patio = $800 \times 500 = 400,000$ cm^2
Area of one slab = $25 \times 25 = 625$ cm^2

Number of paving slabs = $\dfrac{\text{area of patio}}{\text{area of one slab}} = \dfrac{400,000}{625} = 640$

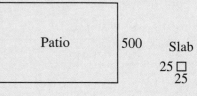

Exercise 19.3 ▼

(Remember: if necessary, change all lengths to the same unit.)

1. A plot of ground 100 m long and 60 m wide is surrounded by a fence. A path 4 m wide is laid around the edge, inside the fence. The path is covered with square paving slabs, with side of length 2 m, costing €5 each. Calculate:
   (i)   the area of the plot of land
   (ii) the area of the path
   (iii) the number of paving slabs required to cover the path, and the cost of the paving slabs.

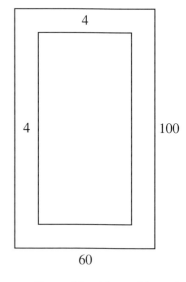

2. A room 18 m long and 7.5 m wide is to be covered by square tiles with sides of length 30 cm. How many tiles will be needed to cover the room? The tiles are sold in boxes of 100 at a cost of €50 a box. Calculate the cost of the tiles.
3. A rectangular metal plate measuring 3 m by 1.5 m is cut up into small squares with sides of length 15 cm. How many squares will be cut?
4. A rectangular lawn is surrounded by a path. The lawn is 40 m long and 20 m wide. The path is 1 m wide. (The diagram is not to scale.) The path is covered with square paving slabs with sides of length 50 cm.

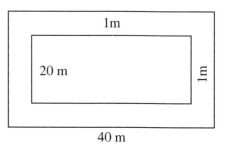

Calculate:

(i) the area of the lawn

(ii) the area of the path

(iii) the number of paving slabs required to cover the path.

5. The floor of a room 15 m long by 12 m wide is to be covered with tiles. Each tile is a square of length 20 cm.

   (a) Find the number of tiles required to cover the floor.

   (b) If each tile costs 28c, find the cost of the tiles.

   (c) If other materials and labour cost 20c per tile, find the cost of tiling the floor.

6. Paint is sold in litre tins costing €15.40 per litre. A wall is 60 m long and 2.5 m high. How many litres of paint are required to paint one side of the wall if one litre of paint will cover 7.5 m²? Calculate the cost of the paint.

7. A rectangular bungalow measures 18 m long by 8.5 m wide. How much will it cost to put a concrete path measuring 1.5 m wide all round the bungalow at a cost of €10 per square metre?

Circumference and area of a circle

The length of the perimeter of a circle is called the **circumference**.

Part of the circumference is called an **arc**.

The value of $\dfrac{\text{circumference}}{\text{diameter}} = \pi$ (pronounced 'pie'), and is the same value for all circles.

An exact value for π cannot be stated. However, the usual approximations are $\pi = 3.14$ or $\pi = \frac{22}{7}$. In an exam you will be given the value of π to use.

Here are the formulas required for circles and sectors of circles:

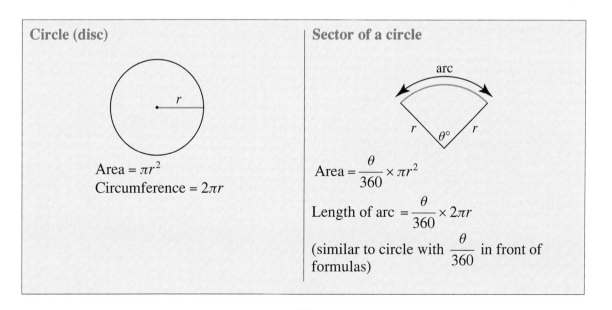

Circle (disc)	Sector of a circle

Area = πr^2

Circumference = $2\pi r$

Area = $\dfrac{\theta}{360} \times \pi r^2$

Length of arc = $\dfrac{\theta}{360} \times 2\pi r$

(similar to circle with $\dfrac{\theta}{360}$ in front of formulas)

Notes: **1.** When using $\pi = \frac{22}{7}$, it is good practice to write the radius as a fraction. For example, $21 = \frac{21}{1}$ or $10.5 = \frac{21}{2}$.

2. If a question says 'give your answer in terms of π,' then leave π in the answer: do not put 3.14 or $\frac{22}{7}$.

Example ▼

Calculate **(i)** the circumference and **(ii)** the area of a circle of radius 8 cm. (Assume $\pi = 3 \cdot 14$.)

Solution:

(i) $C = 2\pi r$
$= 2 \times 3.14 \times 8$
$= 50.24$
Therefore the circumference is 50·24 cm.

(ii) $A = \pi r^2$
$= 3.14 \times 8 \times 8$
$= 200.96$
Therefore the area is 200·96 cm².

Example ▼

The diagram shows a sector of a circle.
Calculate:

(i) the area of the sector
(ii) the length of the arc pq.

(Assume $\pi = \frac{22}{7}$.)

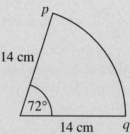

Solution:

(i) Area of sector
$= \dfrac{\theta}{360}\pi r^2$

$= \dfrac{72}{360} \times \dfrac{22}{7} \times \dfrac{14}{1} \times \dfrac{14}{1}$
  ↑   ↑
(fraction) × (area of full circle)

$= \dfrac{1}{5} \times \dfrac{22}{7} \times \dfrac{14}{1} \times \dfrac{14}{1}$

$= 123\frac{1}{5}$ or 123.2

Therefore the area of the sector
$= 123\frac{1}{5}$ cm² or 123.2 cm²

(ii) Length of arc pq
$= \dfrac{\theta}{360} \times 2\pi r$

$= \dfrac{72}{360} \times \dfrac{2}{1} \times \dfrac{22}{7} \times \dfrac{14}{1}$
  ↑   ↑
(fraction) × (full circumference)

$= \dfrac{1}{5} \times \dfrac{2}{1} \times \dfrac{22}{7} \times \dfrac{14}{1}$

$= 17\frac{3}{5}$ or 17.6

Therefore the length of the arc pq
$= 17\frac{3}{5}$ cm or 17.6 cm

Taking π to be 3.14, calculate the circumference and area of a circle of radius:

1. 5 cm	**2.** 10 m	**3.** 20 mm	**4.** 12 cm	**5.** 6 m
6. 4 mm	**7.** 13 cm	**8.** 30 cm	**9.** 8.5 m	**10.** 2.5 cm

Taking π to be $\frac{22}{7}$, calculate the circumference and area of a circle of radius:

11. 14 cm	**12.** 7 cm	**13.** 21 mm	**14.** 28 cm	**15.** 35 mm
16. 2.1 m	**17.** 10.5 cm	**18.** 1.4 m	**19.** 3.5 cm	**20.** 4.9 cm

Taking π to be 3.14, calculate the circumference and area of a circle of diameter:

21. 18 cm	**22.** 4 m	**23.** 6 cm	**24.** 1 m	**25.** 15 cm

Calculate, in terms of π, the circumference and area of a circle of radius:

26. 3 cm	**27.** 2 m	**28.** 11 mm	**29.** 4.5 cm	**30.** 1.5 m

Calculate **(i)** the area, **(ii)** the length of the arc and **(iii)** the perimeter of each of the following sectors (taking π to be 3.14; all dimensions in centimetres):

31.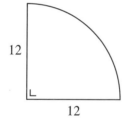

32.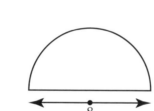

33.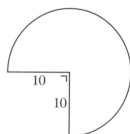

34.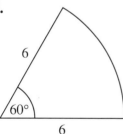

35.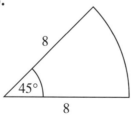

36.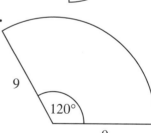

Calculate the areas of the following figures (taking π to be 3.14; all dimensions in centimetres):

37.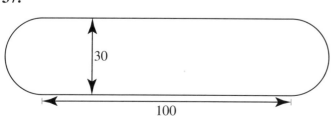

38.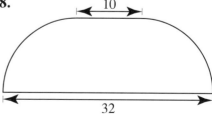

217

Find the area of each of the following shaded regions (taking π to be 3.14; all dimensions in centimetres):

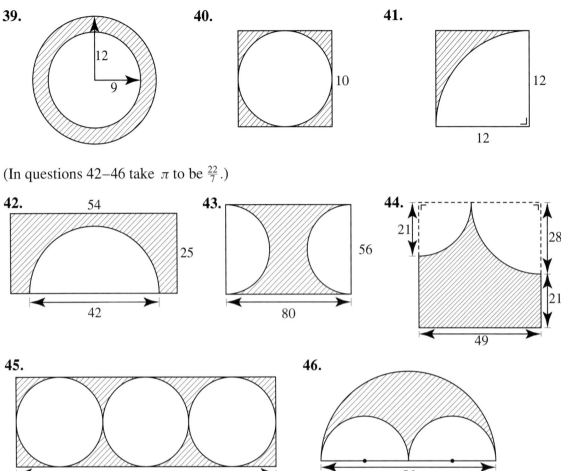

39.

12
9

40.

10

41.

12

12

(In questions 42–46 take π to be $\frac{22}{7}$.)

42.

54

25

42

43.

56

80

44.

21

28

21

49

45.

84

46.

56

Given the circumference or area

In some questions we are given the circumference or area and asked to find the radius (or diameter). As before, write down the '**equation given in disguise**' and solve this equation to find the radius, r.

Example ▼

(i)   If $\pi r^2 = 1{,}256$, calculate r (assume $\pi = 3.14$).
(ii) The circumference of a circle is 12π cm. Calculate the radius.
(iii) The area of a circle is 154 cm^2. Calculate its diameter (assume $\pi = \frac{22}{7}$).

Solution:

(i) Given: $\pi r^2 = 1256$

$\Rightarrow \quad 3.14 r^2 = 1256$ (put in 3.14 for π)

$\Rightarrow \quad\quad r^2 = 400$ (divide both sides by 3.14)

$\Rightarrow \quad\quad r = \sqrt{400}$ (take the square of both sides)

$\Rightarrow \quad\quad r = 20$

(ii) Given: circumference $= 12\pi$ cm

$\Rightarrow \quad\quad\quad 2\pi r = 12\pi$ (circumference $= 2\pi r$)

$\Rightarrow \quad\quad\quad \pi r = 6\pi$ (divide both sides by 2)

$\Rightarrow \quad\quad\quad r = 6$ (divide both sides by π)

The radius is 6 cm

(iii) Given: area $= 154$ cm^2

$\Rightarrow \quad\quad \pi r^2 = 154$ (area $= \pi r^2$)

$\Rightarrow \quad\quad \frac{22}{7} r^2 = 154$ (put in $\frac{22}{7}$ for π)

$\Rightarrow \quad 22 r^2 = 1078$ (multiply both sides by 7)

$\Rightarrow \quad\quad r^2 = 49$ (divide both sides by 22)

$\Rightarrow \quad\quad r = \sqrt{49}$ (take the square root of both sides)

$\Rightarrow \quad\quad r = 7$

$d = 2r = 2(7) = 14$

The diameter is 14 cm.

Exercise 19.5 ▼

The table below shows certain information on circles, including the value of π used. In each case write down the equation given in disguise and use this to find the radius and complete the tables:

	π	Circumference	Area	Radius
1.	π	8π cm		
2.	π	18π cm		
3.	3.14		314 cm^2	
4.	3.14		706.5 m^2	
5..	$\frac{22}{7}$	132 mm		
6.	$\frac{22}{7}$		616 cm^2	
7.	π		16π cm^2	
8.	3.14	78.5 m		

	π	Circumference	Area	Radius
9.	$\frac{22}{7}$		2,464 cm^2	
10.	π		81π cm^2	
11.	$\frac{22}{7}$	220 m		
12.	3.14		2,826 mm^2	
13.	π		121π m^2	
14.	3.14		5,024 cm^2	
15.	$\frac{22}{7}$		38.5 m^2	
16.	$\frac{22}{7}$	66 cm		

17. The area of a circle is 154 cm^2. Find its circumference (taking π to be $\frac{22}{7}$)

18. The circumference of a circle is 10π m. Find its area in terms of π.

19. The area of a circle is 12.56 cm^2. Find its circumference (taking π to be 3.14).

20. The area of a circle is 20.25π m^2. Find the radius of the circle.

Practical problems

Example ▼

A bicycle wheel, including the tyre, has a diameter of 56 cm. Find the number of turns the wheel must make in travelling 352 m without slipping. (Take π to be $\frac{22}{7}$.)

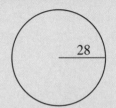

Solution:

Change all dimensions to the smaller unit, centimetres.

352 m = 352 × 100 cm = 35200 cm

$$\text{Number of turns of the wheel}$$
$$= \frac{\text{distance travelled}}{\text{circumference of the wheel}}$$
$$= \frac{35200}{176}$$

$$\text{Radius} = r = \frac{56}{2} = 28$$

Circumference of wheel
$$= 2\pi r$$
$$= \frac{2}{1} \times \frac{22}{7} \times \frac{28}{1}$$
$$= 176 \text{ cm}$$

Therefore the wheel will turn 200 times.

Exercise 19.6 ▼

1. A bicycle wheel, including the tyre, has a diameter of 42 cm.
   (i) Calculate the length of the radius of the wheel.
   (ii) Find the distance moved by the bicycle if the wheel makes one full turn,
   (iii) How far, in metres, will the bike have travelled after 250 turns without slipping?
   (iv) Calculate how many turns the wheel makes when the bicycle moves 264 m without slipping. (Take π to be $\frac{22}{7}$.)

2. A window is in the shape of a rectangle combined with a semicircle, as shown. The rectangular part of the window is 70 cm long and 90 cm high. Find the area of the window in cm^2. (Take π to be $\frac{22}{7}$.)

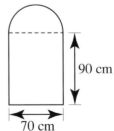

90 cm

70 cm

3. A wire frame consists of a circle and a diameter. The diameter is 28 cm. Find the length of wire needed for a frame. (Take π to be $\frac{22}{7}$.)

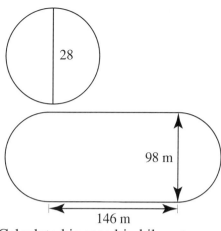

4. An athletics track is in the shape of a rectangle with semi-circular ends, as shown.

   (i) Write down the radius of the semi-circular ends.

   (ii) Calculate the length of both semi-circular ends. (Take π to be $\frac{22}{7}$.)

   (iii) Calculate the length of the track.

   (iv) Calculate the number of laps an athlete would have to complete in a 5.4 km race.

   (v) Another athlete ran four laps in ten minutes. Calculate his speed in kilometres per hour.

5. If the diameter of a disc is 14 cm, calculate its area. (Take π to be $\frac{22}{7}$.)

From a rectangular strip of tin 14 cm wide, five disks of radius 7 cm are cut out.

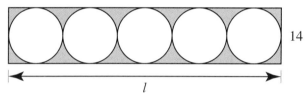

Calculate *l*, the shortest length of strip required.

Find also the area of tin remaining from this latter strip after the five discs have been cut out.

6. A piece of wire is 176 cm in length.

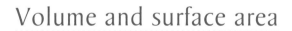

The wire is bent into the shape of a circle.
Calculate the radius of the circle.
(Take π to be $\frac{22}{7}$.)

Volume and surface area

The **volume** of a solid is the amount of space it occupies.
Volume is measured in cubic units, such as cubic metres (m^3) or cubic centimetres (cm^3).
Capacity is the volume of a liquid or gas and is usually measured in litres.

Note: 1 litre = 1,000 cm^3 = 1,000 ml
The **surface area** of a solid is the '**total area of its outer surface**'.
It is measured in square units such as square metres or square centimetres.
To calculate the surface area of a solid you have to find the area of each face and add them together (often called the 'total surface area'). With some objects, such as a sphere, the surface area is called the 'curved surface area'.

Note: It is usual to denote volume by V and surface area by SA.

Formulas required:

1. Rectangular solid (cuboid)	2. Cube
$V = lbh$	$V = l^3$
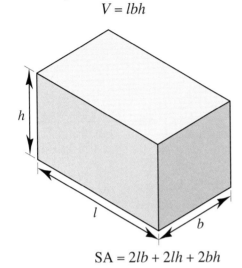	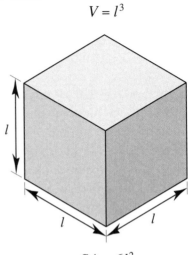
SA = $2lb + 2lh + 2bh$	SA = $6l^2$

Example ▼

Find **(i)** the volume and **(ii)** the surface area of a cube with sides of length 2 cm.

Solution:

(i) $V = l^3 = (2 \text{ cm})^3 = 8 \text{ cm}^3$

(ii) $SA = 6\,l^2$
$= 6\,(2 \text{ cm})^2$
$= 6\,(4 \text{ cm}^2)$
$= 24 \text{ cm}^2$

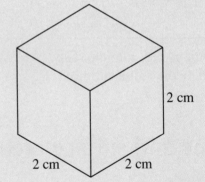

2 cm

2 cm   2 cm

Example ▼

A rectangular glass tank has internal dimensions of length 1.2 m, breadth 80 cm, and height 60 cm.
(i) How many litres of water can it contain?
(ii) If water is poured into the tank at the rate of 8 litres per minute, how long does it take to fill the tank?

Solution:
As 1 litre = 1,000 cm^3, we change all dimensions to centimetres.

Length = 1.2 m = 120 cm

(i) Volume of the tank = $l.b.h$

$$= (120)(80)(60)$$
$$= 576,000 \text{ cm}^3$$

$$\text{Number of litres} = \frac{\text{volume of the tank (cm}^3)}{1000 \text{ cm}^3}$$

$$= \frac{576,000}{1000}$$

$$= 576$$

(ii) Time taken to fill the tank $= \dfrac{\text{volume of the tank (litres)}}{\text{number of litres poured per minute}}$

$$= \frac{576}{8}$$

$$= 72 \text{ minutes, or 1 hour and 12 minutes.}$$

Exercise 19.7 ▼

Calculate **(i)** the volume and **(ii)** the surface area of each of the following solids (all dimensions in centimetres):

1.

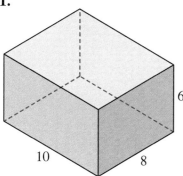

2.

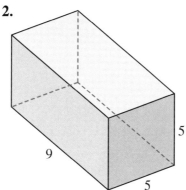

3.

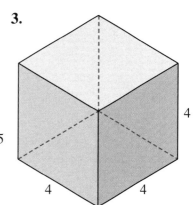

Complete the following table, which gives certain information about various rectangular blocks (it may help to draw a diagram in each case):

	Length	Breadth	Height	Volume	Surface area
4.	10 cm	8 cm	6 cm		
5.	9 cm	7 cm	4 cm		
6.	3 m	2 m	5 m		
7.	40 mm	30 mm	20 mm		
8.	8 m	2 m	3 m		
9.	5 m	5 m	5 m		
10.	50 cm	40 cm	80 cm		
11.	25 mm	15 mm	12 mm		
12.	3 cm	3 cm	3 cm		
13.	2.5 m	0.8 m	1.2 m		

14. (i) Calculate the volume of a cube with sides of length 2 cm.

(ii) How many of these cubes will exactly fill a rectangular box with a square base of sides 6 cm and height 4 cm?

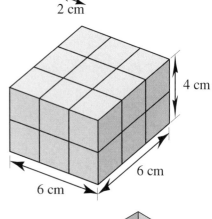

15. A box measures 6 cm by 6 cm by 15 cm. It has seven cubes stacked tightly inside. Each cube measures 3 cm by 3 cm 3 cm. How many more such cubes must be stacked inside so as to fill the box?

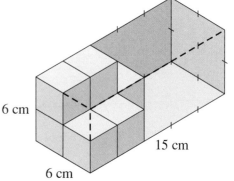

16. How many cubes of side 4 cm will fit exactly into a rectangular box with dimensions 0.8 m by 0.4 m by 60 cm?

17. How many rectangular packets of butter 20 cm by 6 cm by 6 cm will fit exactly in a box 0.6 m by 48 cm by 36 cm?

18. A rectangular block of metal has dimensions 48 cm by 24 cm by 16 cm. It is melted down and recast into cubes of length 8 cm, without loss of volume. How many cubes will be cast?

Calculate the volume of each of the following solids (all measurements in centimetres):

19.   **20.**   **21.**

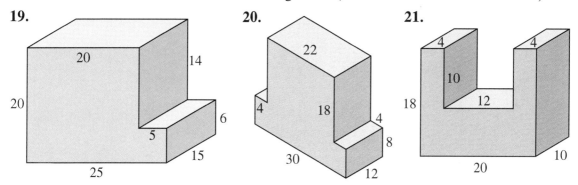

22. A rectangular glass tank has internal dimensions of length 60 cm, breadth 30 cm, and height 20 cm.

    (i)   Calculate its capacity (internal volume) in litres.

    (ii) If water is poured into the tank at the rate of 3 litres per minute, how long does it take to fill the tank?

23. A rectangular tank, full of oil, has internal measurements of 1.8 m by 30 cm by 40 cm. If 4 litres are drained off every minute, how long will it take to empty the tank?

24. Butter is sold in rectangular blocks 5 cm by 5 cm by 14 cm.
Find the volume of butter in the block.
The mass of this block is 454 grams.
What mass of butter would be in a similar block 10 cm by 10 cm by 28 cm?

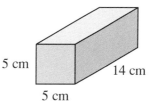

25. A rectangular piece of cardboard measured 80 cm by 60 cm.
Squares of sides 10 cm were cut off from the corners, as shown. The strips at the edges were folded along the dotted lines so as to make an open rectangular box.
Calculate the volume of this box, in litres.

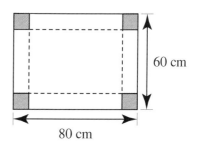

Given the volume or surface area, to find the missing lengths

In some questions we are given the volume or surface area and asked to find a missing dimension. As before, write down the '**equation given in disguise**', and solve this equation to find the missing dimension.

Example ▼

The volume of a rectangular block is 560 cm^3.
If its length is 14 cm and its breadth is 8 cm,
find **(i)** its height and **(ii)** its surface area.

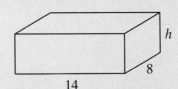

Solution:

(i) Equation given in disguise:
$$\text{volume} = 560 \text{ cm}^3$$
$$\Rightarrow \quad (14)(8)h = 560$$
$$\Rightarrow \quad 112h = 560$$
$$\Rightarrow \quad h = \frac{560}{112} = 5 \text{ cm}$$

(ii) Surface area $= 2lb + 2lh + 2bh$
$$= 2(14)(8) + 2(14)(5) + 2(8)(5)$$
$$= 224 + 140 + 80$$
$$= 444 \text{ cm}^2$$

Example ▼

The surface area of a cube is 54 cm^2.
Calculate its volume.

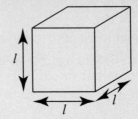

Solution:

Let the length of one side of the cube be l cm.
Equation given in disguise:
$$\text{Surface area} = 54 \text{ cm}^2$$
$$\Rightarrow \quad 6l^2 = 54$$
$$\Rightarrow \quad l^2 = 9$$
$$\Rightarrow \quad l = 3 \text{ cm}$$

$$\text{Volume} = l^3$$
$$= 3^3$$
$$= 27 \text{ cm}^3$$
Therefore the volume of the cube is 27 cm^3.

1. The volume of a rectangular block is 2,400 cm^3. If its length is 20 cm and its breadth is 15 cm, calculate **(i)** its height and **(ii)** its surface area.
2. The volume of a cube is 64 cm^3. Calculate **(i)** the length of a side and **(ii)** its surface area.
3. The surface area of a cube is 24 cm^2. Calculate **(i)** the length of a side and **(ii)** its volume.
4. The volume of a rectangular block is 720 cm^3. If its breadth is 9 cm and its height is 8 cm, calculate **(i)** its length and **(ii)** its surface area.
5. The volume of a cube is 125 cm^3. Calculate its surface area.
6. An oil storage tank is in the shape of a cuboid. Its rectangular base has dimensions 2.2 m by 80 cm and its height is 90 cm. When the tank is full, 704 litres are drawn off into another vessel. Calculate the drop in height (depth) of the oil.

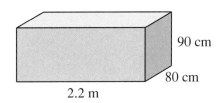

90 cm

80 cm

2.2 m

Cylinder

Formulas required:

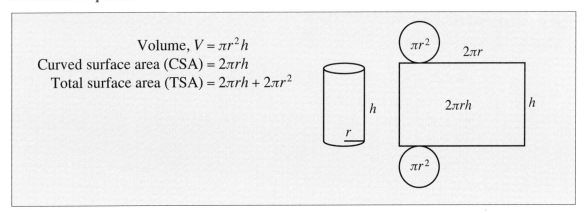

Volume, $V = \pi r^2 h$
Curved surface area (CSA) $= 2\pi rh$
Total surface area (TSA) $= 2\pi rh + 2\pi r^2$

πr^2

$2\pi r$

h

$2\pi rh$

h

r

πr^2

The top and bottom lids of a cylindrical can are circles, each of area πr^2.
The curved part will open out into a flat surface in the shape of a rectangle.
The length of this rectangle is $2\pi r$ (circumference of a lid), and its breadth will be h (height of the cylinder). Therefore the curved surface area is $2\pi r \times h$ or simply $2\pi rh$.

Find **(i)** the volume and **(ii)** the total surface area of a closed cylindrical can of radius 7 cm and height 12 cm (taking π to be $\frac{22}{7}$).

Solution:

(i) $V = \pi r^2 h$

$$= \frac{22}{7} \times \frac{7}{1} \times \frac{7}{1} \times \frac{12}{1}$$

$$= 1{,}848 \text{ cm}^3$$

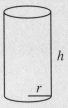

(ii) $\text{TSA} = 2\pi rh + 2\pi r^2$

$$= \frac{2}{1} \times \frac{22}{7} \times \frac{7}{1} \times \frac{12}{1} + \frac{2}{1} \times \frac{22}{7} \times \frac{7}{1} \times \frac{7}{1}$$

$$= 528 + 308$$

$$= 836 \text{ cm}^2$$

A hollow concrete pipe has an external diameter 20 cm and is 2 cm thick. Calculate the volume of concrete in 50 cm of pipe. (Take π to be 3.14.)

Solution:

Volume of concrete = volume of outside cylinder – volume of inside cylinder

Outside cylinder	Inside cylinder
$V = \pi r^2 h$	$V = \pi r^2 h$
$= 3.14 \times 10 \times 10 \times 50$	$= 3.14 \times 8 \times 8 \times 50$
$= 15{,}700 \text{ cm}^3$	$= 10{,}048 \text{ cm}^3$

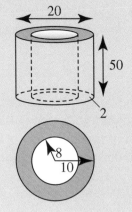

Volume of concrete $= 15{,}700 \text{ cm}^3 - 10{,}048 \text{ cm}^3$

$$= 5{,}652 \text{ cm}^3.$$

Complete the following table, which gives certain information about various closed cylinders:

	π	Radius	Height	Volume	Curved surface area	Total surface area
1.	$\frac{22}{7}$	7 cm	10 cm			
2.	$\frac{22}{7}$	14 cm	8 cm			
3.	$\frac{22}{7}$	21 cm	20 cm			
4.	3.14	10 mm	5 mm			
5.	3.14	15 m	30 m			
6.	$\frac{22}{7}$	28 cm	20 cm			
7.	3.14	12 cm	50 cm			
8.	$\frac{22}{7}$	3.5 m	5 m			
9.	3.14	2.5 mm	40 mm			
10.	$\frac{22}{7}$	4.9 cm	10 cm			

11. A closed cylinder has a diameter of 42 cm and a height of 10 cm.
Calculate **(i)** its volume and **(ii)** its curved surface area (assume $\pi = \frac{22}{7}$).

12. (i) Calculate, in terms of π, the capacity of a cylinder of:
   (a) radius 12 cm and height 40 cm   **(b)** radius 3 cm and height 10 cm.
   (ii) A cylindrical jug full of water has a radius of 12 cm and is 40 cm tall. Water from it is poured into cylindrical glasses of diameter 6 cm and height 10 cm. How many such glasses can be filled?

13. A hollow metal pipe has an external diameter of 40 cm and is 2.5 cm thick.
Calculate the volume, in cubic centimetres, of metal in 2 m of pipe (assume $\pi = 3.14$).

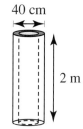

14. (a) Calculate the volume of a solid cylinder of diameter 10 cm and height 14 cm (assume $\pi = \frac{22}{7}$).
   (b) Two such identical cylinders fit exactly into a rectangular box:
   Find:
   (i)   the dimensions of the box
   (ii) the internal volume of the box
   (iii) the volume of air in the box when the two cylinders are placed inside it.

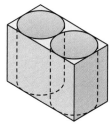

15. A semi-circular tunnel of height 5 m and length 600 m has been driven through a mountain.
Calculate the volume, in cubic metres, of material that has been removed from the mountain.
(Assume $\pi = 3.14$.)

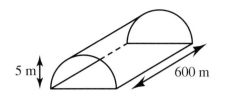

5 m
600 m

Sphere

Formulas required:

Volume, $V = \frac{4}{3} \pi r^3$

Curved surface area (CSA) $= 4\pi r^2$

r

Example ▼

A solid sphere has a radius of 6 cm. Calculate **(i)** its volume and **(ii)** its curved surface area.
(Assume $\pi = 3.14$.)

Solution:

(i) $V = \frac{4}{3} \pi r^3$

$\quad = \frac{4}{3} \times 3.14 \times 6 \times 6 \times 6$

$\quad = 904.32 \text{ cm}^3$

(ii) CSA $= 4\pi r^2$

$\quad = 4 \times 3.14 \times 6 \times 6$

$\quad = 452.16 \text{ cm}^2$

Example ▼

A solid metal sphere of radius 1.5 cm fits exactly inside a cubic box, and then oil is poured in until the box is full.
Taking π to be 3.14, find the volume of:

(i) the box
(ii) the sphere
(iii) the oil.

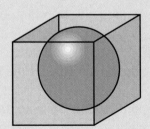

230

Solution:

(i) Let l = the length of a side of the box
$l = 2$ (radius of the sphere)
$= 2(1.5 \text{ cm}) = 3 \text{ cm}$
Volume of the box $= l^3$
$= (3 \text{ cm})^3 = 27 \text{ cm}^3$

(ii) Volume of sphere
$= \frac{4}{3}\pi r^3$
$= \frac{4}{3} \times 3.14 \times 1.5 \times 1.5 \times 1.5$
$= 14.13 \text{ cm}^3$

(iii) Volume of oil = volume of the box – volume of the sphere
$= 27 \text{ cm}^3 - 14.13 \text{ cm}^3$
$= 12.87 \text{ cm}^3$

Exercise 19.10 ▼

Complete the following table, which gives certain information about various spheres:

	π	Radius	Volume	Curved surface area
1.	3.14	3 cm		
2.	3.14	9 cm		
3.	3.14	12 mm		
4.	3.14	4.5 cm		
5.	3.14	7.5 mm		
6.	$\frac{22}{7}$	21 cm		
7.	$\frac{22}{7}$	42 mm		
8.	$\frac{22}{7}$	$\frac{21}{2}$ cm		
9.	π	6 cm		
10.	π	1.5 m		

Taking π to be 3.14, and giving all answers where necessary to two places of decimals, find the volume and the curved surface area of a sphere of radius:

11. 10 cm   **12.** 2 m   **13.** 4 cm   **14.** 5 mm   **15.** 2.5 cm

16. The diameter of a sphere is 6 cm. Find, in terms of π:
   (i) its volume   **(ii)** its curved surface area.

17. A sphere of diameter 12 cm fits exactly into a cylindrical box. Show that
   (i) both have the same curved surface area
   (ii) volume of the sphere
   $= \frac{2}{3}$ (volume of the cylinder)
   (In this question use $\pi = 3.14$.) Show that you get the same result by giving the curved surface areas and the volumes in terms of π.

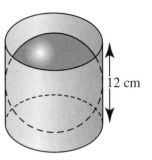

12 cm

18. A ball bearing has a radius of 3 mm. Calculate its volume. Three similar ball bearings fit exactly into a cylindrical metal tube, and then oil is poured in until the tube is full. Calculate:
   (i) the height, h, of the tube
   (ii) the internal radius of the tube
   (iii) the internal volume of the tube
   (iv) the volume of oil in the tube.
      (Assume $\pi = 3.14$.)

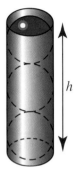

h

19. A solid metal sphere has a diameter of 42 cm. Find the mass of the sphere if 1 cm³ of metal weighs 10 g. (Assume $\pi = \frac{22}{7}$.)

20. Sphere A has a radius of 6 cm, and sphere B has a radius of 3 cm. Calculate the ratio of
   (i) curved surface area of sphere A to curved surface area of sphere B
   (ii) volume of sphere A to volume of sphere B.

Given the volume or surface area of cylinders and spheres

In some questions we are given the volume or surface area and asked to find a missing dimension. As before, write down the '**equation given in disguise**', and solve this equation to find the missing dimension.

Notes:

1. Moving liquids
   In many questions we have to deal with moving liquid from one container to another container of different dimensions or shape. To help us solve the problem we use the following fact :

> The volume of the moved liquid does not change

2. Recasting

Many of the questions we meet require us to solve a recasting problem. What happens is that a certain solid object is melted down and its shape is changed. We use the following fact:

> The volume remains the same after it is melted down

3. Displaced liquid

In many questions we have to deal with situations where liquid is displaced by immersing, or removing, a solid object. In all cases the following principle helps us to solve these problems:

> Volume of displaced liquid = volume of immersed, or removed, solid object

In problems on moving liquids and recasting or displaced liquids, it is good practice not to put in a value for π (i.e. do **not** put in $\pi = \frac{22}{7}$ or $\pi = 3.14$), as the π's normally cancel when you write down the equation given in disguise.

Example ▼

(i) The curved surface area of a sphere is 25π cm^2. Calculate its radius.

(ii) The curved surface area of a cylinder is 220 cm^2 and its radius is $3\frac{1}{2}$ cm. Calculate its height (assume $\pi = \frac{22}{7}$).

(iii) A cylinder has a volume of 401.92 m^3. If its height is 8 m, calculate its radius. (Assume $\pi = 3.14$.)

Solution:

(i) Given: curved surface area $= 25\pi$ cm^2

$\Rightarrow \qquad\qquad\qquad 4\pi r^2 = 25\pi$ (curved surface area $= 4\pi r^2$)

$\Rightarrow \qquad\qquad\qquad 4r^2 = 25$ (divide both sides by π)

$\Rightarrow \qquad\qquad\qquad r^2 = 6.25$ (divide both sides by 4)

$\Rightarrow \qquad\qquad\qquad r = \sqrt{6.25}$ (take the square root of both sides)

$\Rightarrow \qquad\qquad\qquad r = 2.5$

The radius is 2.5 cm

(ii) Given: curved surface area $= 220$ cm^2

$\Rightarrow \qquad\qquad\qquad 2\pi r h = 220$ (curved surface area $= 2\pi r h$)

$\Rightarrow \qquad 2 \times \frac{22}{7} \times \frac{7}{2} \times h = 220$ (put in $\pi = \frac{22}{7}$ and $r = \frac{7}{2}$)

$\Rightarrow \qquad\qquad\qquad 22h = 220$ (simplify left-hand side)

$\Rightarrow \qquad\qquad\qquad h = 10$ (divide both sides by 22)

The height is 10 cm.

(iii) Given: volume of cylinder $= 401.92 \text{ m}^3$

$\Rightarrow \qquad\qquad \pi r^2 h = 401.92$ (volume of cylinder $= \pi r^2 h$)

$\Rightarrow \qquad 3.14 \times r^2 \times 8 = 401.92$ (put in $\pi = 3.14$ and $h = 8$)

$\Rightarrow \qquad\qquad 8r^2 = 128$ (divide both sides by 3.14)

$\Rightarrow \qquad\qquad r^2 = 16$ (divide both sides by 8)

$\Rightarrow \qquad\qquad r = \sqrt{16}$ (take the square root of both sides)

$\Rightarrow \qquad\qquad r = 4$

The radius is 4 m.

Example ▼

A solid cylinder of radius 4 cm and height 18 cm is melted down and recast as a solid sphere. Calculate the radius of the sphere.

Solution:

Equation given in disguise

Volume of sphere = volume of cylinder

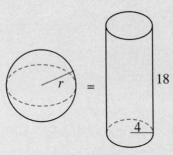

$\frac{4}{3}\pi r^3 = \pi R^2 H$

$\frac{4}{3}\pi r^3 = \pi \times 4 \times 4 \times 18$ (put in $R = 4$ and $H = 18$)

$\frac{4}{3}\pi r^3 = 288\pi$ (simplify right-hand side)

$\frac{4}{3}r^3 = 288$ (divide both sides by π)

$4r^3 = 864$ (multiply both sides by 3)

$r^3 = 216$ (divide both sides by 4)

$r = 6$ (take the cube root of both sides)

The radius is 6 cm.

1. A solid cylinder has a volume of 72π cm^3. If the radius is 3 cm, calculate its height.
2. A solid cylinder has a volume of 300π cm^3. If the height is 12 cm, calculate its radius.
3. The curved surface area of a sphere is 36π cm^2. Calculate its radius.
4. The curved surface area of a cylinder is 628 cm^2 and its radius is 5 cm.
   Calculate **(i)** its height and **(ii)** its volume (assume $\pi = 3.14$).
5. The volume of a sphere is 972π cm^3. Calculate its radius.
6. The volume of a sphere is 904.32 mm^3. Calculate its radius (assume $\pi = 3.14$).
7. The curved surface area of a sphere is 144π cm^2.
   Calculate **(i)** its radius and **(ii)** its volume in terms of π.
8. A solid cylinder has a volume of 2,816 cm^3 and a radius of 8 cm. Calculate its height (assume $\pi = \frac{22}{7}$).
9. A cylinder has a volume of 792 m^3. If the height is 28 m, calculate its radius (assume $\pi = \frac{22}{7}$).
10. A solid cylinder has a volume of 176 cm^3. If the radius is 2 cm, calculate its height (assume $\pi = \frac{22}{7}$).
11. The curved surface area of a cylinder is 660 cm^2. If the diameter of the base is 10 cm, calculate **(i)** its height and **(ii)** its volume. (Assume $\pi = \frac{22}{7}$.)
12. A cylindrical jug has a radius of 6 cm and height of 40 cm. If the jug is full of lemonade, how many cylindrical tumblers, each with radius 4 cm and height 10 cm, can be filled from the jug?

Find the missing dimension. In each case the volumes are equal (all dimensions in centimetres).

13.   **14.**

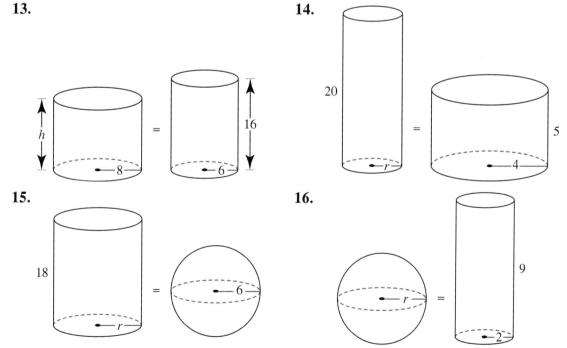

17. A cylinder of internal diameter 8 cm and height 18 cm is full of liquid. The liquid is poured into a second cylinder of internal diameter 12 cm. Calculate the depth of the liquid in this second cylinder.

18. A solid metal sphere has a radius of 3 cm. Express the volume of the sphere in terms of π. A cylindrical container is partly filled with water. The sphere is completely submerged in this container. If the level of water in the container rises by 1 cm, calculate the radius of the base of the cylinder.

19. A solid metal sphere of radius 9 cm is completely immersed in a cylinder containing water. The sphere is removed, and the level of water drops by 3 cm. Calculate the diameter of the base of the cylinder.

20. A cylinder with diameter 20 cm and height 35 cm is full of water. If 2.2 litres of the water are removed, calculate **(i)** the drop in the level of the water and **(ii)** the percentage of water remaining in the cylinder (assume $\pi = \frac{22}{7}$).

| Exercise 19.12 ▼ |

Chapter test

Find **(i)** the perimeter and **(ii)** the area of each of the following figures (all dimensions in centimetres):

1.

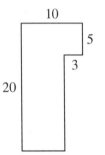

2.

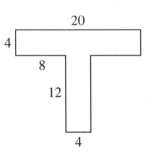

(In questions 3 and 4 assume $\pi = \frac{22}{7}$.)

3.

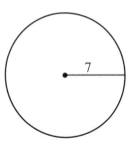

4.

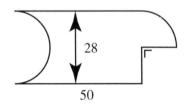

Find the area of the shaded parts shown (assume $\pi = \frac{22}{7}$; all dimension in centimetres):

5.

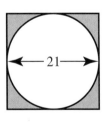

6.

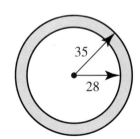

7.

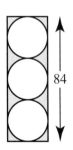

8. The floor of a room 3.2 m long by 2.7 m wide is to be covered with tiles. Each tile is 10 cm by 15 cm.
    (a) Find the number of tiles required to cover the floor.
    (b) If each tile costs €1.20, find the cost of the tiles.
    (c) If adhesive costs €2.50 per 48 tiles and labour costs €30 per 96 tiles, find the total cost of tiling the floor.

9. A piece of cardboard is in the shape of a square with sides of length 20 cm. Calculate its area.

   Two semi-circular pieces, each with a diameter of 20 cm, are cut from the piece of cardboard, as shown in the diagram.

   Taking π to be 3.14, calculate
    (i) the area of the two pieces that are cut out
    (ii) the percentage of the area of the square that remains.

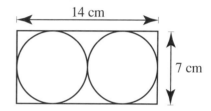

10. Calculate the area enclosed by a circle of radius 3.5 cm, taking π to be $\frac{22}{7}$.

    A rectangular piece of cardboard measures 14 cm by 7 cm. Two circular pieces, each of radius 3.5 cm, are cut out from this rectangular piece of cardboard, as shown.
    (i) Calculate the area of the remaining piece of cardboard.
    (ii) Express the area of the remaining piece of cardboard as a percentage of the area of the original rectangular piece.
       Give your answer correct to two places of decimals.

11. A closed cylindrical metal can has an external radius of 7 cm and a height of 10 cm.
    (i) Calculate the curved surface area of the can. Assume $\pi = \frac{22}{7}$.
    (ii) Calculate the total surface area of the can. Assume $\pi = \frac{22}{7}$.
    (iii) A rectangular sheet of metal measuring 50 cm by 25 cm was used to make the can. What area of the metal sheet was left over?

12. Find, in terms of π, the volume of liquid in a large cylinder of radius 10 cm and height 15 cm.

    Calculate the number of small cylinders of radius 2.5 cm and height 1.5 cm that can be filled from one supply of liquid in the large cylinder.

13. A machine part consists of a hollow sphere floating in a closed cylinder full of oil. The height of the cylinder is 28 cm; the radius of the cylinder is 15 cm; and the radius of the sphere is $\frac{21}{2}$ cm.

    Taking π to be $\frac{22}{7}$, find the volume of
    (i) the cylinder
    (ii) the sphere
    (iii) the oil.

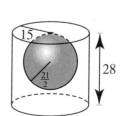

14. Find the volume, in cubic centimetres, of a cylindrical can with a radius of 20 cm and height of 70 cm, taking π to be $\frac{22}{7}$.

This can is filled with liquid. How many litres of liquid does it contain?
(1 litre = 1,000 cm³.)

The same amount of liquid fills fifity smaller, identical cylindrical cans.
How many litres of liquid fill one of these smaller cans?

If a smaller can has a height of 35 cm, calculate its radius, taking π to be $\frac{22}{7}$.

15. Find the volume, in cubic centimetres, of a cylindrical carton with radius of 5 cm and height of 7 cm, taking π to be $\frac{22}{7}$.

Cartons of this type are filled with yoghurt. How many cartons must be filled so that the total amount of yoghurt contained in them is 22 litres?
(1 litre = 1,000 cm³.)

Larger cylindrical cartons are filled with ice-cream. Each larger cylindrical carton has a height of 14 cm and a volume of 4.4 litres.

Calculate the radius length of these larger cartons, taking $\pi = \frac{22}{7}$.

16. (i) Calculate, in terms of π, the volume of a sphere of radius 4.5 cm.

Four of these spheres exactly fit into a cylinder of radius 4.5 cm and of height h cm, as shown. Calculate

(ii) the height, h, of the cylinder

(iii) the volume of the cylinder, in terms of π

(iv) the fraction of the volume of the cylinder taken up by the four spheres.

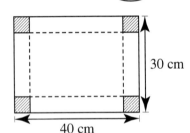

17. A rectangular piece of plastic measured 40 cm by 30 cm. Squares of sides 5 cm were cut off from the corners, as shown.

(i) Find the area of the remainder in square centimetres.

(ii) The strips at the edges were folded along the dotted lines so as to make an open rectangular box. Calculate the volume of the box, in litres.

18. (i) Find the volume, in cubic centimetres, of a cylindrical cup of radius 3 cm and height 7 cm, taking π to be $\frac{22}{7}$.

(ii) A fish tank has a square base measuring 30 cm by 30 cm. It has four rectangular sides, each 55 cm high. Find the volume of the tank in cubic centimetres.

(iii) The cylindrical cup is filled with water and then totally emptied into the fish tank. This is done fifty times. What is the total volume of water put into the fish tank?

(iv) If the fish tank was empty at the start, what is the depth of water in it at the end?

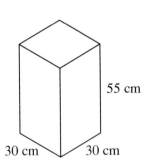

19. A solid metal rectangular block 30 cm by 24 cm by 15 cm is melted down and recast into cubes of sides 3 cm. How many such cubes were made?

20. The length, width and height of a rectangular box are in the ratio $3 : 4 : 2$.
If the length of the box is 6 cm, find its width and height.
Hence, calculate the volume of the box.

21. A cylinder has a radius of 5 cm and a volume of 200π cm^3. Calculate its height.

22. A cylinder has a volume of 502.4 cm^3. If its height is 10 cm, calculate its radius (assume $\pi = 3.14$).

23. A solid lead sphere of radius 6 cm is melted down and recast as a solid cylinder of height 18 cm. Calculate the radius of the cylinder.

24. The curved surface area of a cylinder is 219.8 cm^2 and its radius is 3.5 cm. Taking π to be 3.14, find:
(i) the height of the cylinder **(ii)** the volume of the cylinder.

25. A piece of wire is bent to form a right-angled triangle. It is then bent into a square.

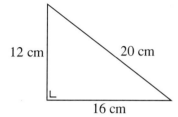

Calculate the difference in area between the square and the triangle.

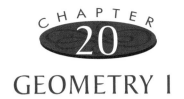

GEOMETRY I

Definitions: points and lines

Point:
A point has no dimensions: it has no length, breadth, or thickness. It represents a position and is indicated by a dot. A point is denoted by a lower-case letter.

Line:
A line can be denoted in two ways:
1. By naming two points on it.　　**2.** Using a capital letter.
Here is a diagram of the line *ab* or the line *L*.

A line extends indefinitely in both directions, as indicated by the arrows.

Line segment:
A part or section of a line is called a line segment.
Here is a diagram of the line segment *ab*, denoted by [*ab*].

The length of the line segment [*ab*] is written $|ab|$.

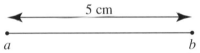

The diagram shows the line segment [*ab*] with $|ab| = 5$ cm.

Collinear points:
Points that are on the same line are said to be collinear.

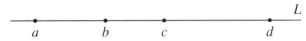

The points *a*, *b*, *c* and *d* are collinear, as they are all on the same line.
Note: Through any two points only one line can be drawn.

Pairs of lines:

Consider the lines L and K:

intersecting	**parallel**	**perpendicular**
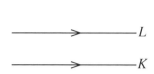		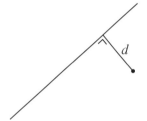
L intersects K at p written: $L \cap K = \{p\}$	L is parallel to K written: $L \| K$ Parallel lines never meet and are often indicated by arrows.	L is perpendicular to K written: $L \perp K$ The symbol $\llcorner$ is placed where the two lines meet to show that they are perpendicular.

Distance from a point to a line

The distance, d, from a point to a line is defined as the **shortest** distance from the point to the line. This distance is often called the '**perpendicular**' distance.

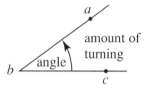

Angles

An angle is formed when two lines meet. The size of the angle measures the amount of turning from one line to the other line, about their common point. In the diagram, ba and bc are called the '**arms**' of the angle, and the common point 'b' is called the '**vertex**' of the angle. An angle is denoted by the symbol $\angle$.

An angle can be named in one of three ways:

1. Three letters	**2. A number**	**3. A capital letter**
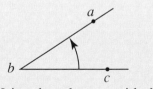	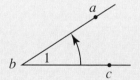	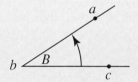
Using three letters, with the centre at the vertex. The angle is then referred to as $\angle abc$ or $\angle cba$.	Putting a number at the vertex of the angle. The angle can then be referred to by the number, for example $\angle 1$.	Putting a capital letter at the vertex of the angle (provided there is no confusion). The angle can then be referred to by the capital letter, for example $\angle B$.

Note: Lower-case letters are often used in diagrams with missing angles.
The size, or measure, of $\angle abc$ is written $|\angle abc|$.
Therefore $|\angle abc| = |\angle 1| = |\angle B|$.

Measuring angles

An angle may be considered to be an amount of turning or rotation. Angles are usually measured in degrees, using the symbol °. A complete turn, or revolution, is 360°.
Angles are named according to the amount of turning:

Types of angles

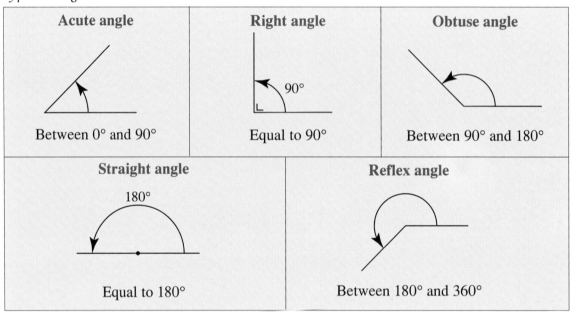

Properties of angles

It is very important to know the following properties of angles:

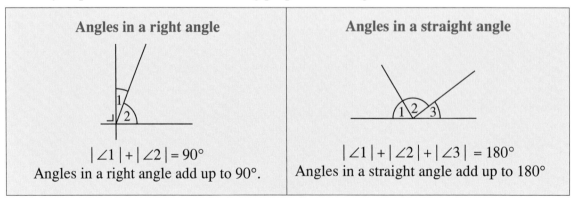

Angles at a point	Vertically opposite angles
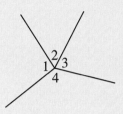	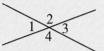
	$\|\angle 1\| = \|\angle 3\|$ and $\|\angle 2\| = \|\angle 4\|$ When two lines meet at a point they form two pairs of **vertically opposite angles**, which are equal in measure. Look for the ✕ shape.
$\|\angle 1\| + \|\angle 2\| + \|\angle 3\| + \|\angle 4\| = 360°$ Angles at a point add up to 360°.	

We regularly use these properties to find missing angles in diagrams.

Example ▼

Calculate the value of the letter representing the angle in each of the following diagrams:

(i)  **(ii)** 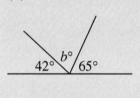 **(iii)** 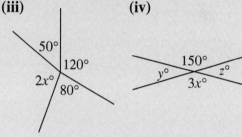 **(iv)**

Solution:

(i)
$$a° + 35° = 90° \quad \text{(angles in a right angle add up to 90°)}$$
$$a + 35 = 90$$
$$a = 55 \quad \text{(subtract 35 from both sides)}$$

(ii)
$$42° + b° + 65° = 180° \quad \text{(angles in a straight angle add up to 180°)}$$
$$42 + b + 65 = 180$$
$$b + 107 = 180$$
$$b = 73 \quad \text{(subtract 107 from both sides)}$$

(iii)
$$2x° + 50° + 120° + 80° = 360° \quad \text{(angles at a point add up to 360°)}$$
$$2x + 50 + 120 + 80 = 360$$
$$2x + 250 = 360$$
$$2x = 110 \quad \text{(subtract 250 from both sides)}$$
$$x = 55 \quad \text{(divide both sides by 2)}$$

Exercise 20.1 ▼

Calculate the value of the letter representing the angle in each of the following diagrams:

1.

2.

3.

4.

5.

6.

7.
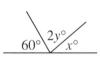

8.

9.
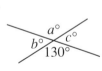

10.

11.
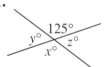

12.
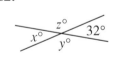

13.
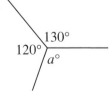

14.
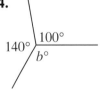

15.
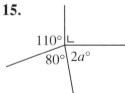

16.
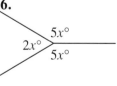

17.
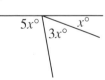

18.
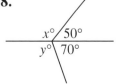

19.
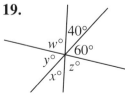

20.
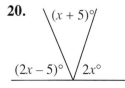

21. Calculate:

   (i) $|\angle bac|$

   (ii) $|\angle dae|$

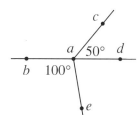

22. Calculate:

   (i) $|\angle xoy|$

   (ii) $|\angle woz|$

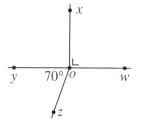

Angles and parallel lines

When a line cuts a pair of parallel lines, eight angles are formed, in such a way that:

1. all the acute angles are equal
2. all the obtuse angles are equal

Some of these angles have special names.

Note: If you know one of these angles then you can work out all the others.

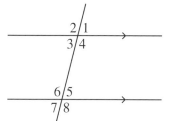

Corresponding angles

Corresponding angles are equal and occur in pairs. A pair of corresponding angles is marked on each of the diagrams:

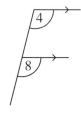 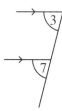 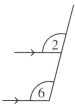 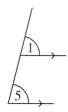

$|\angle 4| = |\angle 8|$ $|\angle 3| = |\angle 7|$ $|\angle 2| = |\angle 6|$ $|\angle 1| = |\angle 5|$

Looking for a **F** or **⌐|** shape can help you to spot corresponding angles.

Alternate angles

Alternate angles are equal and occur in pairs. A pair of alternate angles is marked on each of the diagrams.

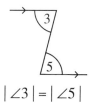 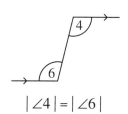

$|\angle 3| = |\angle 5|$ $|\angle 4| = |\angle 6|$

Looking for a **Z** or **⌐⌐** shape can help you to spot alternate angles.

Interior angles

Interior angles add up to 180°. A pair of interior angles is marked on each of the diagrams.

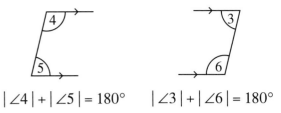

$$|\angle 4| + |\angle 5| = 180° \qquad |\angle 3| + |\angle 6| = 180°$$

Looking for a $\llcorner$ or $\lrcorner$ shape can help you to spot interior angles.

Example ▼

Calculate the value of:
(i) a (ii) b (iii) c

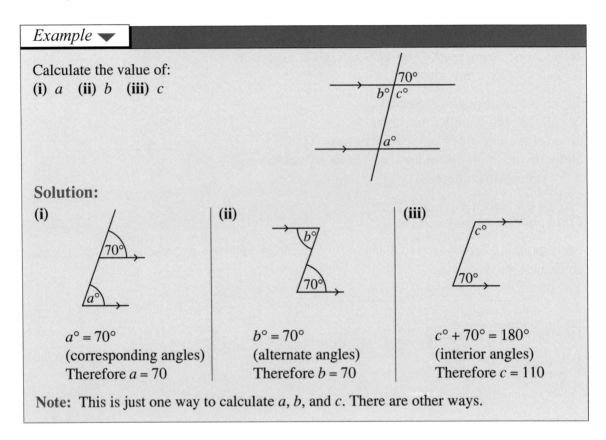

Solution:

(i)

$a° = 70°$
(corresponding angles)
Therefore $a = 70$

(ii)

$b° = 70°$
(alternate angles)
Therefore $b = 70$

(iii)

$c° + 70° = 180°$
(interior angles)
Therefore $c = 110$

Note: This is just one way to calculate a, b, and c. There are other ways.

Exercise 20.2 ▼

Calculate the value of the letter representing the angle in each of the following diagrams (arrows indicate parallel lines):

1. 2. 3. 4.

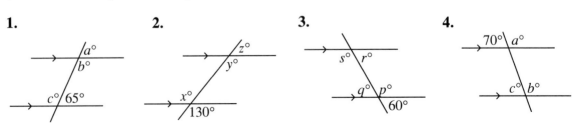

5.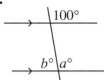

6.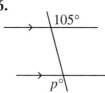

7.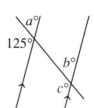

8.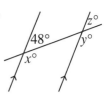

9.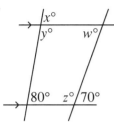

10.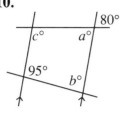

11.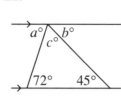

12.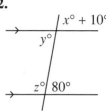

Triangles

Angle sum of a triangle	Exterior angle of a triangle
The three angles of a triangle add up to 180°.	If one side is produced, the exterior angle is equal to the sum of the two interior opposite angles.
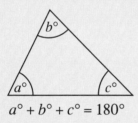	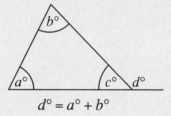
$a° + b° + c° = 180°$	$d° = a° + b°$

Types of triangles

Equilateral triangle	Isosceles triangle	Scalene triangle
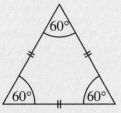	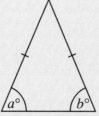	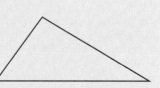
3 sides equal 3 equal angles All angles are equal to 60°	2 sides equal base angles are equal $a° = b°$ (base angles are the angles opposite the equal sides)	3 unequal sides 3 unequal angles

Notes on triangles:

1. The marks on the sides of the triangle indicate sides with equal lengths.
2. If two sides are of unequal length, the angles opposite these sides are also unequal.
3. The largest angle is opposite the largest side, and the smallest angle is opposite the smallest side.
4. The lengths of any two sides added together are always greater than the length of the third side.

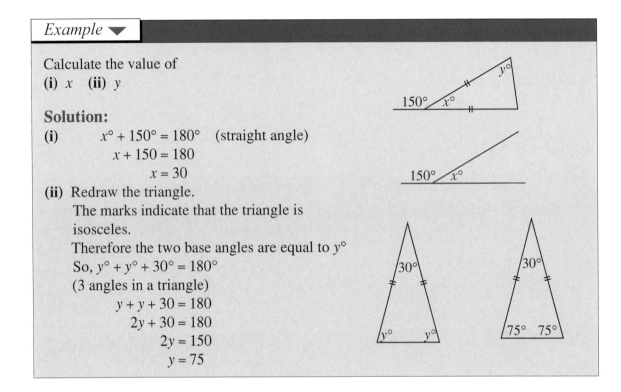

Example ▼

Calculate the value of
(i) x (ii) y

Solution:

(i) $x° + 150° = 180°$ (straight angle)
$x + 150 = 180$
$x = 30$

(ii) Redraw the triangle.
The marks indicate that the triangle is isosceles.
Therefore the two base angles are equal to $y°$
So, $y° + y° + 30° = 180°$
(3 angles in a triangle)
$y + y + 30 = 180$
$2y + 30 = 180$
$2y = 150$
$y = 75$

Exercise 20.3 ▼

Calculate the value of the letter representing the angle in each of the following diagrams (arrows indicate parallel lines):

1.

$x°$

$60°$ $45°$

2.

$80°$

$70°$ $y°$

3.

$70°$

$z°$ $60°$

4.

$a°$

$40°$

5.

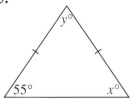

6.

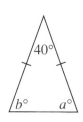

7.

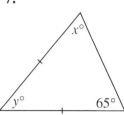

8.

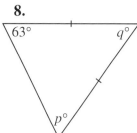

9.

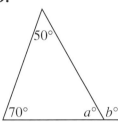

10.

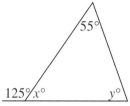

11.

12.

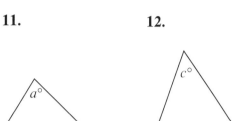

13.

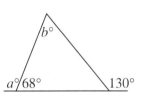

14.

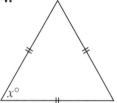

15.

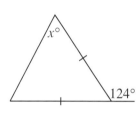

16.

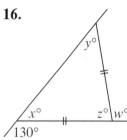

17.

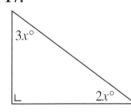

18.

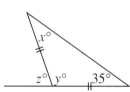

19.

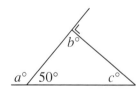

20.

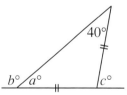

21.

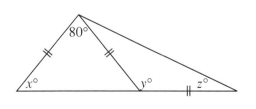

22.

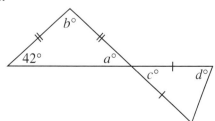

23. Calculate:

    (i) $|\angle xzw|$

    (ii) $|\angle xyz|$

    (iii) $|\angle yxz|$

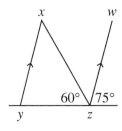

24. Calculate:

    (i) $|\angle bcd|$

    (ii) $|\angle dbc|$

    (iii) $|\angle dba|$

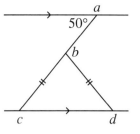

25. In $\triangle pqr$,
$|\angle pqr| = |\angle prq|$,
$|pr| = 10$ cm and $|qr| = 14$ cm.
Calculate the perimeter of $\triangle pqr$.

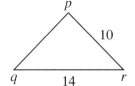

Quadrilaterals

A quadrilateral is a figure that has four sides and four vertices. It has two diagonals that join the opposite vertices.

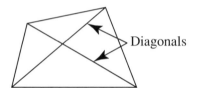

The four angles of a quadrilateral add up to 360°.
$a° + b° + c° + d° = 360°$
(This is because a quadrilateral can be divided up into two triangles.)

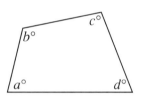

Note: $a°$ and $c°$ are called opposite angles, and $b°$ and $d°$ are also called opposite angles.
Some quadrilaterals have special names and special properties.

Parallelogram

1. Opposite sides are parallel

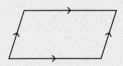

2. Opposite sides are equal

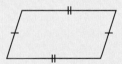

3. Opposite angles are equal

4. Diagonals bisect each other

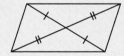

Rhombus

1. Opposite sides are parallel

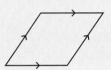

2. All sides are equal

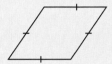

3. Opposite angles are equal

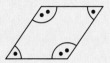

4. Diagonals bisect each other

5. Diagonals intersect at right angles

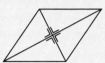

6. Diagonals bisect opposite angles

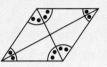

Rectangle

1. Opposite sides are parallel

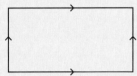

2. Opposite sides are equal

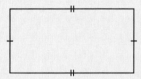

3. All angles are right angles

4. Diagonals are equal and bisect each other

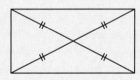

Square

1. Opposite sides are parallel

2. All sides are equal

3. All angles are right angles

4. Diagonals are equal and bisect each other

5. Diagonals intersect at right angles

6. Diagonals bisect each angle

xyzw is a rhombus.
Calculate the value of:
(i) *a*   **(ii)** *b*   **(iii)** *c*

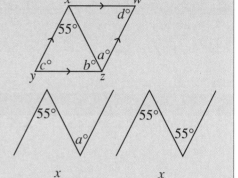

Solution:
(i) $a° = 55°$ (alternate angles, ⌐ shape)
        Therefore $a = 55$

(ii) △*xyz* is isosceles (because *xyzw* is a rhombus)
        $b° = 55°$ (base angles)
        Therefore $b = 55$
        $55° + b° + c° = 180°$ (three angles in a triangle)
        Therefore $55 + b + c = 180$
        $55 + 55 + c = 180$ ($b = 55$)
                    $c = 70$
(iii) $d° = 70°$ (opposite angles)
        Therefore $d = 70$

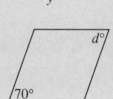
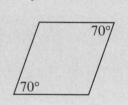

Exercise 20.4 ▼

Calculate the value of the letter representing the angle in each of the following diagrams (arrows indicate parallel lines):

1.

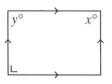

2.

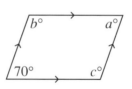

3.

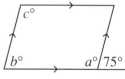

4.

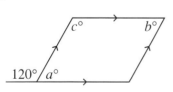

5.

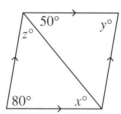

6.

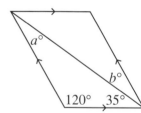

7.

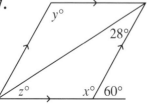

8.

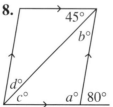

9.

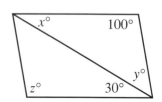

10.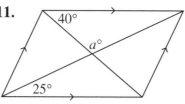

125° a° b° c° 30°

11. 40° a° 25°

12. 40° 85° y° x°

13. $pqrs$ is a parallelogram, with
$|\angle pqt| = 30°$ and $|\angle qru| = 110°$
$|\angle qus| = x°$
$|\angle uts| = y°$

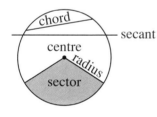

u x° t y° p s 30° 110° q r

Calculate **(i)** x **(ii)** y

14. $pqrs$ is a rhombus with diagonals inter-secting at o.

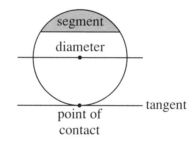

p 30° s o q r

If $|\angle psq| = 30°$, calculate:
(i) $|\angle sqr|$ **(ii)** $|\angle sop|$
(iii) $|\angle spr|$ **(iv)** $|\angle prq|$

Circle

The diagrams below show some of the terms we use when dealing with a circle:

chord secant centre radius sector

segment diameter tangent point of contact

Circle theorems

1. Angle in a semicircle

| The angle in a semicircle is always a right angle |

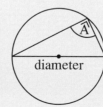

A diameter

Angle A is the angle in a semicircle
$|\angle A| = 90°$

2. Tangent-radius theorem

> A tangent to a circle is perpendicular to a radius at the point of contact

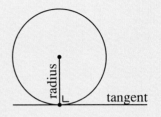

3. Cyclic quadrilateral

A cyclic quadrilateral has its four vertices on the circumference of a circle.

> The opposite angles in a cyclic quadrilateral add up to 180°

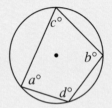

$a° + b° = 180°$ and $c° + d° = 180°$

Example ▼

The centre of the circle is o.
Calculate the value of:
(i) a **(ii)** b **(iii)** c

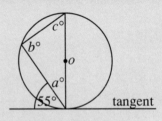

Solution:

(i) $\qquad 55° + a° = 90°$ (tangent perpendicular to radius)
$\qquad$ Therefore $55 + a = 90$
$\qquad\qquad\qquad a = 35$ (subtract 55 from both sides)

(ii) $\qquad\qquad b = 90°$ (the angle in a semicircle is always a right angle)

(iii) $\qquad a° + b° + c° = 180°$ (three angles in a triangle)
$\qquad$ Therefore $a + b + c = 180$
$\qquad\qquad 35 + 90 + c = 180$ ($a = 35$, $b = 90$)
$\qquad\qquad\quad 125 + c = 180$
$\qquad\qquad\qquad\quad c = 55$ (subtract 125 from both sides)

Example ▼

The centre of the circle is c.
Calculate the value of:
(i) x **(ii)** y

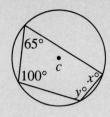

Solution:

(i) $x° + 100° = 180°$ (opposite angles in a cyclic quadrilateral)
      Therefore $x + 100 = 180$
            $x = 80$ (subtract 100 from both sides)

(ii) $y° + 65° = 180°$ (opposite angles in a cyclic quadrilateral)
      Therefore $y + 65 = 180$
            $y = 115$ (subtract 65 from both sides)

Exercise 20.5 ▼

Calculate the value of the letter representing the angle in each of the following diagrams, where o is the centre of the circle in each case and lines touching circles are tangents:

1.

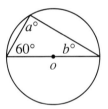

2.

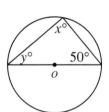

3.

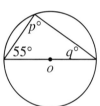

4.

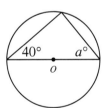

5.

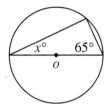

6.

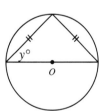

7.

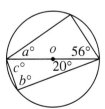

8.

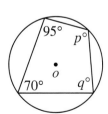

9.

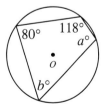

10.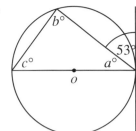

11.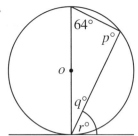

12.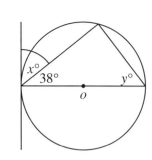

In questions 13 to 18 look for the isosceles and equilateral in the diagrams.
Remember: All radii in a diagram are equal in length.

13.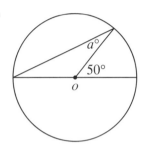

14.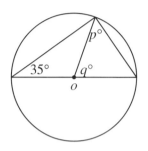

15.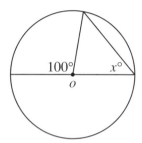

16.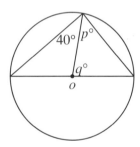

17.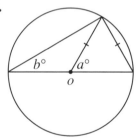

18.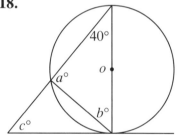

19. *pt* is a tangent to a circle of centre *k*.
If $|\angle pqr| = 58°$, calculate the value of:
(i) *x*   **(ii)** *y*

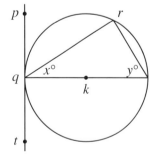

20. Circle *K* has centre *c*.
ab is a tangent to *K*.
$|\angle qst| = 54°$

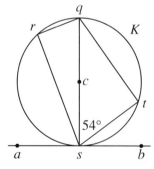

Find:
(i) $|\angle qrs|$ **(ii)** $|\angle sqt|$

(iii) $|\angle tsb|$ **(iv)** $|\angle rqt| + |\angle rst|$

Chapter test

1. *M* and *N* are parallel lines.

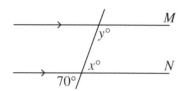

Calculate the value of **(i)** *x* **(ii)** *y*.

2. Calculate the value of **(i)** *a* **(ii)** *b*.

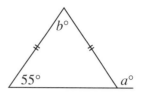

3. [*bd*] is a diagonal of the parallelogram *abcd*.
Calculate the value of
(i) *x* **(ii)** *y* **(iii)** *z* **(iv)** *w*

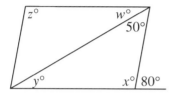

4. *xy* || *wz*.
Calculate the value of **(i)** *p* **(ii)** *q* **(iii)** *r*.

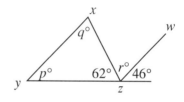

5. Calculate the value of **(i)** *a* **(ii)** *b*.

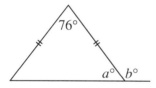

6. *k* is the centre of the circle and
| ∠*xwk* | = 40°.
Calculate | ∠*ykw* |.

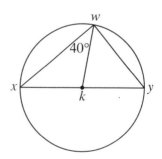

7. *M* and *N* are parallel lines.
Calculate the value of *x*.

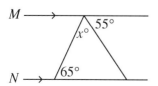

8. Calculate the value of *y* in the diagram.

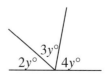

9. *abcd* is a parallelogram.
Calculate $|\angle bdc|$.

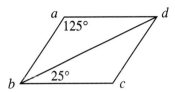

10. *wxyz* is a parallelogram with
$|\angle wxy| = 70°$ and $|wy| = |xy|$.
Calculate **(i)** $|\angle wyx|$ **(ii)** $|\angle wyz|$.

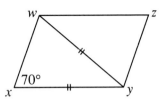

11. *L* and *M* are parallel lines.
Find the value of *x* and the value of *y*.

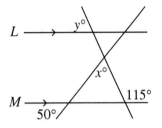

12. *A* and *B* are parallel lines.
Find the value of *p*.

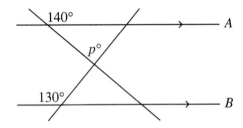

13. The centre of the circle is *c*.
If $|\angle acd| = 46°$, find $|\angle bac|$.

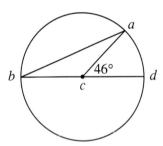

14. *pqr* are points of a circle, centre *c*.
If $|\angle pcr| = 58°$, show that $|\angle pqc| = 29°$.

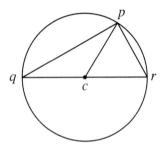

15. The centre of the circle is *k*.
If $|\angle pqr| = 75°$ and $|\angle srq| = 110°$.
Calculate **(i)** $|\angle qps|$ **(ii)** $|\angle rsp|$.

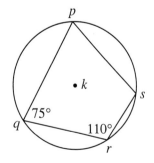

16. *k* is the centre of the circle.
$|\angle tps| = 30°$.
Calculate $|\angle sur|$.

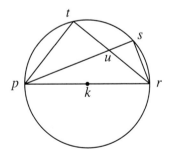

17. $ab \parallel cd$, $|\angle abc| = 40°$, and $|pc| = |pd|$.
Name another angle that measures 40°.
Hence, calculate $|\angle bpd|$.

18. Calculate the value of **(i)** a **(ii)** b.

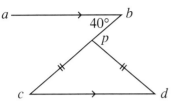

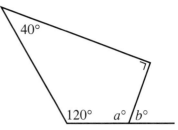

19. The three angles in a triangle are in the ratio $1 : 2 : 3$.
Find the three angles, in degrees.

20. The diagram shows the rhombus $abcd$, with diagonals intersecting at m.
If $|\angle dab| = 112°$, evaluate
(i) $|\angle dcb|$ **(ii)** $|\angle abc|$
(iii) $|\angle mbc|$ **(iv)** $|\angle mab|$
(v) $|\angle amb|$.

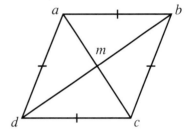

21

TRANSFORMATION GEOMETRY

Transformations

The word '**transformation**' means change. In geometry a transformation changes the position of a figure.

Object and image

The original position of a figure is called the '**object**'. The new position of a figure is called the '**image**'.
In other words, the image is where the object moves to.

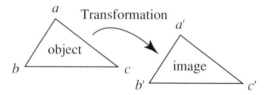

Notice that each letter on the image is dashed. Transformations are sometimes called '**mappings**', and the object is said to be mapped onto the image.
On our course we will look at three types of transformations:
1. Translations   **2.** Axial symmetries   **3.** Central symmetries
Each of these transformations changes the position of a figure but not its size or shape.

Translation

> A translation moves a figure in a straight line.

A translation is often called a '**slide**' or '**shift**'.
The figure does not turn or flip over.

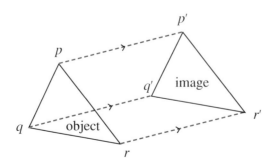

Under a translation, every point (on the figure) moves the **same distance** and in the **same direction**.

To define a translation we must give the distance and direction moved.

The translation above could be described as $p \rightarrow p'$, written $\overrightarrow{pp'}$ (or $\overrightarrow{qq'}$ or $\overrightarrow{rr'}$).

Notice that under a translation, a line is parallel to the original line.

As can be seen from the diagram, $pr \,||\, p'r'$, $pq \,||\, p'q'$, and $qr \,||\, q'r'$.

Example ▼

abcd and aced are parallelograms.
Under the translation $\overrightarrow{bc}$, write down the image of:
(i) $\triangle abc$ **(ii)** $[ac]$ **(iii)** $\angle bac$.
Name two other translations equal to $\overrightarrow{bc}$.

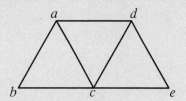

Solution:
The image of a point is where the point moves to after the transformation.

Under the translation $\overrightarrow{bc}$:

$a \rightarrow d$ (a moves to d)
$b \rightarrow c$ (b moves to c)
$c \rightarrow e$ (c moves to e)

(i) $\triangle abc \rightarrow \triangle dce$

(ii) $[ac] \rightarrow [de]$

(iii) $\angle bac \rightarrow \angle cde$

Two other translations equal to $\overrightarrow{bc}$ are $\overrightarrow{ad}$ and $\overrightarrow{ce}$ (same length and direction)

Note: It is good practice, but not necessary, to keep the order of the images of points asked in the question.

Exercise 21.1 ▼

1. pqrs and prts are parallelograms.
   Under the translation $\overrightarrow{ps}$, write down the image of:
   (i) $\triangle pqr$ **(ii)** $[qr]$ **(iii)** $\angle qpr$.
   Name two other translations equal to $\overrightarrow{ps}$.
   Find the image of s under the translation $\overrightarrow{rq}$.

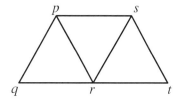

2. rstu is a square, and ustv is a parallelogram.
   Under the translation $\overrightarrow{st}$, write down the image of:
   (i) $\triangle rsu$ **(ii)** $[su]$ **(iii)** $\angle sru$.
   Under the translation $\overrightarrow{ur}$, write down the image of:
   (iv) $\triangle uvt$ **(v)** $[ut]$ **(vi)** $\angle tvu$.
   Name one translation equal to:
   (vii) $\overrightarrow{su}$ **(viii)** $\overrightarrow{vt}$ **(ix)** $\overrightarrow{tu}$.

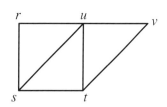

3. *pqrs* is a rectangle. The midpoint of [*qr*] is *z*.
$|qz| = |xy|$, and $|px| = \lfloor ys \rfloor$.
Under the translation $\vec{qz}$, write down the image of:
(i) $\triangle xqz$ **(ii)** [*xz*] **(iii)** $\angle qxz$.
Name two parallelograms that are not rectangles.
Name two angles equal to $\angle xqz$.
If $|pq| = 5$ cm and $|px| = 2$ cm, calculate the area of the
rectangle *pqrs*.

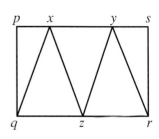

4. The diagram shows two identical squares, *abcd* and *dcef*,
with their diagonals intersecting at *x* and *y*, respectively.
Under the translation $\vec{ad}$, write down the image of:
(i) *c* **(ii)** [*ab*] **(iii)** $\triangle axd$
(iv) [*bx*] **(v)** [*xd*] **(vi)** $\angle xad$.
Name another square.
If the area of $\triangle abx$ is 4 cm^2, find the area of:
(vii) $\triangle bad$ **(viii)** $\triangle acf$ **(ix)** the rectangle *abef*.

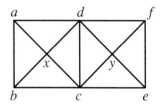

5. The diagram shows four equilateral triangles.
Under the translation $\vec{qr}$, write down the image of:
(i) *s* **(ii)** [*qp*] **(iii)** $\triangle psr$ **(iv)** $\angle rps$.
Name a translation under which $\triangle prs$ is the image of
$\triangle suv$.
If the area of the parallelogram *pquv* is 20 cm^2, what is
the area of the parallelogram *prus*? Calculate $|\angle pru|$.

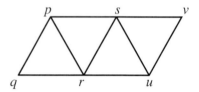

Axis of symmetry

If a figure is **identical** on each side of a line drawn through it then it is said to have 'line symmetry'. A figure with line symmetry is balanced on each of the line. The line that divides the
figure into two identical halves is called an '**axis of symmetry**' (often called a 'line of symmetry').

Consider the kite shown opposite.
The kite can be folded, so that one half fits
exactly on top of the other. The fold line (its
main diagonal) is an 'axis of symmetry'. Each
side of an axis of symmetry is said to be the
mirror image of the other. Figures that have an
axis of symmetry are said to be '**symmetrical**'
about the line. Some figures (shapes) have no axis of
symmetry, for example certain parallelograms.
Other figures have more than one axis of symmetry.
For example, a square has four axes of symmetry.

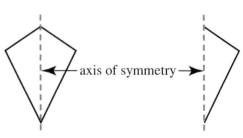

For each figure, state the number of lines of symmetry it possesses if any (it may help to indicate, where appropriate, an axis of symmetry with a broken line):

1.

2.

3.

4.

5.

6.

7.

8.

9.

10.

11.

12.

13.

14.

15.

16.

Axial symmetry

Axial symmetry is a reflection in a line

A reflection in a line, an axial symmetry, gives an image that looks like the reflection of an object in a mirror. The object and the image are the **same distance** on either side of the line. However, under a reflection in a line, a figure flips over.

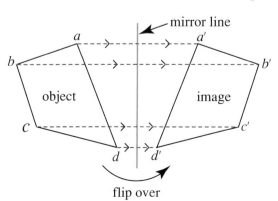

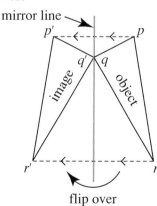

Notes: **1.** If a point lies on the mirror line, its image is the same point.
In the second diagram, the image of *q* is still *q*.

2. By the same distance on either side of the line we mean the same perpendicular distance.

Example ▼

pqrs and *sruv* are two squares with diagonals intersecting at *a* and *b*, respectively. Under the axial symmetry in *sr*, write down the image of:

(i) △*pqs* **(ii)** [*pq*] **(iii)** ∠*aps*.

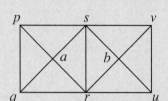

Solution:
Under the axial symmetry in *sr*:

$p \rightarrow v$

$q \rightarrow u$

$s \rightarrow s$ (own image)

$a \rightarrow b$

(i)   △*pqs* → △*vus*
(ii)   [*pq*] → [*vu*]
(iii)   ∠*aps* → ∠*bvs*

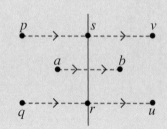

Exercise 21.3 ▼

1. *abcd* and *dcef* are squares with diagonals intersecting at *x* and *y*, respectively.

  (a) Under the axial symmetry in *dc*, write down the image of:
  (i) *a* **(ii)** *b* **(iii)** *e* **(iv)** *f*
  (v) *d* **(vi)** *c* **(vii)** *x* **(viii)** *y*
  (ix) [*ab*] **(x)** △*dfy* **(xi)** ∠*xad* **(xii)** ∠*ycd*.

  (b) Under the axial symmetry in *ac*, write down the image of:
  (i) *b* **(ii)** *d* **(iii)** *a* **(iv)** *c* **(v)** *x*
  (vi) △*abx* **(vii)** ∠*bxc* **(viii)** [*xd*].

2. *pqrs* is a kite with diagonals intersecting at *o*.
Under the axial symmetry in *pr*, write down the image of:
(i) *q* **(ii)** *s* **(iii)** △*pos* **(iv)** ∠*pso*.

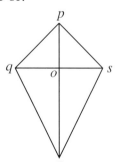

3. *pqrs* and *tsvu* are identical squares.
Write down the image of:
(i)   *p* under the axial symmetry in *qu*
(ii) [*rs*] under the axial symmetry in *pv*
(iii) △*pqr* under the axial symmetry *pr*
(iv) ∠*tuv* under the axial symmetry in *tv*.

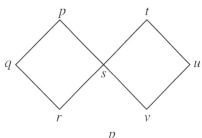

4. [*pq*] and [*rs*] are two diameters of a circle
that are perpendicular to each other.
Write down the image of:
(i)   *p* under the axial symmetry in *rs*
(ii) [*po*] under the axial symmetry in *rs*
(iii) △*qor* under the axial symmetry in *pq*.

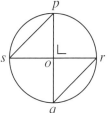

5. *abcd* is a rhombus with diagonals
intersecting at *k*.
(i)   Find the image of △*bck* under the axial symmetry in *bd*.
(ii) What is the image of *abcd* under the axial symmetry in *ac*?
(iii) Name four isosceles triangles.
(iv) Find the image of [*ab*] under the translation $\overrightarrow{bc}$.

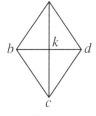

6. The diagram shows a rectangle *abcd* divided into four smaller
rectangles of equal size. The diagonals of the rectangle
abcd meet at *z*.
(a) Under the axial symmetry in *pr*, write down the image
of:
(i) *a* (ii) *b* (iii) *s* (iv) △*czs* (v) ∠*zpd*.
(b) Under the axial symmetry in *qs*, write down the image
of:
(i) *b* (ii) *p* (iii) *c* (iv) △*qbr* (v) the rectangle *rzsc*.
(c) Find the image of [*qz*] under the translation $\overrightarrow{ds}$.
(d) If the area of △*apq* = 4 cm², what is the area of the rectangle *abcd*?

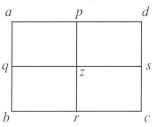

Centre of symmetry

> A reflection in a point *o* is where a point is moved in a straight line to *o*
> and then moved in a straight line the same distance beyond.

The diagram shows three points, *a*, *b*, and *c*, and
the images of the three points *a′*, *b′* and *c′* under a
reflection in the point *o*.

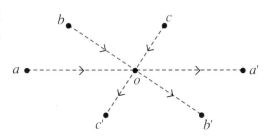

Notice that | *ao* | = | *oa′* |, | *bo* | = | *ob′* |, and
| *co* | = | *oc′* |.

Some figures are symmetrical about a point. The point is called the '**centre of symmetry**'. The following figures have a centre of symmetry, indicated by *o*.

Circle

Rectangle

Square

Letter X

In each case, if any point is taken on the figure, its image under a reflection in the point *o* is always another point on the figure.

Not all figures have a centre of symmetry. For example, a triangle has no centre of symmetry.

Exercise 21.4 ▼

For each figure, state whether it has a centre of symmetry, and indicate where it is:

1.

2.

3.

4.

5.

6.

7.

8.

9.

10.

11.

12.

13.

14.

15.

16.

Central symmetry

....

Central symmetry is a reflection in a point

Consider below the △*abc* and its image △*a'b'c'* under a central symmetry in the point *o*.

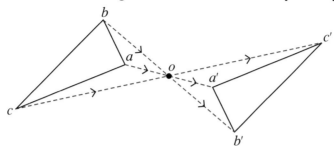

Notice that under a central symmetry, a line is parallel to the original line. As can be seen from the diagram, *ab* || *a'b'*, *ac* || *a'c'*, and *bc* || *b'c'*.

Note: The image of the point *o* under a central symmetry in *o* is the point itself. We say that *o* is its own image.

Example ▼

abcd and *edgf* are two identical parallelograms with diagonals intersecting at *p* and *q*, respectively.
Under the central symmetry in *d*, write down the image of:
(i) △*apd* **(ii)** [*ab*] **(iii)** ∠*qfe*

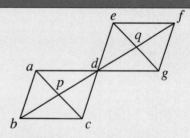

Solution:

Under the central symmetry in *d*:

$a \to g$
$p \to q$
$d \to d$ (own image)
$b \to f$
$q \to p$
$f \to b$
$e \to c$

(i) △*apd* → △*gqd*

(ii) [*ab*] → [*gf*]

(iii) ∠*qfe* → ∠*pbc*

Exercise 21.5 ▼

1. *abcd* is a parallelogram with diagonals intersecting at *m*. Under the central symmetry in *m*, write down the image of:
(i) *a* **(ii)** *b* **(iii)** [*dc*] **(iv)** [*ad*]
(v) △*abm* **(vi)** ∠*bcm*.

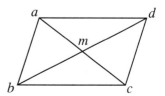

2. *pqrs* is a square divided into four equal squares by [*wy*] and [*xy*]. Find the image of:

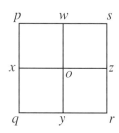

    (i)   *p* under the central symmetry in *o*

    (ii)   *y* under the central symmetry in *o*

    (iii)   *r* under the central symmetry in *z*

    (iv)   *s* under the central symmetry in *w*

    (v)   [*sw*] under the central symmetry in *o*

    (vi)   △*qxo* under the central symmetry in *o*

    (vii) △*xyq* under the central symmetry in *o*

    (viii) the square *wszo* under the central symmetry in *o*.

3. *pqrs* and *tsvu* are two identical parallelograms with diagonals intersecting at *x* and *y*, respectively. Under the central symmetry in *s*, write down the image of:

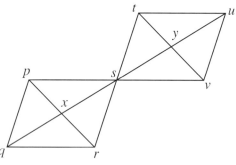

    (i) *t*   **(ii)** *p*   **(iii)** *u*   **(iv)** *x*   **(v)** *s*

    (vi) [*pq*]   **(vii)** [*ps*]   **(viii)** △*pxs*

    (ix) △*uvy*   **(x)** ∠*rxs*.

4. *pqrs* is a square and *sqrt* is a parallelogram with diagonals intersecting at *x* and *y*, respectively.

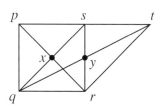

    (i) Name four line segments equal in length to [*ps*].

    Under the central symmetry in *x*, write down the image of:

    (ii) *r*   **(iii)** *q*   **(iv)** [*pq*]   **(v)** △*pxs*.

    Under the central symmetry in *y*, write down the image of:

    (vi) *r*   **(vii)** *q*   **(viii)** [*sq*]   **(ix)** △*sty*   **(x)** ∠*qrt*.

    What is the image of [*ps*] under the translation $\overrightarrow{qr}$?

    What is the image of *p* under the axial symmetry in *sr*?

    If the area of △*psq* = 20 cm², what is the area of the parallelogram *sqrt*?

5. *abcd* is a rectangle. *abdx* and *bycd* are parallelograms.

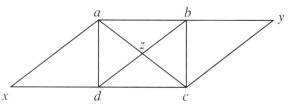

    (i)   Name three line segments equal in length to [*dc*].

    (ii) What is the image of △*bcy* under the central symmetry in *z*?

    (iii) What is the image of △*axd* under the axial symmetry in the line *ad*?

    (iv) What is the image of [*ax*] under the translation $\overrightarrow{by}$?

    (v) If | ∠*axd* | = 40°, write down the measure of | ∠*adz* | .

    (vi) If the area of △*adz* = 8 cm², what is the area of the figure *axcy*?

    (vii) What is the centre of symmetry of the figure *axcy*?

Chapter test

1. *abcd* is a square with diagonals intersecting at *o*. Write down the image of:

   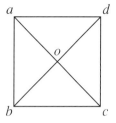

   (i) [*bc*] under the translation $\overrightarrow{cd}$
   (ii) △*cod* under the central symmetry in *o*
   (iii) △*abc* under the axial symmetry in *ac*.
   If the area of △*ocd* = 10 cm², write down the area of the square *abcd*.

2. *xyzw* is a parallelogram with diagonals intersecting at *o*. Write down the image of:

   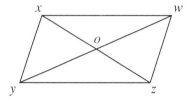

   (i) *z* under the translation $\overrightarrow{wx}$
   (ii) △*woz* under the central symmetry in *o*
   (iii) [*yz*] under the translation $\overrightarrow{zw}$.
   If the area of △*xyz* = 3 cm², write down the area of the parallelogram *xyzw*.

3. *abcd* and *edfg* are squares. Write down the image of:

   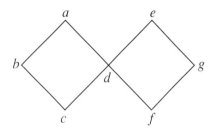

   (i) △*abc* under the central symmetry in *d*
   (ii) [*ab*] under the translation $\overrightarrow{cf}$
   (iii) *a* under the axial symmetry in *bg*
   (iv) [*eg*] under the translation $\overrightarrow{eb}$.

4. *pqrs* is a rectangle. The midpoint of [*qr*] is *k*, and the midpoint of [*ps*] is *z*.
   If |*xy*| = |*qk*|:

   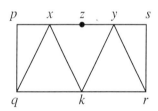

   (i) Name two parallelograms that are not rectangles.
   (ii) Name two angles equal in measure to ∠*xqk*.
   (iii) Find the image of △*xqk* under the translation $\overrightarrow{kr}$.
   (iv) Find the image of *x* under the central symmetry in *z*.
   (v) Find the image of △*ysr* under the axial symmetry in *kz*.
   If the area of △*pqx* is 6 cm², write down the area of the rectangle *pqkz*.

5. *abcd*, *cefg* and *hgji* are three identical rectangles.

x is the midpoint of [*cg*].

y is the midpoint of [*ef*].

Find the image of:

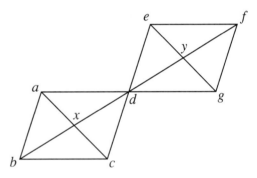

(i)   *a* under the central symmetry in *c*

(ii)   *i* under the central symmetry in *g*

(iii)   [*bc*] under the translation $\overrightarrow{ad}$

(iv)   [*bx*] under the translation $\overrightarrow{xj}$

(v)   the rectangle *abcd* under the translation $\overrightarrow{hj}$

(vi)   △*hgj* under the central symmetry in *g*

(vii) the rectangle *abcd* under the central symmetry in *c*

(viii) *e* under axial symmetry in the line *bj*

(ix)   △*abc* under the axial symmetry in the line *xy*

(x)   the rectangle *hgji* under the axial symmetry in the line *xy*.

If the area of △*abc* = 5 cm², what is the area of the three rectangles added together?

Name the translation under which △*efg* is the image of △*bcd*.

6. *abcd* and *edgf* are identical parallelograms. Supply the missing letters:

(i) $|ad| = |b\quad| = |\quad g|$

(ii) $|bx| = |x\quad| = |\quad y|$

(iii) $|xy| = |a\quad| = |\quad f|$

Find the image of:

(iv)   *d* under the translation $\overrightarrow{bc}$

(v)   [*ed*] under the translation $\overrightarrow{ad}$

(vi)   △*adx* under the central symmetry in *d*

(vii) △*efy* under the central symmetry in *y*

(viii) [*ax*] under the translation $\overrightarrow{bd}$.

Name a translation under which:

(ix)   [*dc*] is the image of [*ab*]

(x)   △*abd* is the image of △*edf*.

Name the central symmetry under which:

(xi)   [*fy*] is the image of [*dy*]

(xii) △*cdx* is the image of △*abx*.

If the area of parallelogram *abcd* is 40 cm², what is the area of △*eyf*?

CO-ORDINATE GEOMETRY

Co-ordinating the plane, and plotting points

A system for describing the position of points on a plane is to draw two perpendicular lines with equal scales intersecting at a point called the origin. The origin is the reference for describing any other point on the plane.

The horizontal line is called the '**x axis**'.

The vertical line is called the '**y axis**'.

The plane is called the '**Cartesian**' (kar-tee-zi-an) plane.

Every point on the plane has two co-ordinates, the x co-ordinate and the y co-ordinate.

Co-ordinates are an ordered pair of numbers, such as $(3, 4)$.

The co-ordinates of any point p are (x, y)

x co-ordinate, y co-ordinate

The first number, x, is always '**across, left or right,**'

and the second number, y, is always '**up or down.**'

Note: The co-ordinates of the origin are $o(0, 0)$.

Example ▼

Draw the x axis from -4 to 4 and the y axis from -3 to 3. Plot the points $a(2, 3)$, $b(3, 2)$, $c(-4, 2)$, $d(-3, -1)$, $e(4, -3)$, $f(1, -1)$, $g(2, 0)$, and $h(0, -3)$.

Solution:

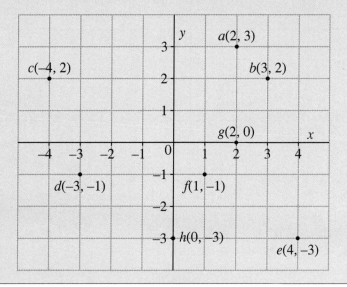

Order is very important. Notice that $a(2, 3) \neq b(3, 2)$.

The points $a(2, 3)$ and $b(3, 2)$ have different positions on the co-ordinated plane.

The word 'axis' means '**line**'. The plural of axis is '**axes**'.

Remember:

x before y

The four quadrants

The intersecting x axis and y axis divide the plane into four regions called '**quadrants**' and are numbered 1, 2, 3, and 4, as shown on the right.

2nd quadrant	1st quadrant
x negative	x positive
y positive	y positive

3rd quadrant	4th quadrant
x negative	x positive
y negative	y negative

Exercise 22.1 ▼

1. Write down the co-ordinates of the points a to z shown on the Cartesian plane:

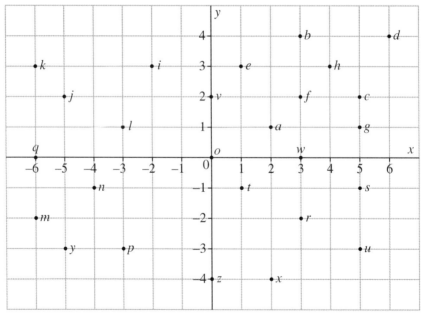

2. Draw a diagram of the co-ordinated plane, with x from -5 to 5 and y from -4 to 4. Plot the following points:

$a(3, 2)$, $b(1, 4)$, $c(5, 3)$, $d(4, 1)$, $e(1, 1)$, $f(-5, 4)$, $g(-2, 3)$, $h(-4, 1)$
$i(-2, 2)$, $j(-4, -2)$, $k(-3, -4)$, $l(-2, -2)$, $m(-5, -3)$, $n(2, -2)$, $o(0, 0)$ $p(4, -1)$,
$q(5, -3)$, $r(1, -4)$, $s(3, 0)$, $t(0, 3)$, $u(-2, 0)$, $v(0, -4)$

3. Draw a diagram of the co-ordinated plane, with x from -1 to 4 and y from -1 to 5.

   (i) Plot the points $a(-1, 4)$, $b(0, 3)$, $c(1, 2)$, $d(2, 1)$, $e(3, 0)$, and $f(4, -1)$.
      Join a to f. What do you notice?

   (ii) Plot the points $g(0, 5)$ and $h(2, 3)$. Join a to g, g to h, and c to h.
      What type of figure is $achg$?

   (iii) Plot the points $i(-1, 2)$ and $j(2, -1)$. Join a to i, i to j, and j to d.
      (a) What type of figure is $aijd$?
      (b) What type of triangle is $\triangle$ ahe?

4. On which axis is each of the following points?
   $a(5, 0)$, $b(0, -2)$, $c(0, 0)$, $d(0, 7)$, $e(-4, 0)$, $f(2, 0)$.

5. Give the co-ordinates of any two points in the
   (i) 1st quadrant   **(ii)** 2nd quadrant   **(iii)** 3rd quadrant   **(iv)** 4th quadrant.

6. Say to which quadrant each of the following points belongs:
   $a(4, 5)$, $b(3, -2)$, $c(-4, 6)$, $d(-3, 5)$, $e(-1, -4)$, $f(-2, -5)$, $g(1, -3)$.

7. Draw a diagram of the co-ordinated plane, with x from 0 to 8 and y from 0 to 7.
   (i) Plot the points $a(1, 1)$, $b(2, 3)$, and $d(4, 7)$. Join a to d.
      Find the value of k if the point $c(3, k)$ is on the line joining a to d.

   (ii) Plot the points $p(2, 1)$, $r(6, 3)$, and $s(8, 4)$. Join p to s.
      Find the value of t if the point $q(t, 2)$ is on the line joining p to s.

Translations

Under a translation, every point moves the **same distance** and in the **same direction**.
When using translations, we look for the **rule** that maps (moves) the points and then apply this rule to the co-ordinates whose images we want to find.

Suppose $a(3, -1)$ and $b(5, -4)$ are two points.
Then the translation (movement) $a \rightarrow b$ can be written $(3, -1) \rightarrow (5, -4)$.
Under this translation:

1. x goes from 3 to 5, i.e. add 2 to x.
2. y goes from -1 to -4, i.e. subtract 3 from y.

This gives the rule: (add 2 to x, subtract 3 from y)
        or $(x, y) \rightarrow (x + 2, y - 3)$.

Note: The translation $a \rightarrow b$ is usually written $\overrightarrow{ab}$.

We will look at two methods of finding the images of points under a translation:

1. Mathematical method   **2.** Graphical method

$p(-2, 4)$ and $q(1, -1)$ are two points. Find the image of the point $(-1, 3)$ under the translation $\overrightarrow{pq}$.

Solution:
Under the translation $\overrightarrow{pq}$, $(-2, 4) \rightarrow (1, -1)$.
          Rule: add 3 to x, subtract 5 from y.

1. **Mathematical method:** (apply the rule directly)
   $(-1, 3) \rightarrow (-1 + 3, 3 - 5) = (2, -2)$
   Therefore the image of $(-1, 3)$ is $(2, -2)$

2. **Graphical method:**
   Plot the point $(-1, 3)$ on the co-ordinated plane.
   Split the move into two parts:
   • horizontal: three steps to the right (add 3 to x)
   • vertical: five steps down (subtract 5 from y)
   Therefore the image of $(-1, 3)$ is $(2, -2)$.

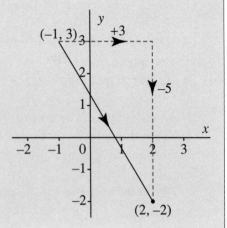

Exercise 22.2 ▼

1. Find the image of the point $(4, 5)$ under the translation $(2, 3) \rightarrow (6, 5)$.
2. Find the image of the point $(3, 2)$ under the translation $(5, 2) \rightarrow (7, 6)$.
3. Find the image of the point $(2, 3)$ under the translation $(1, 4) \rightarrow (4, 2)$.
4. Find the image of the point $(4, 3)$ under the translation $(5, -4) \rightarrow (3, -7)$.
5. Find the image of $(-1, 5)$ under the translation that maps $(2, -1) \rightarrow (-1, 3)$.
6. Find the image of each of the following points under the translation that maps $(0, 5) \rightarrow (2, 4)$:
   (i) $(6, 2)$ **(ii)** $(3, -1)$ **(iii)** $(-4, -3)$ **(iv)** $(-6, 0)$.
7. $a(1, -3)$ and $b(4, -5)$ are two points.
   Find the image of each point under the translation $\overrightarrow{ab}$:
   (i) $(4, -1)$ **(ii)** $(-2, 6)$ **(iii)** $(-5, -2)$ **(iv)** $(9, 5)$
   What is the image of $(1, 1)$ under the translation $\overrightarrow{ba}$?
8. t is the translation $(1, 5) \rightarrow (0, 7)$. Find the image of the point $(4, 5)$ under t.
9. $a(-1, 1)$, $b(3, -2)$ and $c(-2, 6)$ are three points. Find the image of the point c under the translation that maps $a \rightarrow b$.
10. (p, q) is the image of $(1, 2)$ under the translation $(3, 4) \rightarrow (5, 5)$. Find (p, q).

Axial symmetry in the axes and central symmetry in the origin

Note:

> S_x means 'axial symmetry in the x axis'
> S_y means 'axial symmetry in the y axis'
> S_o means 'central symmetry in the origin'

Again we will look at two methods of finding the images of points under axial symmetry in the axes and central symmetry in the origin.

1. Mathematical method.
The following three patterns emerge, and it is worth memorising them:

> **1.** Axial symmetry in the x axis $\rightarrow$ **change the sign of y.**
> **2.** Axial symmetry in the y axis $\rightarrow$ **change the sign of x.**
> **3.** Central symmetry in the origin, $(0, 0)$ $\rightarrow$ **change the sign of both x and y.**

2. Graphical method.

> Plot the point on the co-ordinated plane and use your knowledge of axial symmetry and central symmetry to find the image.

Example ▼

Find the image of $(3, 2)$ under: **(i)** S_x **(ii)** S_y **(iii)** S_o

Solution:
1. Mathematical method
   (i) $S_x(3, 2) = (3, -2)$ (change the sign of y)
   (ii) $S_y(3, 2) = (-3, 2)$ (change the sign of x)
   (iii) $S_o(3, 2) = (-3, -2)$ (change the sign of both x and y)

2. Graphical method
   From the graph it can be seen that
   (i) $S_x(3, 2) = (3, -2)$
   (ii) $S_y(3, 2) = (-3, 2)$
   (iii) $S_o(3, 2) = (-3, -2)$

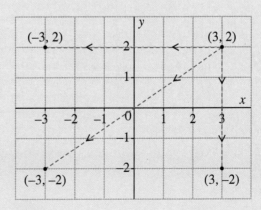

Complete the following table. (If you are using the graphical method, construct your diagram with both *x* and *y* between −5 and 5.)

	Point	Axial symmetry in the *x* axis, S_x	Axial symmetry in the *y* axis, S_y	Central symmetry in the origin, S_o
1.	$(4, 2)$	$(4, 2)$		
2.	$(3, 1)$		$(-3, 1)$	
3.	$(2, 3)$			$(-2, -3)$
4.	$(5, -3)$			
5.	$(4, -5)$			
6.	$(-3, -2)$			
7.	$(-4, 3)$			
8.	$(2, -5)$			
9.	$(3, 0)$			
10.	$(0, -2)$			

11. Find the image of the point $(-3, 4)$ under:
    (i) axial symmetry in the *x* axis, S_x.
    (ii) axial symmetry in the *y* axis, S_y.
    (iii) central symmetry in the origin, S_o.
12. Copy the diagram.

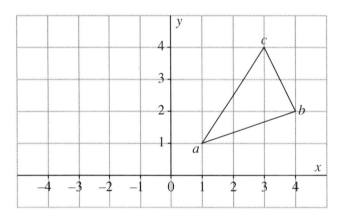

Write down the co-ordinates of the points *a*, *b*, and *c*.
Under the axial symmetry in the *y* axis, draw the image of the △*abc* in the diagram.

Distance between two points

If (x_1, y_1) and (x_2, y_2) are two points, the distance between them is given by the formula

$$D = \sqrt{(x_2 - x_1)^2 + (y_2 - y_1)^2}$$

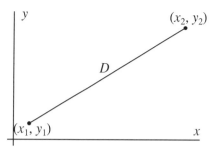

Example ▼

Find the distance between the points

(i) $(5, 2)$ and $(8, 6)$ **(ii)** $(6, -1)$ and $(5, 7)$.

Solution:

(i) $(5, 2)$ and $(8, 6)$
    (x_1, y_1) (x_2, y_2)
$x_1 = 5, y_1 = 2$ $x_2 = 8, y_2 = 6$
$D = \sqrt{(x_2 - x_1)^2 + (y_2 - y_1)^2}$
  $= \sqrt{(8 - 5)^2 + (6 - 2)^2}$
  $= \sqrt{(3)^2 + (4)^2}$
  $= \sqrt{9 + 16}$
  $= \sqrt{25}$
  $= 5$

(ii) $(6, -1)$ and $(5, 7)$
    (x_1, y_1) (x_2, y_2)
$x_1 = 6, y_1 = -1$ $x_2 = 5, y_2 = 7$
$D = \sqrt{(x_2 - x_1)^2 + (y_2 - y_1)^2}$
  $= \sqrt{(5 - 6)^2 + (7 + 1)^2}$
  $= \sqrt{(-1)^2 + (8)^2}$
  $= \sqrt{1 + 64}$
  $= \sqrt{65}$
(leave your answer as $\sqrt{65}$)

Note: Always decide which point is (x_1, y_1) and which point is (x_2, y_2) before you use the formula. The distance between the points a and b is written $|ab|$.

Exercise 22.4 ▼

Find the distance between each of the following pairs of points:

1. $(5, 2)$ and $(8, 6)$
2. $(1, 1)$ and $(7, 9)$
3. $(1, 2)$ and $(6, 14)$
4. $(3, 4)$ and $(5, 5)$
5. $(4, 3)$ and $(8, 1)$
6. $(2, 3)$ and $(5, 5)$
7. $(1, -1)$ and $(2, 3)$
8. $(3, 0)$ and $(-2, 1)$
9. $(-2, 2)$ and $(3, -1)$
10. $(3, -6)$ and $(-3, -4)$
11. $(2, -4)$ and $(-4, 2)$
12. $(-7, -2)$ and $(-3, -6)$

13. $a(3, -2)$, $b(-2, 1)$ and $c(1, 6)$ are three points. Show that $|ba| = |bc| = \sqrt{34}$.
14. A circle has centre $c(2, 2)$, and the point $d(5, 6)$ is on its circumference. Calculate $|cd|$, its radius.
15. $p(2, 1)$, $q(2, 5)$, $r(5, 4)$ and $s(3, 3)$ are four points. Show that $|ps| = |qs| = |rs|$.

16. $a(1, 1)$, $b(4, 5)$ and $c(7, 9)$ are three points. Simplify the ratio $|ab| : |ac|$.

17. $w(1, 3)$, $x(5, 1)$, $y(6, 3)$ and $z(2, 5)$ are the vertices of the rectangle $wxyz$.
Verify that **(i)** $|wx| = |zy|$ **(ii)** $|wz| = |xy|$ **(iii)** $|wy| = |xz|$.

18. $o(0, 0)$, $a(3, 1)$ and $b(2, 2)$ are three points. Verify that $|ao| > |bo|$.

Midpoint of a line segment

If (x_1, y_1) and (x_2, y_2) are two points, their midpoint is given by the formula:

$$\text{Midpoint} = \left(\frac{x_1 + x_2}{2}, \frac{y_1 + y_2}{2} \right)$$

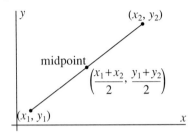

In words: $\left(\dfrac{\text{add the } xs}{2}, \dfrac{\text{add the } ys}{2} \right)$

Example ▼

$p(5, 6)$ and $q(7, -4)$ are two points. Find the midpoint of $[pq]$.

Solution:

$(5, 6)$	$(7, -4)$	$x_1 = 5$,	$y_1 = 6$
(x_1, y_1)	(x_2, y_2)	$x_2 = 7$,	$y_2 = -4$

$$\text{Midpoint} = \left(\frac{x_1 + x_2}{2}, \frac{y_1 + y_2}{2} \right)$$

$$= \left(\frac{5 + 7}{2}, \frac{-4 + 6}{2} \right) = \left(\frac{12}{2}, \frac{2}{2} \right) = (6, 1)$$

Rough diagram: ●————————●————————●
$\quad\quad\quad\quad\quad p(5, 6) \quad\quad (6, 1) \quad\quad q(7, -4)$

Exercise 22.5 ▼

Find the midpoint of the line segment joining each of the points:

1. $(3, 2)$ and $(5, 4)$ **2.** $(1, 1)$ and $(5, 9)$ **3.** $(0, 4)$ and $(2, 2)$

4. $(5, 4)$ and $(7, 2)$ **5.** $(10, 3)$ and $(-4, 1)$ **6.** $(2, 1)$ and $(8, 9)$

7. $(5, -1)$ and $(3, -3)$ **8.** $(-8, 7)$ and $(4, -3)$ **9.** $(8, 8)$ and $(-2, -2)$

10. $(-7, 5)$ and $(9, -7)$ **11.** $(7, 1)$ and $(-4, 4)$ **12.** $(2\frac{1}{2}, 1\frac{1}{4})$ and $(3\frac{1}{2}, \frac{3}{4})$

13. Find the co-ordinates of m, the midpoint of the line segment joining $p(7, 4)$ and $q(-1, -2)$.
Show that $|pm| = |qm|$.

14. The diagram shows the $\triangle abc$ with vertices $a(2, 1)$, $b(6, 3)$, and $c(4, 5)$. Copy the diagram. Calculate the co-ordinates of p, q, and r, the midpoints of the sides of the triangle. Verify that $|ap| = |rq|$ and $|qb| = |rp|$.

15. Show that the midpoint of the line segment joining $(4, -2)$ and $(6, 2)$ is on the x axis.

16. The parallelogram $abcd$ has vertices $a(6, 3)$, $b(4, -1)$, $c(-2, -1)$, and $d(0, 3)$. Find the point m, where the diagonals intersect. Show that $|am| = |mc|$ and $|bm| = |md|$.

17. $a(6, 4)$ and $b(2, 0)$ are two points. Calculate the midpoint of $[ab]$. Find the distance from $(7, 5)$ to the midpoint of $[ab]$.

18. $a(-3, 2)$ and $e(9, 10)$ are two points.

(i) Calculate the co-ordinates of c, the midpoint of $[ae]$.

(ii) Calculate the co-ordinates of b, the midpoint of $[ac]$.

(iii) Calculate the co-ordinates of d, the midpoint of $[ce]$.

Verify that $|ab| = |de|$.

Slope for a line

We read words on a page from left to right. A slope is also read from left to right.

$$m = \text{slope} = \frac{\text{vertical change}}{\text{horizontal change}}$$

Note: The letter m is usually used to denote the slope of a line.

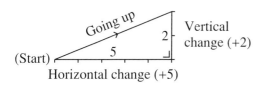

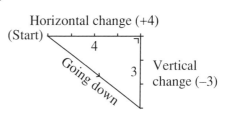

$$m = \text{slope} = \frac{\text{vertical change}}{\text{horizontal change}} = \frac{2}{5}$$

(positive slope, going up)

$$m = \text{slope} = \frac{\text{vertical change}}{\text{horizontal change}} = \frac{-3}{4} = -\frac{3}{4}$$

(negative slope, going down)

Slope of a line containing the two points (x_1, y_2) and (x_2, y_2)

If a line contains the two points (x_1, y_1) and (x_2, y_2), then the slope of the line is given by the formula

$$m = \frac{y_2 - y_1}{x_2 - x_1}$$

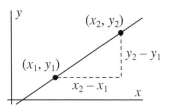

Example ▼

Find the slope of the line containing the points $(-1, 3)$ and $(4, 1)$.

Solution:

$$(-1, 3) \qquad (4, 1) \qquad x_1 = -1 \qquad y_1 = 3$$
$$(x_1, y_1) \qquad (x_2, y_2) \qquad x_2 = 4 \qquad y_2 = 1$$

$$\text{Slope} = m = \frac{y_2 - y_1}{x_2 - x_1} = \frac{1 - 3}{4 + 1} = \frac{-2}{5} = -\frac{2}{5}$$

Parallel lines have equal slopes

Consider the parallel lines L_1 and L_2.
Let m_1 be the slope of L_1
and m_2 be the slope of L_2.
If $L_1 \| L_2$, then $m_1 = m_2$.
i.e. L_1 and L_2 have equal slopes.

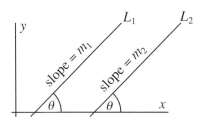

Example ▼

$a(2, 4)$, $b(7, 8)$, $c(2, 0)$ and $d(7, 4)$ are four points. Show that $ab \| cd$.

Solution:

Let $m_1 = $ the slope of ab and $m_2 = $ the slope of cd.

$$a(2, 4) \qquad b(7, 8) \qquad x_1 = 2 \qquad\qquad c(2, 0) \qquad d(7, 4) \qquad x_1 = 2$$
$$(x_1, y_1) \qquad (x_2, y_2) \qquad y_1 = 4 \qquad\qquad (x_1, y_1) \qquad (x_2, y_2) \qquad y_1 = 0$$
$$x_2 = 7 \qquad\qquad\qquad\qquad\qquad\qquad\qquad x_2 = 7$$
$$y_2 = 8 \qquad\qquad\qquad\qquad\qquad\qquad\qquad y_2 = 4$$

$$m_1 = \frac{y_2 - y_1}{x_2 - x_1} \qquad\qquad\qquad\qquad m_2 = \frac{y_2 - y_1}{x_2 - x_1}$$

$$= \frac{8 - 4}{7 - 2} \qquad\qquad\qquad\qquad\qquad = \frac{4 - 0}{7 - 2}$$

$$= \frac{4}{5} \qquad\qquad\qquad\qquad\qquad\qquad = \frac{4}{5}$$

$$m_1 = m_2$$
Therefore $ab \| cd$

Find the slope of the line containing each of the given pairs of points:

1. $(1, 4)$ and $(5, 7)$ **2.** $(3, 2)$ and $(5, 3)$ **3.** $(2, 2)$ and $(7, 4)$

4. $(3, 2)$ and $(8, 6)$ **5.** $(4, 8)$ and $(7, 9)$ **6.** $(2, 1)$ and $(7, 8)$

7. $(4, 3)$ and $(7, 5)$ **8.** $(1, 1)$ and $(5, 2)$ **9.** $(2, 3)$ and $(6, 8)$

10. $(3, 2)$ and $(7, 8)$ **11.** $(2, 3)$ and $(5, 1)$ **12.** $(-1, -2)$ and $(3, 2)$

13. $(-7, 3)$ and $(-5, 1)$ **14.** $(-3, -6)$ and $(-5, -4)$ **15.** $(2, 3)$ and $(-3, -7)$

16. $a(-2, -1)$, $b(1, 3)$, $c(1, 1)$ and $d(4, 5)$ are four points. Show that $ab \,||\, cd$.

17. $p(-6, 6)$, $q(-1, 4)$, $r(1, 1)$ and $s(6, -1)$ are four points. Show that $pq \,||\, rs$.

18. Plot the points $a(-1, 6)$, $b(4, 5)$, $c(3, -2)$, and $d(-2, -1)$.

   (i)   Verify that $ab \,||\, dc$ and $ad \,||\, bc$.

   (ii) Verify that $|ab| = |dc|$ and $|ad| = |bc|$.

   (iii) Plot m, the midpoint of $[ac]$.

   (iv) Verify that $|am| = |mc|$ and $|bm| = |md|$.

   Is $am \,||\, bm$? Give a reason for your answer.

Equation of a line I

Let us plot the points $(-1, 5)$, $(0, 4)$, $(1, 3)$, $(2, 2)$, $(3, 1)$, $(4, 0)$, and $(5, -1)$.

The points all lie on the same straight line. In this set of points there is the same relationship (connection, link) between the x coordinate and the y co-ordinate for each point. If we add the co-ordinates of each point the result is always 4,

i.e. $x + y = 4$.

This result will hold for every other point on the line. We say '$x + y = 4$' is the equation of the line.

(**Note:** $x + y - 4 = 0$ is also the equation of the line.)

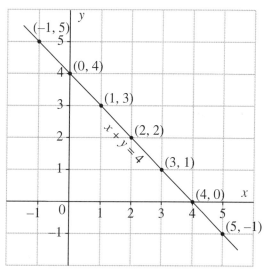

Let us now plot two other sets of points:
$L : (-2, 3), (-1, 3), (0, 3), (1, 3), (2, 3),$ and $(3, 3)$.
$K : (2, -1), (2, 0), (2, 1), (2, 2), (2, 3),$ and $(2, 4)$.
Is there a co-ordinate pattern?
In L all the points lie on the same straight line.
The y co-ordinate is **always** 3.
Therefore $y = 3$ is the equation of the line L.
In K all the points lie on the same straight line.
The x co-ordinate is **always** 2.
Therefore $x = 2$ is the equation of the line K.

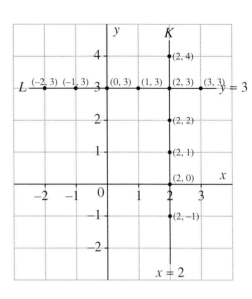

Note:

> $y = 0$ is the equation of the x axis
> $x = 0$ is the equation of the y axis

To verify that a point belongs to a line

If a point belongs to a line, its co-ordinates will satisfy the equation of the line.
We substitute the co-ordinates of the point in the equation of the line.
If they satisfy the equation, then the point is **on** the line. Otherwise, the point is **not** on the line.

Example ▼

Which of the points $(2, -1)$ and $(5, -4)$ is on the line $5x + 3y - 7 = 0$?

Solution:

$(2, -1)$
$5x + 3y - 7 = 0$
Substitute $x = 2$ and $y = -1$
$5(2) + 3(-1) - 7$
$= 10 - 3 - 7$
$= 10 - 10$
$= 0$
Satisfies equation
Therefore $(2, -1)$ is on the line

$(5, -4)$
$5x + 3y - 7 = 0$
Substitute $x = 5$ and $y = -4$
$5(5) + 3(-4) - 7$
$= 12 - 12 - 7$
$= 25 - 19$
$= 6 \neq 0$
Does not satisfy equation
Therefore $(5, -4)$ is not on the line

Exercise 22.7 ▼

Find which of the given points is on the corresponding line:

1. $(4, 1)$; $x + y - 5 = 0$
2. $(3, 1)$; $2x + 3y - 3 = 0$
3. $(2, 2)$; $5x - 4y - 1 = 0$
4. $(-3, -2)$; $6x - 7y + 4 = 0$

5. $(-4, 3);$ $3x + 2y - 8 = 0$

6. $(5, 2);$ $3x - 7y - 1 = 0$

7. $(-3, -1);$ $4x + y - 15 = 0$

8. $(-5, 2);$ $2x + 5y + 3 = 0$

9. $(1, 3);$ $3x - y = 0$

10. $(2, \frac{1}{2});$ $x - 4y = 0$

11. L is the line $x - 4y - 5 = 0$. Verify that the point $p(1, -1) \in L$.

12. M is the line $3x - 2y - 8 = 0$. Verify that the point $s(2, -1)$ is on M.

13. K is the line $3x - y - 11 = 0$. Investigate whether the points $a(2, -5)$ and $b(3, 2)$ are on the line K.

14. The point $(a, 4)$ is on the line $3x - 2y + 2 = 0$. Find the value of a.

15. The point $(-3, k)$ is on the line $5x + 4y + 3 = 0$. Find the value of k.

Graphing lines

To draw a line, only two points are needed. The easiest points to find are those where lines cut the x and y axes.

This is known as the **intercept method**. We use the following fact:

On the x axis $y = 0$. On the y axis $x = 0$.

To draw a line do the following:

1. Let $y = 0$ and find x.
2. Let $x = 0$ and find y.
3. Plot these two points.
4. Draw the line through these points.

Example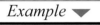

Graph the line $3x - 2y - 12 = 0$.

Solution:

1 and 2.

$$\begin{array}{c|c} \multicolumn{2}{c}{3x - 2y = 12} \\ \hline y = 0 & x = 0 \\ 3x = 12 & -2y = 12 \\ x = 4 & 2y = -12 \\ (4, 0) & y = -6 \\ & (0, -6) \end{array}$$

3. Plot the points $(4, 0)$ and $(0, -6)$.

4. Draw the line through these points.

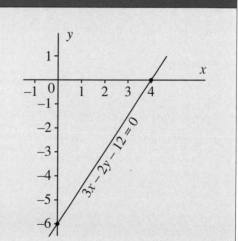

Graph each of the following lines:

1. $2x + 3y - 6 = 0$ **2.** $x + y - 5 = 0$ **3.** $3x - 5y + 15 = 0$

4. $2x - y - 4 = 0$ **5.** $x - y - 3 = 0$ **6.** $2x - 5y + 10 = 0$

7. $4x + 3y - 24 = 0$ **8.** $x - 3y - 12 = 0$ **9.** $4x + 5y + 40 = 0$

10. $x + y + 2 = 0$ **11.** $x + 2y - 6 = 0$ **12.** $x - y - 1 = 0$

13. Draw the line $2x + 3y - 12 = 0$. Show **(i)** graphically and **(ii)** algebraically that the point $(3, 2)$ is on the line.

14. $L : 2x + 3y - 12 = 0$ is a line. The line intersects the x axis at p and the y axis at q. Find the co-ordinates of p and q, without drawing the line.

Without graphing, find the co-ordinates of the points where each of the following lines meets both axes:

15. $x + y - 2 = 0$ **16.** $3x + 2y - 24 = 0$ **17.** $5x + y - 10 = 0$

18. $x + y + 1 = 0$ **19.** $x - 3y - 6 = 0$ **20.** $5x - 4y + 20 = 0$

Point of intersection of two lines

If two lines are non-parallel, then they must meet at one point. We call this point the **point of intersection**. The co-ordinates of this point will satisfy the equations of both lines. Therefore, we must find a point that **simultaneously** satisfies both equations.

We will use two methods:

1. Graph both lines.   **2.** Solve their equations simultaneously.

Example ▼

Graph the lines $x + 3y = 6$ and $x + y = 4$.

(i) From the graph, write down the point of intersection of the two lines.

(ii) Solve the simultaneous equations $x + 3y = 6$ and $x + y = 4$.

Solution:

$x + 3y = 6$	
$y = 0$	$x = 0$
$x = 6$	$3y = 6$
$(6, 0)$	$y = 2$
	$(0, 2)$

$x + y = 4$	
$y = 0$	$x = 0$
$x = 4$	$y = 4$
$(4, 0)$	$(0, 4)$

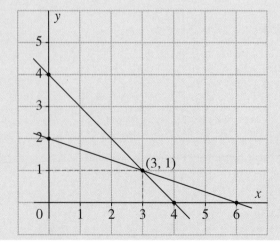

(i) From the graph, the point of intersection is (3, 1).

(ii) Number the equations

$$x + 3y = 6 \quad ①$$
$$x + y = 4 \quad ②$$

Subtract ② from ①

$$2y = 2$$

Divide both sides by 2

$$y = 1$$

Put $y = 1$ into ① or ②

$$x + y = 4 \quad ②$$
$$\downarrow$$
$$x + 1 = 4$$

Subtract 1 from both sides

$$x = 3$$

Therefore the point of intersection of both lines is (3, 1).

Exercise 22.9 ▼

Find the point of intersection of the following pairs of lines using two methods:

1. By graphing both lines and reading the point of intersection from the graph.
2. By solving the equations simultaneously.

1. $x + 2y = 4$ $x + y = 3$	**2.** $2x + y = 6$ $x + y = 5$	**3.** $3x + y = 6$ $x + y = 4$
4. $3x + 2y = 12$ $x + 2y = 8$	**5.** $2x + y = 8$ $x + y = 5$	**6.** $3x + y = 9$ $x + 2y = 8$
7. $x - y = 1$ $x + y = 3$	**8.** $5x + 4y = 40$ $x + 2y = 14$	**9.** $x + 2y = 6$ $x - 2y = 2$
10. $2x + y = 8$ $x - y = -2$	**11.** $3x + 2y = 12$ $3x - y = 3$	**12.** $2x + y = 6$ $x - 2y = -2$

Equation of a line 2

To find the equation of a line we need:

      1. The slope of the line, m **2.** A point on the line, (x_1, y_1)

Then use the formula: $(y - y_1) = m(x - x_1)$

In short: we need the **slope** and a **point**.

Find the equation of the following lines:

(i) containing the point $(2, -3)$ with slope 3.
(ii) containing the point $(-4, 2)$ with slope $-\frac{2}{3}$.

Solution:

(i) containing $(2, -3)$ with slope 3

$$x_1 = 2, \quad y_1 = -3, \quad m = 3$$
$$(y - y_1) = m(x - x_1)$$
$$\Rightarrow \quad (y + 3) = 3(x - 2)$$
$$\Rightarrow \quad y + 3 = 3x - 6$$
$$\Rightarrow \quad -3x + y + 3 + 6 = 0$$
$$\Rightarrow \quad -3x + y + 9 = 0$$
$$\Rightarrow \quad 3x - y - 9 = 0$$

(ii) containing $(-4, 2)$ with slope $-\frac{2}{3}$

$$x_1 = -4, \quad y_1 = 2, \quad m = -\frac{2}{3}$$
$$(y - y_1) = m(x - x_1)$$
$$\Rightarrow \quad (y - 2) = -\frac{2}{3}(x + 4)$$
$$\Rightarrow \quad 3(y - 2) = -2(x + 4)$$
(Multiply both sides by 3)
$$\Rightarrow \quad 3y - 6 = -2x - 8$$
$$\Rightarrow \quad 2x + 3y - 6 + 8 = 0$$
$$\Rightarrow \quad 2x + 3y + 2 = 0$$

Exercise 22.10 ▼

Find the equation of each of the following lines:

1. Containing $(4, 1)$ with slope 2
2. Containing $(2, 3)$ with slope 3
3. Containing $(1, 5)$ with slope 4
4. Containing $(3, 2)$ with slope 1
5. Containing $(2, 3)$ with slope -2
6. Containing $(5, -2)$ with slope -1
7. Containing $(-3, -2)$ with slope -3
8. Containing $(-1, -1)$ with slope -4
9. Containing $(0, -2)$ with slope 5
10. Containing $(0, 0)$ with slope -5
11. Containing $(5, -2)$ with slope $\frac{1}{2}$
12. Containing $(-1, -3)$ with slope $\frac{2}{3}$
13. Containing $(7, -2)$ with slope $-\frac{4}{5}$
14. Containing $(1, 1)$ with slope $-\frac{1}{2}$
15. Containing $(0, 0)$ with slope $-\frac{1}{4}$
16. Containing $(-3, -4)$ with slope $-\frac{2}{5}$
17. Find the equation of the line K through $(2, -1)$, the slope of K being -1.
18. Find the equation of the line L through $(3, -2)$, the slope of L being $-\frac{1}{2}$.

Equation of a line 3

To find the equation of a line we need the **slope** and **one point** on the line.
However, in many questions one or both of these are missing. Consider the following example:

Find the equation of the line that contains the points $(-4, 7)$ and $(1, 3)$.

Solution:
The slope is missing. We first find the slope and use **either one** of the two points to find the equation.

$(-4, 7)$ $(1, 3)$ $x_1 = -4$ containing $(-4, 7)$ with slope $-\frac{4}{5}$

(x_1, y_1) (x_2, y_2) $y_1 = 7$

$x_2 = 1$ $x_1 = -4,$ $y_1 = 7,$ $m = -\frac{4}{5}$

$y_2 = 3$

$m = \dfrac{y_2 - y_1}{x_2 - x_1}$

$\Rightarrow$ $(y - y_1) = m(x - x_1)$

$= \dfrac{3 - 7}{1 + 4}$

$\Rightarrow$ $(y - 7) = -\frac{4}{5}(x + 4)$

$= \dfrac{-4}{5}$

$\Rightarrow$ $5(y - 7) = -4(x + 4)$

(Multiply both sides by 5)

$= -\dfrac{4}{5}$

$\Rightarrow$ $5y - 35 = -4x - 16$

$\Rightarrow$ $4x + 5y - 35 + 16 = 0$

$\therefore m = -\dfrac{4}{5}$

$\Rightarrow$ $4x + 5y - 19 = 0$

Exercise 22.11 ▼

Find the equation of the line containing the given pair of points:

1. $(2, 5)$ and $(6, 9)$ **2.** $(1, 8)$ and $(3, 4)$ **3.** $(4, 4)$ and $(5, 7)$

4. $(3, 8)$ and $(5, 6)$ **5.** $(6, 6)$ and $(8, 10)$ **6.** $(4, 1)$ and $(2, 9)$

7. $(1, 6)$ and $(4, -3)$ **8.** $(-1, 2)$ and $(1, 10)$ **9.** $(-3, -5)$ and $(3, 1)$

10. $(-1, -2)$ and $(2, 4)$ **11.** $(1, 4)$ and $(3, 5)$ **12.** $(-4, -1)$ and $(-1, -2)$

13. $(-1, 5)$ and $(4, 7)$ **14.** $(2, 7)$ and $(4, 6)$ **15.** $(-1, 2)$ and $(2, 4)$

16. $a(-2, 2)$ and $b(1, 8)$ are two points.
    Find   **(i)** the slope of ab and   **(ii)** the equation of ab.

17. $p(5, 1)$ and $q(2, 7)$ are two points.
    Find   **(i)** the slope of pq and   **(ii)** the equation of pq.
    Show that the point $r(3, 5)$ is on the line pq.

18. $a(3, 5)$ and $b(1, 7)$ are two points. Find:
    (i) $|ab|$ **(ii)** the midpoint of $[ab]$
    (iii) the slope of ab **(iv)** the equation of ab.
    (v)   Verify that the point $c(-1, 9)$ is on the line ab.
    (vi) If the line ab contains the point $(k, 10)$, find the value of k.
    (vii) The line ab intersects the x axis at p and the y axis at q.
         Calculate the co-ordinates of p and q.

Formulas provided on the exam paper for the points (x_1, y_1) and (x_2, y_2):

Distance formula:	$\sqrt{(x_2 - x_1)^2 + (y_2 - y_1)^2}$
Midpoint formula:	$\left(\dfrac{x_1 + x_2}{2}, \dfrac{y_1 + y_2}{2}\right)$
Slope formula:	$m = \dfrac{y_2 - y_1}{x_2 - x_1}$
Equation of a line:	$(y - y_1) = m(x - x_1)$

Exercise 22.12 ▼

Chapter test

1. Find the image of the point $(-2, 2)$ under the translation $(0, 0) \rightarrow (7, 4)$.
2. Find the image of the point $(3, 4)$ under the axial symmetry in the y axis.
3. Find the image of the point $(2, -3)$ under the axial symmetry in the x axis.
4. Find the image of the point $(1, 3)$ under the central symmetry in the origin, $(0, 0)$.
5. Verify that the point $(2, 1)$ is on the line $3x + 2y - 8 = 0$.
6. The line $2x + 5y - 20 = 0$ cuts the x axis at the point p. Calculate the co-ordinates of the point p.
7. The line $3x - 4y + 8 = 0$ cuts the y axis at the point q. Calculate the co-ordinates of the point q.
8. The point $(k, 1)$ is on the line $5x + 3y - 13 = 0$. Calculate the value of k.
9. Find the midpoint of the line segment joining the points $(3, -2)$ and $(5, -4)$.
10. A line passes through the point $(2, -1)$ and has slope 3. Find the equation of the line.
11. The line $5x + 3y - 15 = 0$ cuts the x axis at p and the y axis at q.
    Find the co-ordinates of p and q and hence draw the line.
    Calculate the area of Δopq, where o is the origin, $(0, 0)$.
12. The line $3x - 4y - 12 = 0$ cuts the x axis at a and the y axis at b.
    Find the co-ordinates of a and b, and calculate $|ab|$.
13. On the same axis and scales, graph the lines $2x + y = 8$ and $x - 3y = -3$.
    (i) From the graph, write down the point of intersection of the lines.
    (ii) Solve the simultaneous equations to verify your answer in **(i)**.

14. The point $p(4, 2)$ is shown.
   (i) Copy the diagram and plot the point $q(-2, 4)$.
   (ii) Calculate the co-ordinates of k, the midpoint of $[pq]$.
   (iii) Calculate $|pk|$.
   (iv) Find the slope of pq.
   (v) Find the equation of pq.

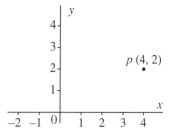

15. The point $p(4, 5)$ is shown.
   (i) Copy the diagram and plot the point $q(-2, 2)$.
   (ii) Show that $|pq| = \sqrt{45}$.
   (iii) Find the slope of pq.
   (iv) Find the equation of pq.
   (v) pq cuts the y axis at the point $d(0, y)$.
      Calculate the value of y. Hence, find the area of
      the triangle dpr, where r is the point $(0, 5)$.

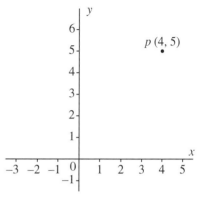

16. The point $a(2, 4)$ is shown in the diagram.
   (i) Copy the diagram, and on it plot the point
      $b(1, -2)$.
   (ii) Find the midpoint of $[ab]$.
   (iii) Find the slope of ab.
   (iv) Find the equation of ab.
   (v) Use your equation to find the co-ordinates of the
      point at which the line ab intersects the y axis.
   (vi) If the line ab contains the point $(k, 10)$, find the
      value of k.

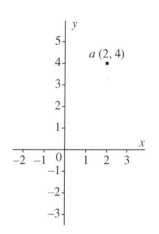

17. $b(3, 6)$ is a point, as in the diagram.
   (i) Copy the diagram and plot the point $a(-2, 1)$.
   (ii) Show that $|ab| = \sqrt{50}$.
   (iii) Find the slope of ab.
   (iv) Find the equation of the line ab.
   (v) Calculate the co-ordinates of the point q, where
      the line ab cuts the x axis.

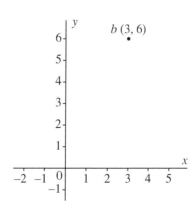

18. $a(3, 0)$ is a point, as in the diagram.

  (i) Copy the diagram, and on it plot the point $b(1, 2)$.

  (ii) Verify that $|ab| = \sqrt{8}$.

  (iii) q is the midpoint of $[ab]$.
  Find the co-ordinates of q, and plot q on your diagram.

  (iv) Find the slope of ab.

  (v) Find the equation of ab.

  (vi) The line ab cuts the y axis at c. Calculate the co-ordinates of c.

  (vii) Find the area of $\triangle ocq$, where o is $(0, 0)$.

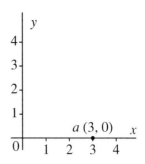

19. The point $p(-3, 1)$ is shown in the diagram.

  (i) Copy the diagram, and on it plot the point $q(1, 4)$.

  (ii) Find the slope of pq.

  (iii) Find the equation of pq.

  (iv) pq cuts the y axis at the point k.
  Calculate the co-ordinates of the point k.

  (v) Calculate the ratio $|pk|:|pq|$.
  Give your answer as a fraction.

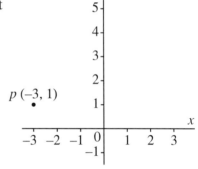

20. $a(1, 5)$ and $b(7, -1)$ are two points.

  (i) Verify that $|ab| = \sqrt{72}$.

  (ii) Find the co-ordinates of m, the midpoint of $[ab]$, and verify that $|am| = |mb|$.

  (iii) Find the slope ab.

  (iv) Find the equation of the line ab.

  (v) The line ab meets the x axis at p and the y axis at q.
  Calculate the co-ordinates of the points p and q.

  (vi) Verify that the points $a(1, 5)$, $b(7, -1)$ and $c(9, -3)$ are in a straight line.

FUNCTIONS

Terminology

Number machine: input to output

You can think of a function as a number machine that changes one number (input) into another number (output) according to some rule.

When the numbers (inputs) are entered, the machine works on them and produces other numbers (outputs).

Number machine

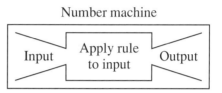

A function does exactly the same to each input number and produces only one output number for each input number.

The set of numbers that are put into a function is called the '**domain**'.
The set of numbers that comes out of a function is called the '**range**'.
A function connects **every** input in the domain to an input in the range.
A function is another way of writing an algebraic formula that links input to output.

Everyday examples of functions

This idea of a function has many everyday applications. Below are some examples of such applications:

---

1. **Bar-codes**. In a supermarket check-out machine, the bar-code on an item ('input') is transformed by the machine ('function') into a price ('output').
2. **Calculator**. If one of the 'function' keys is chosen, e.g. $\sqrt{\ }$, the number keyed in ('input') is transformed by the $\sqrt{\ }$ key ('function') into the answer ('output'), i.e. the square root of the number.
3. **Teletext**. When a particular screen, e.g. 'football scores', is required, the code number of that screen ('input') is transferred by the teletext machine ('function') into the relevant screen ('output').

Let us consider the number machine that applies the rule:

double the input and then add on 3

i.e. $2(\text{input}) + 3 = \text{output}$.

Let us look at what happens when we put in the numbers 0, 1, 2, 3, 4, and 5.
We set up the number machine in the form of a table.

Input (numbers put in)	Rule 2(input) + 3	Output (numbers that come out)
0	0 + 3	3
1	2 + 3	5
2	4 + 3	7
3	6 + 3	9
4	8 + 3	11
5	10 + 3	13

A function can be represented by a set of ordered pairs of couples (input, output):
i.e. $\{(0, 3), (1, 5), (2, 7), (3, 9), (4, 11), (5, 13)\}$

A function can also be represented by a table:

Input	0	1	2	3	4	5
Output	3	5	7	9	11	13

We can also see that:
domain $= \{0, 1, 2, 3, 4, 5\}$, the set of inputs.
range $= \{3, 5, 7, 9, 11, 13\}$, the set of outputs.

Exercise 23.1 ▼

In each case, complete the table by working out the outputs, and write out each function as a set of ordered pairs (inputs, outputs).
Write down the domain and range in each case.

1.

input	3(input) + 2	output
1		
2		
3		
4		
5		

2.

input	4(input) + 1	output
0		
2		
4		
6		
8		

3.

input	2(input) + 1	output
−3		
−2		
−1		
0		
1		
2		

4.

input	(input) + 3	output
−2		
−1		
0		
1		
2		
3		

5.

input	5(input) + 3	output
−5		
−4		
−3		
−2		
−1		
0		
1		
2		

6.

input	3(input) − 4	output
−2		
−1		
0		
1		
2		
3		
4		
5		

7.

input	2(input) − 5	output
−3		
−2		
−1		
0		
1		
2		

8.

input	(input) − 3	output
−1		
0		
1		
2		
3		
4		

9.

input	$(\text{input})^2 + 3$	output
0		
1		
2		
3		
4		
5		
6		

10.

input	$(\text{input})^2 + 3\,(\text{input})$	output
−2		
−1		
0		
1		
2		
3		
4		

Notation

A function changes input into output according to some rule.

Functions are often represented by the letter f.

For example, let's represent the function 'double input and then add one' by the letter f.

Then f is the rule that 'doubles input and then adds one.'

Let's look at this rule on a mapping diagram:

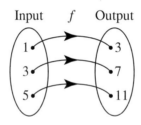

A mapping diagram is a diagram showing the linkage between inputs and outputs.

Generally, f changes x into $2x + 1$,

which can be written as: $f : x \rightarrow 2x + 1$ or $f(x) = 2x + 1$

$$(\text{input}, \text{output}) = (x, f(x)) = (x, 2x + 1)$$

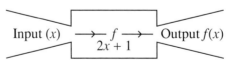

$f(x)$, which denotes the output, is read as 'f of x'.

Note: A **function** is also called a '**mapping**' or simply a '**map**'.

One number is mapped onto another number.

In the above example, x is mapped onto $2x + 1$, written $f : x \rightarrow 2x + 1$.

Input number

If $f(x) = 3x + 2$, then $f(1)$ means input 1 into the function
i.e. 'it is the result of applying f to the number 1.'

$$f(x) = 3x + 2$$
$$f(1) = 3(1) + 2 \qquad \text{(put in 1 for } x)$$
$$= 3 + 2$$
$$= 5 \qquad \text{(output)}$$
$$(\text{input, output}) = (1, f(1)) = (1, 5)$$

Example ▼

A function f is defined as $f : x \longrightarrow 3x + 4$.
Find the value of $f(2) + f(-3)$.

Solution:

$$f(x) = 3x + 4$$

$f(2) = 3(2) + 4$	$f(-3) = 3(-3) + 4$	Thus, $f(2) + f(-3)$
$\quad = 6 + 4$	$\quad = -9 + 4$	$\quad = 10 - 5$
$\quad = 10$	$\quad = -5$	$\quad = 5$

Example ▼

A function f is defined as $f : x \longrightarrow 2x^2 + 3$.
Find **(i)** $f(1)$ **(ii)** $f(-2)$ **(iii)** $f(3)$.

Solution:

$$f(x) = 2x^2 + 3$$

(i) $f(1) = 2(1)^2 + 3$	**(ii)** $f(-2) = 2(-2)^2 + 3$	**(iii)** $f(3) = 2(3)^2 + 3$
$\quad = 2(1) + 3$	$\quad = 2(4) + 3$	$\quad = 2(9) + 3$
$\quad = 2 + 3$	$\quad = 8 + 3$	$\quad = 18 + 3$
$\quad = 5$	$\quad = 11$	$\quad = 21$

Exercise 23.2 ▼

1. A function f is defined as $f : x \longrightarrow 2x + 5$.
    Find **(i)** $f(1)$ **(ii)** $f(2)$ **(iii)** $f(3)$ **(iv)** $f(4)$.

2. A function f is defined as $f : x \longrightarrow 3x + 4$.
    Find **(i)** $f(0)$ **(ii)** $f(2)$ **(iii)** $f(4)$ **(iv)** $f(6)$.

3. A function f is defined as $f : x \longrightarrow 4x + 3$.
    Find **(i)** $f(5)$ **(ii)** $f(1)$ **(iii)** $f(3)$ **(iv)** $f(2)$.

4. A function f is defined as $f : x \rightarrow 2x - 3$.

    Find   **(i)** $f(2)$ **(ii)** $f(0)$ **(iii)** $f(3)$ **(iv)** $f(6)$.

5. A function f is defined as $f : x \rightarrow 3x - 1$.

    Find   **(i)** $f(0)$ **(ii)** $f(-1)$ **(iii)** $f(1)$ **(iv)** $f(-2)$.

6. A function f is defined as $f : x \rightarrow 5x - 2$.

    Find   **(i)** $f(1)$ **(ii)** $f(2)$ **(iii)** $f(-1)$ **(iv)** $f(-2)$.

7. A function f is defined as $f : x \rightarrow x + 2$.

    Find   **(i)** $f(3)$ **(ii)** $f(5)$ **(iii)** $f(1) + f(-3)$ **(iv)** $2f(4)$.

8. A function f is defined as $f : x \rightarrow 3x$.

    Find   **(i)** $f(-2)$ **(ii)** $f(-1)$ **(iii)** $f(1) + f(2)$ **(iv)** $5f(2)$.

9. A function f is defined as $f : x \rightarrow 1 - x$.

    Find   **(i)** $f(1)$ **(ii)** $f(-1)$ **(iii)** $f(-3) + f(2)$ **(iv)** $4f(-2)$.

    Verify that $f(3) < 0$.

10. A function f is defined as $f : x \rightarrow 3 - 2x$.

    Find   **(i)** $f(0)$ **(ii)** $f(1)$ **(iii)** $f(2)$ **(iv)** $f(-1) - f(0)$.

    Verify that $f(-2) > 0$.

11. A function f is defined as $f : x \rightarrow 2x^2 + 5$.

    Find   **(i)** $f(1)$ **(ii)** $f(2)$ **(iii)** $f(-1)$ **(iv)** $f(-2)$.

    Verify that $f(3) = f(-3)$.

12. A function f is defined as $f : x \rightarrow \sqrt{x}$.

    Find   **(i)** $f(4)$ **(ii)** $f(9)$ **(iii)** $f(16)$ **(iv)** $f(1)$ **(v)** $f(0)$.

    Verify that $f(36) > f(25)$.

13. A function f is defined as $f : x \rightarrow x^2 + 2x$

    Find   **(i)** $f(1)$ **(ii)** $f(2)$ **(iii)** $f(-1)$ **(iv)** $f(-3)$.

    Find the two values of x for which $f(x) = 8$.

14. A function f is defined as $f : x \rightarrow x^2 - 3x - 4$.

    Find   **(i)** $f(1)$ **(ii)** $f(2)$ **(iii)** $f(3)$.

    Find the two values of x for which $f(x) = 0$.

Representing functions with mapping diagrams and sets of couples

Functions can also be represented by mapping diagrams or sets of couples, or both. Consider the next example.

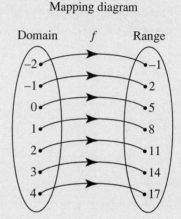

Example ▼

A function f is defined as $f : x \rightarrow 3x + 5$. The domain of f is $\{-2, -1, 0, 1, 2, 3, 4\}$.
Represent f **(i)** with a mapping diagram **(ii)** as a set of couples.
Write down the range of f.

Solution:
A table is used to work out the couples. The domain $= \{-2, -1, 0, 1, 2, 3, 4\}$.

(i) Mapping diagram

x	$3x + 5$	$f(x)$
-2	$-6 + 5$	-1
-1	$-3 + 5$	2
0	$0 + 5$	5
1	$3 + 5$	8
2	$6 + 5$	11
3	$9 + 5$	14
4	$12 + 5$	17

(ii) $f = \{(-2, -1), (-1, 2), (0, 5), (1, 8), (2, 11), (3, 14), (4, 17)\}$
Range $= \{-1, 2, 5, 8, 11, 14, 17\}$

Exercise 23.3 ▼

1. A function f is defined as $f : x \rightarrow 2x + 5$. The domain of f is $\{1, 2, 3, 4, 5\}$.
   Find the range of f. Write f as a set of couples.
2. A function f is defined as $f : x \rightarrow 3x + 2$. The domain of f is $\{2, 4, 6, 8\}$.
   Find the range of f. Write f as a set of couples.
3. A function f is defined as $f : x \rightarrow 4x - 3$. The domain of f is $\{0, 1, 2, 3, 4\}$.
   Find the range of f. Write f as a set of couples.
4. A function f is defined as $f : x \rightarrow 2x - 1$. The domain of f is $\{-2, -1, 0, 1, 2, 3\}$.
   Find the range of f. Write f as a set of couples.
5. A function f is defined as $f : x \rightarrow x + 4$. The domain of f is $\{-3, -2, -1, 0, 1, 2\}$.
   Find the range of f. Write f as a set of couples.
6. $f : x \rightarrow 3x + 4$ is a function. The domain of f is $\{1, 2, 3\}$. Find the range of f.
7. $f : x \rightarrow 5x - 2$ is a function. The domain of f is $\{0, 1, 2\}$. Find the range of f.
8. $f : x \rightarrow 2x + 5$ is a function. The domain of f is $\{-2, -1, 0, 1, 2\}$. Find the range of f.
9. $f : x \rightarrow 3x - 5$ is a function. The domain of f is $\{-1, 0, 1, 2\}$. Find the range of f.
10. $f : x \rightarrow 1 - 2x$ is a function. The domain of f is $\{-2, 0, 2, 4\}$. Find the range of f.

Mapping diagrams with numbers missing

Sometimes we have to solve problems where parts of the domain and the range are missing. Consider the next example.

Example ▼

A function f is defined as $f : x \rightarrow 3x - 2$.
Copy the mapping diagram and fill in the missing numbers a, b, and c.

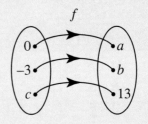

Solution:
$f(x) = 3x - 2$
$f(0) = 3(0) - 2 = 0 - 2 = -2$
$\therefore a = -2$

$f(-3) = 3(-3) - 2 = -9 - 2 = -11$
$\therefore b = -11$

To find c we are given an equation in disguise.

Given: Output = 13,   find input, c.
$\Rightarrow$ $f(x) = 13$
$\Rightarrow$ $3x - 2 = 13$
$\Rightarrow$ $3x = 15$
$\Rightarrow$ $x = 5$
Therefore $c = 5$

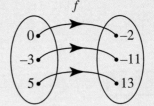

Exercise 23.4 ▼

1. A function f is defined as $f : x \rightarrow 2x + 3$.
   Copy the mapping diagram and fill in the missing numbers a, b, and c.

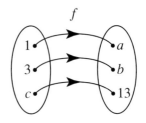

2. A function f is defined as $f : x \rightarrow 3x + 1$.
   Copy the mapping diagram and fill in the missing numbers p, q, and r.

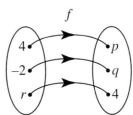

3. A function f is defined as $f : x \rightarrow 5x - 3$.
Copy the mapping diagram and fill in the missing numbers, a, b, and c.

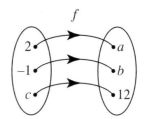

4. A function f is defined as $f : x \rightarrow 4x - 3$.
Copy the mapping diagram and fill in the missing numbers, r, s, and t.

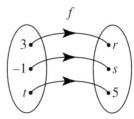

5. A function f is defined as $f : x \rightarrow 1 - x$.
Copy the mapping diagram and fill in the missing numbers x, y, and z.

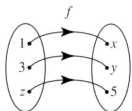

6. A function f is defined as $f : x \rightarrow 3x$.
Copy the mapping diagram and fill in the missing numbers, a, b and c in the domain.

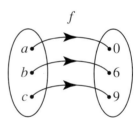

7. A function f is defined as $f : x \rightarrow x + 3$.
Fill in the missing numbers p, q, r and s of the following four couples of f:

(i) $(2, p)$ **(ii)** $(-2, q)$

(iii) $(r, 6)$ **(iv)** $(s, 0)$.

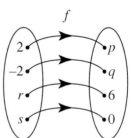

8. A function f is defined as $f : x \rightarrow 2x - 1$.
Fill in the missing numbers, a, b, c and d of the following four couples of f:
(i) $(5, a)$ **(ii)** $(-2, b)$ **(iii)** $(c, 5)$ **(iv)** $(d, 1)$.

9. A function f is defined as $f : x \rightarrow 4x + 1$. Complete the following four couples:
(i) $(2, \ )$ **(ii)** $(0, \ )$ **(iii)** $(\ , 5)$ **(iv)** $(\ , -3)$.

10. A function f is defined as $f : x \rightarrow 2x - 5$. Complete the following four couples:
(i) $(3, \ )$ **(ii)** $(-3, \ )$ **(iii)** $(\ , 3)$ **(iv)** $(\ , -7)$.

Chapter test

1. **(a)** A function f is defined as $f : x \rightarrow 2x + 5$.
    Find the value of **(i)** $f(4)$ **(ii)** $f(3)$.
    (b) A function f is defined as $f : x \rightarrow 3x + 4$.
    The domain of f is $\{-2, -1, 0, 1, 2\}$.
    Find the range of f.
    (c) A function f is defined as $f : x \rightarrow 4x + 1$.
    Copy the mapping diagram and fill in the
    missing numbers a, b, and c.

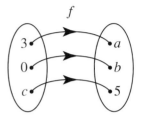

2. **(a)** A function f is defined as $f : x \rightarrow 2x - 3$.
    The domain of f is $\{-1, 0, 1, 2, 3, 4\}$.
    Represent f as a set of couples.
    (b) A function f is defined as $f : x \rightarrow 3x - 2$.
    Copy the mapping diagram and fill in the
    missing numbers p, q, and r.
    (c) A function f is defined as $f : x \rightarrow 5x + 3$.
    Find the value of
    (i) $f(2)$ **(ii)** $f(-1)$ **(iii)** $f(1) + f(0)$.
    Verify that $f(-2) < f(3)$.

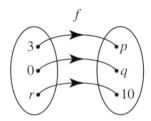

3. **(a)** A function is defined as the set of couples
    $f = \{(-2, -13), (-1, -8), (0, -3), (1, 2), (2, 7)\}$.
    Write down **(i)** the domain and **(ii)** the range of f.
    (b) A function f is defined in the following table:

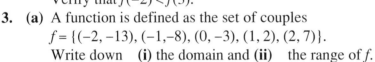

x	-2	-1	0	1	2	3	4	5
$f(x)$	10	4	0	-2	-2	0	4	10

    Write down **(i)** the domain and **(ii)** the range of f.
    (c) A function f is defined as $f : x \rightarrow 3x - 5$. The domain of f is $\{-2, -1, 0, 1, 2, 3\}$.
    Represent f as a set of couples. Write down the range of f.
    (d) A function is defined as $f : x \rightarrow 2x - 3$.
    Find the missing numbers a, b, c and d of the
    following four couples of f:
    (i) $(5, a)$
    (ii) $(-2, b)$
    (iii) $(c, 5)$
    (iv) $(d, -5)$.
    Graph on the number line the values of x for
    which $f(x) > 5$, $x \in \mathbf{R}$

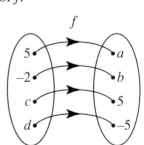

GRAPHING FUNCTIONS

Graphs

A function can be written as a set of couples, (input, output), (x, y) or $(x, f(x))$. When the couples are plotted and joined by a line or curve, we get the graph of the function. When graphing functions, always put the inputs, x, on the horizontal axis and the outputs, y or $f(x)$, on the vertical axis. A graph of a function is a diagram or picture showing the relationship (link) between the inputs and the outputs.

Note: It is very important not to draw a graph outside the given inputs (the given values of x).

Notation

The notation $y = f(x)$ means 'the value of the output y depends on the value of the input x, according to some rule called f. Hence, y and $f(x)$ are interchangeable, and the y axis can also be called the $f(x)$ axis.

Graphing linear functions

The first four letters in the word '**linear**' spell '**line**'. Therefore the graph of a linear function will be a straight line. A linear function is usually given in the form $f : x \rightarrow ax + b$, where $a \neq 0$ and a, b are constants. For example, $f : x \rightarrow 2x + 5$. As the graph is a straight line, two points are all that are needed to graph it. In the question, you will always be given a set of inputs, x, called the domain.

To graph a linear function do the following:

1. Choose two suitable values of x, in the given domain.
   (Two suitable values are the smallest and largest values of x.)
2. Substitute these in the function to find the two corresponding value of y.
3. Plot the points and draw the line through them.

Note: $-3 \leqslant x \leqslant 2$ means 'x is between -3 and 2, including -3 and 2.'

Graph the function $f : x \rightarrow 2x + 1$, in the domain $-3 \leqslant x \leqslant 2,$ $\quad x \in \mathbf{R}.$

Solution:

Let $y = f(x) \implies y = 2x + 1$

1. Let $x = -3$ and $x = 2$

2.

$$y = 2x + 1$$

$x = -3$	$x = 2$
$y = 2(-3) + 1$	$y = 2(2) + 1$
$y = -6 + 1$	$y = 4 + 1$
$y = -5$	$y = 5$
$(-3, -5)$	$(2, 5)$

3. Plot the points $(-3, -5)$ and $(2, 5)$ and join them with a straight line.

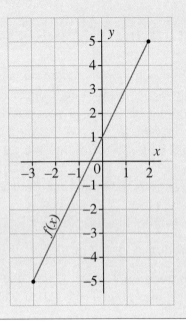

Graph each of the following functions in the given domain:

1.	$f : x \rightarrow 2x + 3$	in the domain	$-4 \leqslant x \leqslant 2,$	$x \in \mathbf{R}.$
2.	$g : x \rightarrow 3x + 1$	in the domain	$-2 \leqslant x \leqslant 3,$	$x \in \mathbf{R}.$
3.	$f : x \rightarrow 4x + 3$	in the domain	$-2 \leqslant x \leqslant 2,$	$x \in \mathbf{R}.$
4.	$g : x \rightarrow 5x + 1$	in the domain	$-1 \leqslant x \leqslant 4,$	$x \in \mathbf{R}.$
5.	$f : x \rightarrow 2x - 3$	in the domain	$-1 \leqslant x \leqslant 4,$	$x \in \mathbf{R}.$
6.	$g : x \rightarrow 3x - 5$	in the domain	$-2 \leqslant x \leqslant 4,$	$x \in \mathbf{R}.$
7.	$f : x \rightarrow x + 4$	in the domain	$-5 \leqslant x \leqslant 2,$	$x \in \mathbf{R}.$
8.	$g : x \rightarrow 2x$	in the domain	$-3 \leqslant x \leqslant 3,$	$x \in \mathbf{R}.$
9.	$f : x \rightarrow 3x$	in the domain	$-2 \leqslant x \leqslant 4,$	$x \in \mathbf{R}.$
10.	$g : x \rightarrow x - 2$	in the domain	$-3 \leqslant x \leqslant 4,$	$x \in \mathbf{R}.$
11.	$f : x \rightarrow 1 - x$	in the domain	$-1 \leqslant x \leqslant 5,$	$x \in \mathbf{R}.$
12.	$g : x \rightarrow 3 - 2x$	in the domain	$-1 \leqslant x \leqslant 4,$	$x \in \mathbf{R}.$
13.	$f : x \rightarrow 2 - 3x$	in the domain	$-2 \leqslant x \leqslant 4,$	$x \in \mathbf{R}.$
14.	$g : x \rightarrow -1 - x$	in the domain	$-3 \leqslant x \leqslant 4,$	$x \in \mathbf{R}.$
15.	$f : x \rightarrow 4 - 3x$	in the domain	$-2 \leqslant x \leqslant 4,$	$x \in \mathbf{R}.$
16.	$g : x \rightarrow -1 - 2x$	in the domain	$-3 \leqslant x \leqslant 3,$	$x \in \mathbf{R}.$

Graphing quadratic functions

A **quadratic** function is usually given in the form $f: x \rightarrow ax^2 + bx + c$, $a \neq 0$, and a, b, c are constants. For example, $f: x \rightarrow 2x^2 - x + 3$. Because of its shape, quite a few points are needed to plot the graph of a quadratic function. In the question, you will always be given a set of inputs, x, called the domain. With these inputs, a table is used to find the corresponding set of outputs, y or $f(x)$, called the range. When the table is completed, plot the points and join them with a '**smooth curve**'.

Notes on making out the table

1. Work out each column separately, i.e. all the x^2 values first, then all the x values, and finally the constant. (Watch for patterns in the numbers.)
2. Work out each corresponding value of y.
3. The **only** column that changes sign is the x term (middle) column. If the given values of x contain 0, then the x term column will make **one** sign change, either from + to − or from − to +, where $x = 0$.
4. The other two columns **never** change sign. They remain either all pluses or all minuses. These columns keep the sign given in the question.

Note: Decide where to draw the x and y axes by looking at the table to see what the largest and smallest values of x and y are. In general, the units on the x axis are larger than the units on the y axis. Try to make sure that the graph extends almost the whole width and length of the page.

Example ▼

Graph the function $f: x \rightarrow x^2 + 3x - 2$, in the domain $-5 \leqslant x \leqslant 2$, $\quad x \in \mathbf{R}$.

Solution:
A table is drawn with the given values of x, from −5 to 2, to find the corresponding values of y.

$$\text{Let } y = f(x) \quad \Rightarrow \quad y = x^2 + 3x - 2$$

x	$x^2 + 3x - 2$	y
−5	25 − 15 − 2	8
−4	16 − 12 − 2	2
−3	9 − 9 − 2	−2
−2	4 − 6 − 2	−4
−1	1 − 3 − 2	−4
0	0 + 0 − 2	−2
1	1 + 3 − 2	2
2	4 + 6 − 2	8

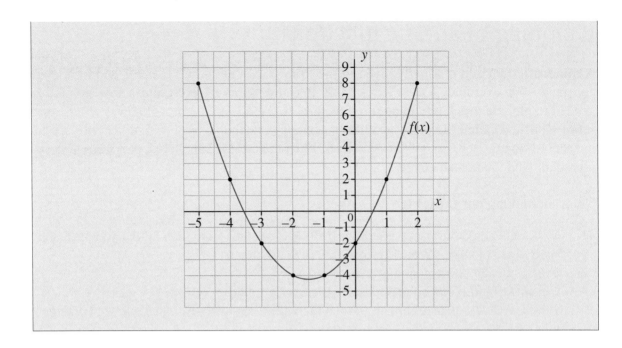

Exercise 24.2 ▼

Graph each of the following functions in the given domain:

1. $f : x \rightarrow x^2 + 2x - 8$ in the domain $-5 \leqslant x \leqslant 3$, $x \in R$.
2. $f : x \rightarrow x^2 - 3x + 2$ in the domain $-2 \leqslant x \leqslant 5$, $x \in R$.
3. $f : x \rightarrow x^2 - 2x - 3$ in the domain $-2 \leqslant x \leqslant 4$, $x \in R$.
4. $f : x \rightarrow x^2 + 3x - 4$ in the domain $-5 \leqslant x \leqslant 2$, $x \in R$.
5. $f : x \rightarrow x^2 + x - 6$ in the domain $-4 \leqslant x \leqslant 3$, $x \in R$.
6. $f : x \rightarrow x^2 - x - 2$ in the domain $-2 \leqslant x \leqslant 3$, $x \in R$.
7. $f : x \rightarrow x^2 - 7x + 6$ in the domain $0 \leqslant x \leqslant 7$, $x \in R$.
8. $f : x \rightarrow x^2 - 4x + 3$ in the domain $-1 \leqslant x \leqslant 5$, $x \in R$.
9. $f : x \rightarrow x^2 - 3x - 4$ in the domain $-2 \leqslant x \leqslant 5$, $x \in R$.
10. $f : x \rightarrow x^2 - 6x + 5$ in the domain $-1 \leqslant x \leqslant 7$, $x \in R$.
11. $f : x \rightarrow x^2 + 2x$ in the domain $-4 \leqslant x \leqslant 2$, $x \in R$.
12. $f : x \rightarrow x^2 - 3x$ in the domain $-2 \leqslant x \leqslant 5$, $x \in R$.
13. $f : x \rightarrow x^2 + 3$ in the domain $-3 \leqslant x \leqslant 3$, $x \in R$.
14. $f : x \rightarrow x^2 - 2$ in the domain $-4 \leqslant x \leqslant 4$, $x \in R$.
15. $f : x \rightarrow 2x^2 + 5x - 3$ in the domain $-4 \leqslant x \leqslant 2$, $x \in R$.
16. $f : x \rightarrow 2x^2 + 3x - 2$ in the domain $-2 \leqslant x \leqslant 3$, $x \in R$.
17. $f : x \rightarrow 2x^2 - x - 1$ in the domain $-2 \leqslant x \leqslant 3$, $x \in R$.
18. $f : x \rightarrow 2x^2 - 5x$ in the domain $-2 \leqslant x \leqslant 4$, $x \in R$.
19. On the same axis and scales, graph the functions
     $f : x \rightarrow x^2 - 2x - 4$, $g : x \rightarrow 2x + 5$,   in the domain $-4 \leqslant x \leqslant 6$, $x \in R$.

Sometimes the coefficient of x^2 is negative. Consider the next example.

Graph the function $f : x \rightarrow 9 + x - x^2$, in the domain $-3 \leqslant x \leqslant 4$, $x \in \mathbf{R}$.

Solution:

A table is drawn with the given values of x, from -3 to 4, to find the corresponding values of y.

Let $y = f(x) \quad \Rightarrow \quad y = -x^2 + x + 9$

x	$-x^2 + x + 9$	y
-3	$-9 - 3 + 9$	-3
-2	$-4 - 2 + 9$	3
-1	$-1 - 1 + 9$	7
0	$-0 + 0 + 9$	9
1	$-1 + 1 + 9$	9
2	$-4 + 2 + 9$	7
3	$-9 + 3 + 9$	3
4	$-16 + 4 + 9$	-3

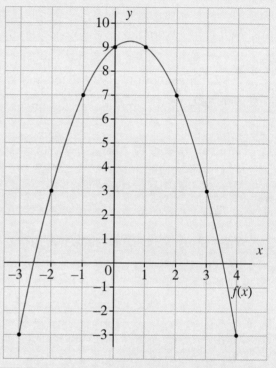

1. $f : x \rightarrow 2 + x - x^2$ in the domain $-2 \leqslant x \leqslant 3,$ $x \in \mathbf{R}.$
2. $f : x \rightarrow 3 + 2x - x^2$ in the domain $-2 \leqslant x \leqslant 4,$ $x \in \mathbf{R}.$
3. $f : x \rightarrow 7 - 2x - x^2$ in the domain $-5 \leqslant x \leqslant 3,$ $x \in \mathbf{R}.$
4. $f : x \rightarrow 5 - 3x - x^2$ in the domain $-5 \leqslant x \leqslant 2,$ $x \in \mathbf{R}.$
5. $f : x \rightarrow 5 + 3x - x^2$ in the domain $-2 \leqslant x \leqslant 5,$ $x \in \mathbf{R}.$
6. $f : x \rightarrow 4 - x - x^2$ in the domain $-4 \leqslant x \leqslant 3,$ $x \in \mathbf{R}.$
7. $f : x \rightarrow 3 + 4x - x^2$ in the domain $-1 \leqslant x \leqslant 5,$ $x \in \mathbf{R}.$
8. $f : x \rightarrow 1 + 5x - x^2$ in the domain $-1 \leqslant x \leqslant 6,$ $x \in \mathbf{R}.$
9. $f : x \rightarrow 2 - 4x - x^2$ in the domain $-5 \leqslant x \leqslant 1,$ $x \in \mathbf{R}.$
10. $f : x \rightarrow 3 + 2x - x^2$ in the domain $-2 \leqslant x \leqslant 4,$ $x \in \mathbf{R}.$
11. $f : x \rightarrow 3 - x^2$ in the domain $-3 \leqslant x \leqslant 3,$ $x \in \mathbf{R}.$
12. $f : x \rightarrow 2x - x^2$ in the domain $-1 \leqslant x \leqslant 5,$ $x \in \mathbf{R}.$

13. $f : x \rightarrow 5 + x - 2x^2$ in the domain $-2 \leqslant x \leqslant 3,$ $x \in R.$

14. $f : x \rightarrow 3 + 5x - 2x^2$ in the domain $-1 \leqslant x \leqslant 4,$ $x \in R.$

15. On the same axis and scales, graph the functions

     $f : x \rightarrow 7 + x - x^2,$ $g : x \rightarrow x - 1,$ in the domain $-3 \leqslant x \leqslant 4,$ $x \in R.$

Using graphs

Once we have drawn the graph, we are usually asked to use the graph to answer some questions. Below are examples of the general type of problems where graphs are used.

Notes: **1.** $y = f(x),$ so $f(x)$ can be replaced by $y.$

        2. In general, if given x find $y,$ and vice versa.

Examples of the main problems, once the graph is drawn:

---

1. Find the values of x for which $f(x) = 0.$

This question is asking:

'Where does the curve meet the x axis?'

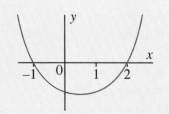

Solution:

Write down the values of x where the graph meets the x axis.

From the graph: $x = -1$ or $x = 2.$

---

2. Find the values of x for which $f(x) = 2.$

This question is asking:

'When $y = 2,$ what are the values of x?'

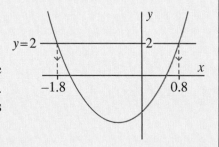

Solution:

Draw the line $y = 2.$ Where this line meets the curve draw broken perpendicular lines onto the x axis. Write down the values of x where these broken lines meet the x axis.

From the graph:

When $y = 2,$ $x = -1.8,$ or $x = 0.8.$

---

3. Find the value of $f(-1.5)$.

This question is asking:
'When $x = -1.5$, what is the value of y?'

Solution:
From $x = -1.5$ on the x axis draw a broken perpendicular line to meet the curve. From this draw a broken horizontal line to meet the y axis. Write down the value of y where this line meets the y axis.
From the graph:
$f(-1.5) = 3.8$

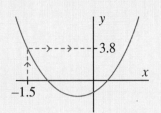

4. Maximum point and maximum value.

Solution:
Consider the graph on the right. The maximum point is $(2, 4)$. The maximum value is found by drawing a horizontal line from the maximum point to the y axis and reading the value where this line meets the y axis.
The maximum value is 4
(the same as the y co-ordinate of the maximum point).

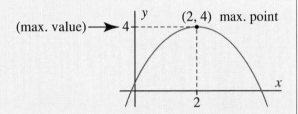

5. Minimum point and minimum value.

Solution:
Consider the graph on the right. The minimum point is $(-1, -3)$. The minimum value is found by drawing a horizontal line from the minimum point to the y axis and reading the value where this line meets the y axis.
The minimum value is -3
(the same as the y co-ordinate of the minimum point).

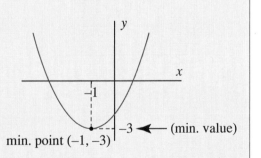

6. Axis of symmetry

Graphs of quadratic functions are symmetrical about a line that passes through the middle of the curve (and also through the maximum and minimum points). The line is called the 'axis of symmetry'.

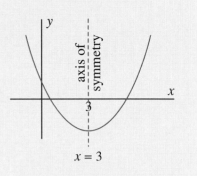

Solution:
From the graph:
The equation of the axis of symmetry is $x = 3$.
3 is where the line meets the x axis.

$x = 3$

Draw the graph of the function $f : x \rightarrow x^2 - 2x - 3$ in the domain $-2 \leqslant x \leqslant 4$, $\quad x \in \mathbf{R}$.
Use your graph to

(i) find the values of x for which $f(x) = 0$
(ii) estimate the values of x for which $5f(x) = f(4)$
(iii) find the minimum point and the minimum value
(iv) estimate $f(2.5)$.

Draw the axis of symmetry of the graph of $f(x)$ and write down its equation.

Solution:

x	$x^2 - 2x - 3$	y
-2	$4 + 4 - 3$	5
-1	$1 + 2 - 3$	0
0	$0 + 0 - 3$	-3
1	$1 - 2 - 3$	-4
2	$4 - 4 - 3$	-3
3	$9 - 6 - 3$	0
4	$16 - 8 - 3$	5

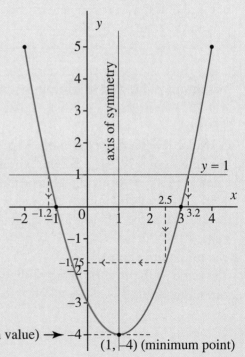

(minimum value) → -4

$(1, -4)$ (minimum point)

(i)   The values of x for which $f(x) = 0$

This question is asking, 'Where does the graph cut the x axis?'

The graph cuts the x axis at -1 and 3.

Therefore $f(x) = 0$ for $x = -1$ and $x = 3$.

Note: Another way of asking the same question is,

'Find the values of x for which $x^2 - 2x - 3 = 0$.'

(ii)   The values of x for which $5f(x) = f(4)$

From the table, $f(4) = 5$ (i.e. when $x = 4$, $y = 5$).

Given: $5f(x) = f(4)$

$\Rightarrow$ $5f(x) = 5$ (put in 5 for $f(4)$)

$\Rightarrow$ $f(x) = 1$ (divide both sides by 5)

$\Rightarrow$ $y = 1$ (replace $f(x)$ with y)

This question is asking, 'When $y = 1$, what are the values of x?'

Draw the line $y = 1$. Where this line meets the curve, drop broken perpendicular lines to meet the x axis. These lines meet the x axis at -1.2 and 3.2.

Therefore $5f(x) = f(4)$ for $x = -1.2$ and $x = 3.2$

Note: Another way of asking the same question is,

'Find the values of x for which $x^2 - 2x - 3 = 1$.'

(iii) Minimum point

From the graph, the minimum point is $(1, -4)$.

Note: A point must have an x value and a y value.

Minimum value

Through the minimum point, draw a broken line parallel to the x axis.

This line meets the y axis at -4.

Therefore the minimum value is -4 (the same as the y co-ordinate of the minimum point).

(iv) $f(2.5)$

This question is asking, 'When $x = 2.5$, what is the value of y?'

From $x = 2.5$ on the x axis draw a broken perpendicular line to meet the curve.

From this a broken horizontal line is drawn to meet the y axis.

This line meets the y axis at -1.75.

Therefore $f(2.5) = -1.75$.

Axis of symmetry of the graph of $f(x)$

Through the minimum point $(1, -4)$ draw a line parallel to the y axis.

This is the axis of symmetry.

As can be seen from the graph, the axis of symmetry meets the x axis at 1.

Therefore $x = 1$ is the equation of the axis of symmetry of the graph of $f(x)$.

1. Below is a graph of the function $f : x \to x^2 + 2x - 3$ in the domain $-4 \leqslant x \leqslant 2$, $\qquad x \in \mathbf{R}$.

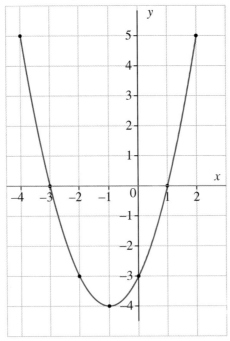

Use the graph to
(i)   find the minimum point and the minimum value
(ii)   find the values of x for which $f(x) = 0$
(iii)   find the values of x for which $f(x) = 5$
(iv)   estimate the value of $f(0.5)$
(v)   estimate the values of x for which $f(x) = f(-4) + f(-2)$
(vi)   find two points on the axis of symmetry of the graph of $f(x)$ and write down the equation of the axis of symmetry
(vii)   find the area of the smallest rectangle that encloses the graph.

2. Below is a graph of the function $f : x \to x^2 - 3x - 4$ in the domain $-2 \leqslant x \leqslant 5$, $\qquad x \in \mathbf{R}$.

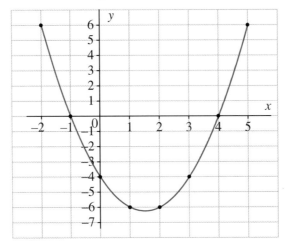

Use the graph to
- **(i)** find the values of x for which $f(x) = 0$
- **(ii)** estimate the value of $f(3.5)$
- **(iii)** find the values of x for which $f(x) = -4$
- **(iv)** estimate the values of x for which $f(x) = f(5) + f(0)$
- **(v)** estimate the minimum value of f.

3. Draw the graph of the function $f : x \rightarrow x^2 - 3x + 2$ in the domain $-1 \leqslant x \leqslant 4$, $x \in \mathbf{R}$.
Use your graph to
- **(i)** find the values of x for which $f(x) = 0$
- **(ii)** estimate the value of $f(2.6)$
- **(iii)** estimate the values of x for which $f(x) = 5$
- **(iv)** estimate the values of x for which $f(x) + f(3) = f(4) - f(0)$.

4. Draw the graph of the function $f : x \rightarrow x^2 - 6x + 5$ in the domain $0 \leqslant x \leqslant 6$, $x \in \mathbf{R}$.
Use your graph to
- **(i)** find the values of x for which $f(x) = 0$
- **(ii)** estimate the value of $f(2.5)$
- **(iii)** find the minimum point of the graph
- **(iv)** find the area of the smallest rectangle that encloses the graph
- **(v)** estimate the values of x for which $f(4) + f(x) = f(1) + f(3)$.

5. Draw the graph of the function $f : x \rightarrow x^2 - x - 2$ in the domain $-3 \leqslant x \leqslant 4$, $x \in \mathbf{R}$.
Use your graph to find
- **(i)** the values of x for which $f(x) = 0$
- **(ii)** the values of x for which $f(x) = 4$
- **(iii)** the values of x for which $f(x) = 2f(3) - f(4)$.

6. Draw the graph of the function $f : x \rightarrow x^2 + 2x - 8$ in the domain $-5 \leqslant x \leqslant 3$, $x \in \mathbf{R}$.
Use your graph to
- **(i)** find the minimum point and the minimum value
- **(ii)** find the values of x for which $f(x) = 0$
- **(iii)** find the values of x for which $f(x) = -5$
- **(iv)** find the equation of the axis of symmetry of the graph of $f(x)$
- **(v)** find the area of the smallest rectangle that encloses the graph.

7. Draw the graph of the function $f : x \rightarrow x^2 + x - 6$ in the domain $-4 \leqslant x \leqslant 3$, $x \in \mathbf{R}$.
Use your graph to
- **(i)** find the values of x for which $f(x) = 0$
- **(ii)** find the values of x for which $f(x) = -4$
- **(iii)** estimate the values of x for which $f(x) = 4$
- **(iv)** estimate the minimum value of f.

8. Draw the graph of the function $f : x \rightarrow x^2 - 4x - 5$ in the domain $-2 \leqslant x \leqslant 6$, $x \in \mathbf{R}$.
Use your graph to
- **(i)** find the values of x for which $f(x) = 0$
- **(ii)** find the minimum point of the graph
- **(iii)** find the values of x for which $f(x) = -8$
- **(iv)** find the equation of the axis of symmetry of the graph of $f(x)$.
Draw the axis of symmetry of the graph.

9. Draw the graph of the function $f : x \rightarrow x^2 - 2x - 3$ in the domain $-3 \leqslant x \leqslant 5$, $\quad x \in \mathbf{R}$.
Use your graph to find
(i)   the minimum point of the graph
(ii)   the values of x for which $f(x) = f(3)$
(iii)   the values of x for which $f(x) = 2 - f(0)$
(iv)   the area of the smallest rectangle that encloses the graph
(v)   the estimate of $f(-2.5)$.

10. Draw the graph of the function $f : x \rightarrow x^2 - 4x + 2$ in the domain $-1 \leqslant x \leqslant 5$, $\quad x \in \mathbf{R}$.
Use your graph to find
(i)   the two values of x for which $f(x) = -1$
(ii)   the minimum point and the minimum value
(iii)   the estimate of $f(4.5)$
(iv)   the two values of x for which $f(x) = 0$.

11. Complete the following table and draw the graph of the function
$f : x \rightarrow x^2 + x - 2$, in the domain $-3 \leqslant x \leqslant 2$, $\quad x \in \mathbf{R}$.

x	-3	-2	-1	0	1	2
$f(x)$	4			-2		

(i)   Use your graph to find the values of x for which $f(x) = 0$.
(ii)   Use your graph to estimate the value of $f(0.5)$.
(iii)   Construct the axis of symmetry of the graph of $f(x)$.
(iv)   Estimate the values of x for which $f(x) = f(0) + f(2)$.

12. Draw the graph of the function $f : x \rightarrow x^2 - 5x + 4$ in the domain $-1 \leqslant x \leqslant 6$, $\quad x \in \mathbf{R}$.
Use your graph to
(i)   find the values of x for which $x^2 - 5x + 4 = 0$
(ii)   find the values of x for which $x^2 - 5x + 4 = -2$
(iii)   estimate the value of $x^2 - 5x + 4$ when $x = 4.5$
(iv)   estimate the minimum value of $f(x)$.
    Draw the axis of symmetry of the graph of $f(x)$.

13. Draw the graph of the function $f : x \rightarrow x^2 + 3x - 4$ in the domain $-5 \leqslant x \leqslant 2$, $\quad x \in \mathbf{R}$.
Use your graph to
(i)   find the values of x for which $x^2 + 3x - 4 = 0$
(ii)   estimate the values of x for which $x^2 + 3x - 4 = 2$
(iii)   estimate the value of $x^2 + 3x - 4$ when $x = -2.2$
(iv)   estimate the minimum value of f.
    Draw the axis of symmetry of the graph of $f(x)$.

14. Draw the x axis from -2 to 4 and the y axis from -5 to 5.
Graph the function $f : x \rightarrow x^2 - 2x - 3$ in the domain $-2 \leqslant x \leqslant 4$, $\quad x \in \mathbf{R}$.
Construct the image of the graph of $f(x)$ under an axial symmetry in the x axis.

15. Draw the graph of the function $f : x \rightarrow 2x^2 - x - 3$ in the domain $-2 \leqslant x \leqslant 3$, $x \in \mathbf{R}$.
Use your graph to estimate
(i)   the two values of x for which $f(x) = 0$
(ii)   the minimum value of f
(iii)   the two values of x for which $f(x) = 3$.

16. Draw the graph of the function $f : x \rightarrow 2x^2 + 3x - 2$ in the domain $-3 \leqslant x \leqslant 1$, $x \in \mathbf{R}$.
Use your graph to estimate
(i)   the value of $f(-2.8)$
(ii)   the two values of x for which $f(x) = 0$
(iii)   the two values of x for which $f(x) + 2 = 0$
(iv)   the minimum value of $f(x)$.

In the following exercises, the coefficient of x^2 is negative.

17. Below is a graph of the function $f : x \rightarrow 3 + 2x - x^2$ in the domain $-2 \leqslant x \leqslant 4$, $x \in \mathbf{R}$

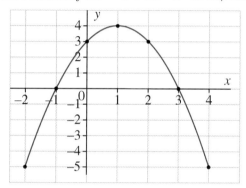

Use the graph to
(i)   find the two values of x for which $f(x) = 0$
(ii)   find the maximum point and the maximum value of $f(x)$
(iii)   find the equation of the axis of symmetry of the graph of $f(x)$
(iv)   find the two values of x for which $f(x) = 3$
(v)   estimate the value of $f(3.5)$
(vi)   find the area of the largest possible triangle abc, where a, b and c are points of the graph and ab is parallel to the x axis.

18. Draw the graph of the function $f : x \rightarrow 3 - 2x - x^2$ in the domain $-4 \leqslant x \leqslant 2$, $x \in \mathbf{R}$.
Use your graph to
(i)   find the maximum point and the maximum value of $f(x)$
(ii)   find the two values of x for which $f(x) = 0$
(iii)   estimate the value of $f(1.7)$
(iv)   find the area of the triangle formed by joining the highest point of the graph to the points where the graph intersects the x axis.

19. Draw the graph of the function $f : x \rightarrow 4 + 3x - x^2$ in the domain $-2 \leqslant x \leqslant 5$, $x \in \mathbf{R}$.
Use your graph to
(i)   find the values of x for which $f(x) = 0$
(ii)   find the values of x for which $f(x) + f(-2) = 0$
(iii)   estimate the value of $f(-1.6)$
(iv)   estimate the maximum value of f.

20. Draw the graph of the function $f : x \rightarrow 8 + 2x - x^2$ in the domain $-3 \leqslant x \leqslant 5$, $x \in \mathbf{R}$.

Use your graph to

   (i)   find the values of x for which $f(x) = 0$

   (ii)   find the maximum point and the maximum value of $f(x)$

   (iii)   find the equation of the axis of symmetry of the graph of $f(x)$

   (iv)   find the values of x for which $f(x) + 3 = f(2)$.

21. Draw the graph of the function $f : x \rightarrow 5x - x^2$ in the domain $-1 \leqslant x \leqslant 6$, $x \in \mathbf{R}$.

Use your graph to

   (i)   estimate the maximum value

   (ii)   find the two values of x for which $f(x) = 0$

   (iii)   find the two values of x for which $f(x) + 2 = f(3)$.

22. Draw the graph of the function $f : x \rightarrow 5 + 3x - 2x^2$ in the domain $-2 \leqslant x \leqslant 3$, $x \in \mathbf{R}$.

Use your graph to

   (i)   estimate the values of x for which $f(x) = 0$

   (ii)   estimate the maximum value of $f(x)$

   (iii)   estimate the values of x for which $f(x) = 4$.

Using graphs to solve real-life problems

Graphs can be used to solve real-life problems.

Example ▼

Draw the graph of the function $f : x \rightarrow x^2 - 4x + 4$ in the domain $-1 \leqslant x \leqslant 5$, $x \in \mathbf{R}$.
The graph shows the wind speed at hourly intervals.

The x axis shows one-hour intervals: for example, $x = -1$ means 23:00, $x = 0$ means 24:00, $x = 1$ means 01:00, etc.

The y axis shows the wind speed in kilometres per hour, where $y = 0$ means calm, $y = 1$ means 10 km/h, $y = 2$ means 20 km/h, etc.

Use your graph to find

   (i)   the times when the wind speed was 22 km/h

   (ii)   the speed of the wind at 04:45

   (iii) the time when there was a calm.

Solution:

x	$x^2 - 4x + 4$	y
-1	$1 + 4 + 4$	9
0	$0 + 0 + 4$	4
1	$1 - 4 + 4$	1
2	$4 - 8 + 4$	0
3	$9 - 12 + 4$	1
4	$16 - 16 + 4$	4
5	$25 - 20 + 4$	9

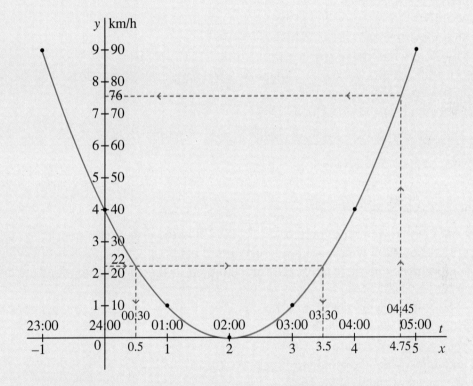

The x axis measures time, t, in hourly intervals from 23:00 to 05:00.

The y axis measures wind speed in km/h.

Each interval on the y axis represents 10 km/h.

Note: If we are given the time, we are required to find the wind speed.
If we are given the wind speed, we are required to find the time.

(i) **The times when the wind speed was 22 km/h**
Given that the wind speed is 22 km/h, find the time.
When wind speed = 22 km/h, y = 2.2.
From 2.2 on the *y* axis (22 km/h) draw a broken horizontal line to meet the curve at two places. Where this line meets the curve, drop broken perpendicular lines to meet the *x* axis (time axis). These lines meet the *x* axis at 0.5 and 3.5.
When *x* = 0.5, *t* = 00:30, and when *x* = 3.5, *t* = 03:30.
Therefore the wind speed was 22 km/h at 00:30 and 03:30.

(ii) **The speed of the wind at 04:45**
When *t* = 04:45, *x* = 4.75.
From 4.75 on the *x* axis (04:45) draw a broken vertical line to meet the curve. Where this line meets the curve, draw a broken horizontal to meet the *y* axis (speed axis). This line meets the *y* axis at 7.6.
When *y* = 7.6, speed = 76 km/h.
Therefore at 04:45 the wind speed was 76 km/h.

(iii) **The time when there was a calm**
From the graph, we see that there was a calm at 02:00 (the lowest point on the graph).
Therefore there was a calm at 02:00.

Exercise 24.5 ▼

1. Draw the graph of the function $f : x \rightarrow x^2 - 5x + 8$ in the domain $0 \leqslant x \leqslant 5$, $x \in \mathbf{R}$.
   The graph shows the wind speed at hourly intervals.
   The *x* axis shows one-hour intervals: for example, *x* = 0 means 12:00, *x* = 1 means 13:00, etc.
   The *y* axis shows wind speed in kilometres per hour: *y* = 0 means 0 km/h, *y* = 1 means 10 km/h, *y* = 2 means 20 km/h, etc.
   Use your graph to estimate
   (i) the times when the wind speed was 33 km/h
   (ii) the speed of the wind at 16:45
   (iii) the time when the wind speed was at its lowest.

2. Draw the graph of the function $f : x \rightarrow x^2 - 6x + 9$ in the domain $0 \leqslant x \leqslant 6$, $x \in \mathbf{R}$.
   Take the graph to represent the speed of a stone thrown straight up into the air.
   The speed in metres per second is shown on the *y* axis, and the time in seconds is shown along the *x* axis.
   Use the graph to find how many seconds after the throw
   (i) the speed of the stone was 6 m/s
   (ii) the stone began to fall back down.

3. Draw the graph of the function $f : x \rightarrow x^2 - x - 3$ in the domain $-3 \leqslant x \leqslant 3$, $\qquad x \in \mathbf{R}$.
The graph shows the temperature taken every two hours between 20:00 ($x = -3$) and 08:00 ($x = 3$). Use the graph to find
(i)   the temperature at midnight
(ii) the time when the temperature was lowest
(iii) the times when the temperature was $0°$.

4. Draw the graph of the function $f : x \rightarrow 4 + x^2$ in the domain $-2 \leqslant x \leqslant 2$, $\qquad x \in \mathbf{R}$.
Assume the graph shows the time of sunset from October until February.

Take -2 on the x axis to be 1 October.
Take -1 on the x axis to be 1 November, etc.
On the other axis, take 4 to be 16:00, 5 to be 17:00, etc.

Estimate, using the graph,
(i)   the time of sunset in mid-December
(ii) the months in which sunset occurs at 18:30.

5. Draw the graph of the function $f : x \rightarrow x^2 - 6x + 10$ in the domain $0 \leqslant x \leqslant 4$, $\qquad x \in \mathbf{R}$.
Using the graph, or otherwise, estimate
(i)   the value of $f(2.5)$
(ii) the value of x when $f(x) = 2.5$.
Let the graph represent the speed of a high-board diver after entering the water.
The seconds under water are shown on the x axis.
The diver's speed at any given second is shown on the y or $f(x)$ axis.
(iii) Find the value of x when the diver's speed is greatest.
(iv) How many seconds after entering the water does the diver's speed begin to increase?

6. Draw the graph of the function $f : x \rightarrow x^2 - 8x + 12$ in the domain $0 \leqslant x \leqslant 5$, $\qquad x \in \mathbf{R}$.
Let the graph represent a science experiment that lowers the temperature of an object from room temperature to below freezing over a period of five hours.
The time, in hours, is shown on the x axis.
The temperature at any given time (in degrees Celsius) is shown on the y axis.
Use the graph to
(i)   find room temperature at the start of the experiment
(ii) find the temperature of the object after $1\frac{1}{2}$ hours
(iii) find the time taken for the temperature of the object to fall to freezing-point
(iv) find the time taken for the temperature of the object to be at its lowest
(v)   find the lowest temperature reached by the object in the experiment.

7. Draw the graph of the function $f : x \rightarrow 5x - x^2$ in the domain $0 \leqslant x \leqslant 5$, $\qquad x \in \mathbf{R}$.
Take the graph to represent the flight of a ball kicked on level ground.
The height, in metres, is shown on the y axis, and the time in seconds is shown on the x axis.
Use the graph to find
(i)   the greatest height reached by the ball
(ii) the time taken to reach this height
(iii) the time taken for the ball to hit the ground
(iv) the times when the ball was 6 m above the ground.

1. Draw the x axis from -1 to 5 and the y axis from -5 to 7.
   (i) Given that $y = x - 1$, complete the table, and hence sketch the line L: $y = x - 1$.

x	0	1	4
y			3

   (ii) Given that $y = 2x - 3$, complete the table, and hence sketch the line K: $y = 2x - 3$ on the same graph as L.

x	0	3	4
y	-3		

   (iii) Use the graph of L and K to solve the simultaneous equations
   $$x - y = 1$$
   $$2x - y = 3.$$

2. Draw the x axis from -2 to 5 and the y axis from 0 to 8.
   (i) Given that $y = x + 3$, complete the table, and hence sketch the line L: $y = x + 3$.

x	-1	2	4
y	2		

   (ii) Given that $y = 5 - x$, complete the table, and hence sketch the line K: $y = 5 - x$ on the same graph as L.

x	-1	3	4
y		2	

   (iii) Use the graph of L and K to solve the simultaneous equations
   $$x - y = -3$$
   $$x + y = 5.$$

3. Draw the x axis from -1 to 5 and the y axis from -4 to 8.
   (i) Given that $y = 4 - x$, complete the table, and hence sketch the line M: $y = 4 - x$.

x	0	1	4
y		3	

   (ii) Given that $y = 6 - 2x$, complete the table, and hence sketch the line N: $y = 6 - 2x$ on the same graph as M.

x	0	3	4
y			-2

   (iii) From the graph, write down the co-ordinates of $M \cap N$.
   (iv) Solve algebraically the simultaneous equations
   $$2x + y = 6$$
   $$x + y = 4,$$
   and verify your answer to part (iii).

GEOMETRY 2

Pythagoras's theorem

The longest side of a right-angled triangle is always opposite the right angle and is called the '**hypotenuse**'.

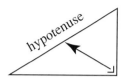

Pythagoras's theorem states that in a right-angled triangle:

The square on the hypotenuse is equal to the sum of the squares on the other two sides.

$$(\text{hypotenuse})^2 = (\text{side 1})^2 + (\text{side 2})^2$$

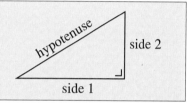

This equation can be written algebraically:

$$h^2 = a^2 + b^2$$

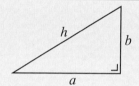

The converse (opposite) also applies:
If $h^2 = a^2 + b^2$, then the triangle must be right-angled.

Note: Pythagoras's theorem applies only to right-angled triangles.
We can use Pythagoras's theorem to find the missing length of a side in a right-angled triangle if we know the lengths of the other two sides.

Example ▼

Find the value of **(i)** x **(ii)** y.

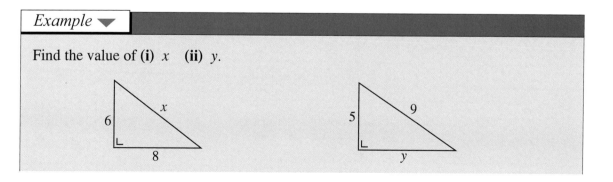

Solution:

(i)

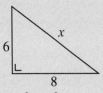

$$h^2 = a^2 + b^2$$
$$\Rightarrow \quad x^2 = 8^2 + 6^2$$
$$\Rightarrow \quad x^2 = 64 + 36$$
$$\Rightarrow \quad x^2 = 100$$
$$\Rightarrow \quad x = \sqrt{100}$$
$$\Rightarrow \quad x = 10$$

(ii)

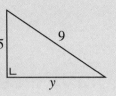

$$a^2 + b^2 = h^2$$
$$\Rightarrow \quad y^2 + 5^2 = 9^2$$
$$\Rightarrow \quad y^2 + 25 = 81$$
$$\Rightarrow \quad y^2 = 81-25$$
$$\Rightarrow \quad y^2 = 56$$
$$\Rightarrow \quad y = \sqrt{56}$$

(It is best to leave your answer in square root (surd) form unless you are told otherwise.)

Note: $(\sqrt{a})^2 = a$. For example, $(\sqrt{20})^2 = 20$; $(\sqrt{50})^2 = 50$.

Example ▼

The diagonal of a square is $\sqrt{32}$. Calculate the length of the side.

Solution:
Draw a square.
Let x = the length of a side.
The diagonal bisects the square to create two right-angled triangles.

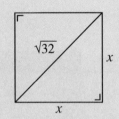

Therefore we can apply Pythagoras's theorem.
$$a^2 + b^2 = h^2 \qquad \text{(Pythagoras's theorem)}$$
$$x^2 + x^2 = (\sqrt{32})^2$$
$$2x^2 = 32$$
$$x^2 = 16 \qquad \text{(divide both sides by 2)}$$
$$x = \sqrt{16} \qquad \text{(take the square root of both sides)}$$
$$x = 4$$
Therefore the length of a side of the square is 4.

Use Pythagoras's theorem to find the length of the side indicated by a letter in each of the following diagrams:

1.

2.

3.
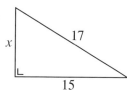

4.

5.
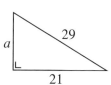

6.
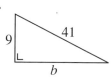

7.
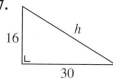

8.

9.
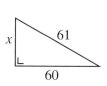

10.

11.
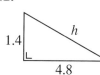

12.
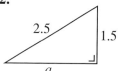

In questions 13–16, remember that $(\sqrt{x})^2 = x$. For exmple, $(\sqrt{5})^2 = 5$, $(\sqrt{8})^2 = 8$.

13.
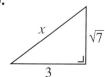

14.
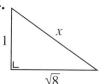

15.

16.
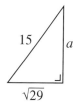

In questions 17–20, leave your answer in square root (surd) form.

17.

18.
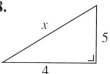

19.
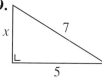

20.

In questions 21–24, the diagrams represent squares.

21.
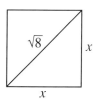

22.
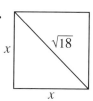

23.

24.

25. The supporting wire to the top of a vertical pole is 17 m and is held to the ground at a distance of 8 m from the foot of the pole.
Calculate *h*, the height of the pole.

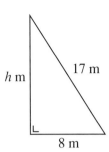

26. The length of a rectangle is 21 cm, and its breadth is 20 cm.
Calculate the length of a diagonal.

27. Is the triangle whose sides are 12.5 cm, 12 cm and 3.5 cm in length a right-angled triangle? Give a reason for your answer.

28. *abcd* is a rhombus whose diagonals intersect at right angles at *o*.
If $|ac| = 6$ cm and $|bd| = 8$ cm, calculate $|ab|$.

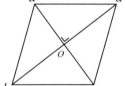

29. In the diagram, $|\angle abd| = 90°$,
$|ab| = 5$, $|ad| = 13$, and
$|bc| = 6$.
Calculate:

(i) $|bd|$ **(ii)** $|cd|$
(iii) $|ac|$ (correct to two decimal places).

30. The diagram shows a circle *K* with centre *o*.
pq is a tangent and *p* is the point of contact.
If $|oq| = 12.5$ cm and $|pq| = 10$ cm, calculate the radius of the circle.

31. In the diagram,
$ab \perp bc$ and $ac \perp cd$.
$|ab| = 3$, $|bc| = 4$, and $|ad| = 13$.
Using Pythagoras's theorem twice,
calculate **(i)** $|ac|$, **(ii)** $|cd|$.

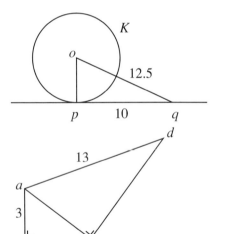

Area of a parallelogram

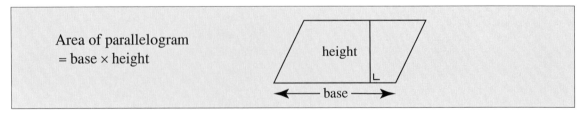

| Area of parallelogram = base × height |

Any side can be taken as the '**base**'. It does not need to be at the bottom of the parallelogram. The height must always be perpendicular to the side chosen as the base.

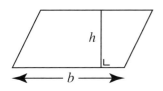 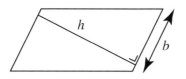

b = length of base
h = perpendicular height
$A = b \times h$

In a parallelogram, therefore, there are two possible values for its base. Each of these 'base lengths' has a corresponding 'perpendicular height'.

Therefore, there are two possible ways to calculate the area of a parallelogram. It depends on the base length and perpendicular height that is known. In some questions we have to use Pythagoras's theorem to find the perpendicular height.

Example ▼

$abcd$ is a parallelogram.
$ae \perp bc$,
$|ab| = 5$, $|ad| = 8$, and $|be| = 3$.

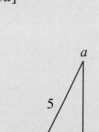

Calculate:

(i) $|ae|$
(ii) the area of the parallelogram $abcd$
(iii) the length of the perpendicular from $[ab]$ to $[cd]$
(iv) the perimeter of the parallelogram $abcd$.

Solution:

(i) $\triangle abe$ is a right-angled triangle.
Using Pythagoras's theorem,

$$|ae|^2 + |be|^2 = |ab|^2$$
$$\Rightarrow \quad |ae|^2 + 3^2 = 5^2$$
$$\Rightarrow \quad |ae|^2 + 9 = 25$$
$$|ae|^2 = 16$$
$$|ae| = \sqrt{16} = 4$$

(ii) Area of parallelogram $abcd$
$$= \text{base} \times \text{height}$$
$$= |ad| \times |ae|$$
$$= 8 \times 4$$
$$= 32$$

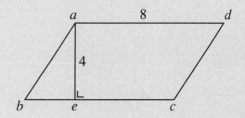

(iii) Let the length of the perpendicular from
[*ab*] to [*cd*] = *h*.

Equation given in disguise:

$$\text{area of parallelogram} = 32$$
$$\Rightarrow \qquad \text{base} \times \text{height} = 32$$
$$\Rightarrow \qquad |ab| \times h = 32$$
$$\Rightarrow \qquad 5 \times h = 32$$
$$\Rightarrow \qquad h = 6.4$$

Therefore the length of the perpendicular from [*ab*] to [*cd*] is 6.4.
(Notice that $8 \times 4 = 5 \times 6.4$. Both are equal to 32.)

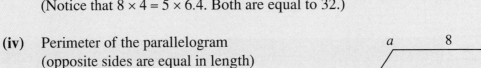

(iv) Perimeter of the parallelogram
(opposite sides are equal in length)
$$= 8 + 5 + 8 + 5$$
$$= 26$$

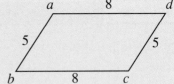

Exercise 25.2 ▼

In questions 1–8, calculate **(i)** the perimeter and **(ii)** the area of each of the following parallelograms (all dimensions are in centimetres):

1. 7 / 5 / 8

2. 6 / 3 / 10

3. 5 / 4 / 7

4. 12 / 8 / 20

5. 8 / 7 / 12

6. 6 / 5 / 7

7. 10 / 8 / 15

8. 7 / 6 / 10

In questions 9–12, calculate the perpendicular height, *h*, in each case, where the area, *A*, is given:

9. 10 / *h* / $A = 80$

10. 20 / *h* / $A = 100$

11. 8 / *h* / $A = 48$

12. 6 / *h* / $A = 33$

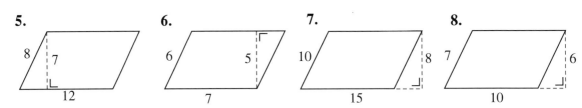

324

In questions 13–16, find **(i)** the area of the parallelogram and **(ii)** the perpendicular height, h:

13.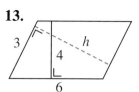

14.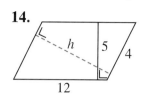

15.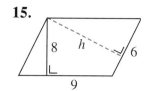

16.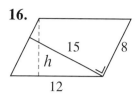

In questions 17–20, use Pythagoras's theorem **(i)** to find the perpendicular and then **(ii)** to find the area of the parallelogram:

17.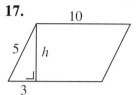

18.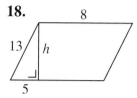

19.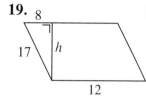

20.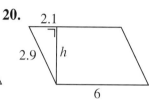

21. The diagram shows a parallelogram and a square. The length of one side of the parallelogram is 24 cm, and its corresponding perpendicular height is 6 cm. The length of a side of the square is x cm.

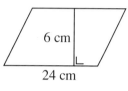

Calculate the value of x if the area of the parallelogram is equal to the area of the square.

Constructions

Any work involving accurate constructions requires a good pencil, a compass, a ruler, and a protractor. It is very important not to rub out any construction lines or marks you make at any stage during a construction. All construction lines or marks should **always** be left on the diagram.

Terminology

1. **Parallel lines** are always the same distance apart and never meet.
2. A **perpendicular** means at right angles, 90°, to another line.
3. A **bisector** divides a line segment or angle into two equal parts.

To construct the perpendicular bisector of a line segment

The perpendicular bisector of a line segment, [xy], is constructed with the following steps:

1. Set your compass to a radius greater than half the length of the line segment [xy]. Keep this radius. 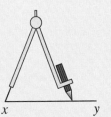	**2.** Place the point of your compass at *x* and draw arcs above and below the line segment. 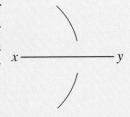
3. Place the point of your compass at *y* and, using the same radius, draw arcs to meet the other arcs. 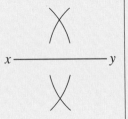	**4.** Draw a line through the points where the arcs cross. This line is the perpendicular bisector of the line segment [xy]. 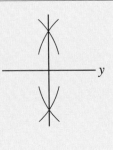

To construct the bisector of an angle

The bisector of an angle is constructed with the following steps:

1. Place the point of your compass on the vertex, *o*, of the angle. Using the same radius, draw two arcs to meet the arms of the angle at *x* and *y*. 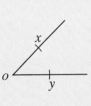	**2.** Place the point of your compass at *x* and draw an arc. 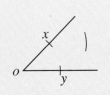
3. Place the point of your compass at *y* and, using the same radius, draw an arc to meet the other arc.	**4.** Draw a line through *o* and the point where the arcs cross. This line is the bisector of the angle. 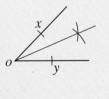

To divide a line segment into three equal parts

A line segment, [xy], is divided into three equal parts with the following steps:

1.	Draw a line through *x* at an acute angle to *xy*.	
2.	Using a compass, mark off three points *a*, *b* and *c* on this line so that $\lvert xa \rvert = \lvert ab \rvert = \lvert bc \rvert$.	
3.	Join *c* to *y*. Using a ruler and a set square, draw lines through *a* and *b* parallel to *cy* to meet the line segment at *w* and *z*. *z* and *w* divide the line segment [xy] into three equal parts.	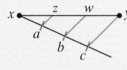

Note: This method can also be used to bisect a line segment or to divide a line segment into any number of equal parts.

Exercise 25.3 ▼

Perpendicular bisector of a line segment

1. Draw a line segment [xy], so that $\lvert xy \rvert = 8$ cm.
    - **(i)** Construct the perpendicular bisector of [xy], showing all your construction lines.
    - **(ii)** Use your ruler to check that the line segment has been bisected.
    - **(iii)** Check with your protractor that your perpendicular bisector is at right angles, 90°, to the line *xy*.
2. Construct the perpendicular bisector of each of the following line segments:
    - **(i)** $\lvert xy \rvert = 6$ cm **(ii)** $\lvert ab \rvert = 7$ cm **(iii)** $\lvert pq \rvert = 9$ cm **(iv)** $\lvert cd \rvert = 84$ mm.
    In each case show all your construction lines and check your answer as in question 1.

Bisector of an angle

3. Draw an angle of 70°, with each arm of the angle about 6 cm in length.
    Construct the bisector of the angle, showing all your construction lines.
    Use your protractor to check that the angle has been bisected.
4. Construct the bisectors of each of the following angles:
    - **(i)** 80° **(ii)** 50° **(iii)** 60° **(iv)** 44° **(v)** 100° **(vi)** 65°.
    In each case show all your construction lines and check your answer as in question 3.

To divide a line segment into three equal parts

5. Draw a line segment [xy], so that $|xy| = 12$ cm.
   (i) Show by construction how to divide the segment into three equal parts, showing all your construction lines.
   (ii) Use your ruler to check that the line segment has been divided into three equal parts.

6. Show by construction how to divide into three equal parts each of the following line segments:
   (i) $|xy| = 9$ cm   (ii) $|ab| = 10\frac{1}{2}$ cm   (iii) $|pq| = 7\frac{1}{2}$ cm   (iv) $|cd| = 99$ mm.
   In each case show all your construction lines and check your answer as in question 5.

Constructing triangles

The following hints are helpful when constructing triangles:

1. Draw a rough sketch first (usually freehand). Label it with the information given.
2. Use a pencil (it's easy to rub out if you make a mistake).
3. Leave all your construction lines on your final drawing (do not rub them out).
4. Draw your final diagram as accurately as possible.
5. Label your final drawing clearly.

The method used for drawing a triangle depends on the information you are given.
We will look at four cases. A triangle can be drawn if you are given:

1. The length of the three sides (SSS).
2. The length of two sides and the angle between them (SAS).
3. The length of one side and two angles (ASA).
4. A right angle, the length of the hypotenuse, and one other side (RHS.).

Note: If you know two angles in a triangles it is possible to calculate the third angle.
The four cases above are related to the '**four cases of congruence**' in the next section.

1. Given the length of the three sides (SSS)

Example ▼

Construct the triangle *abc* so that $|ab| = 6$ cm, $|ac| = 5$ cm, and $|bc| = 4$ cm.

Solution:
A rough sketch, with the given information, is
shown on the right.

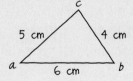

1. Using your ruler, draw a horizontal line segment 6 cm in length. Label the end points *a* and *b*. 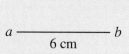	**2.** Set your compass to a radius of 5 cm. Place the compass point on *a*. Draw an arc above the line. 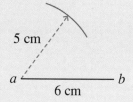
3. Set your compass to a radius of 4 cm. Place the compass point at *b*. Draw an arc above the line to meet the other arc. Label this point *c*. 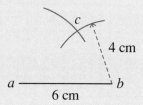	**4.** Using your ruler, join *a* to *c* and *b* to *c*. The triangle *abc* is now drawn, as required. 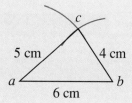

2. Given the length of two sides and the angle between them (SAS)

Example ▼

Construct a triangle *pqr* so that $|pq| = 5$ cm, $|pr| = 4$ cm, and $|\angle qpr| = 60°$.

Solution:
A rough sketch, with the given information, is shown on the right.

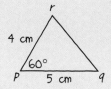

1. Using your ruler, draw a horizontal line segment 5 cm in length. Label the end points *p* and *q*. 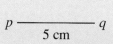	**2.** Use your protractor to draw an angle of 60° at *p*. 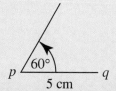

3. Use your ruler, or compass, to mark the point r, so that $\|pr\| = 4$ cm. 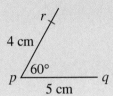	**4.** Using your ruler, join r to q. The triangle pqr is now drawn as required. 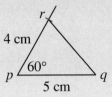

3. Given the length of one side and two angles (ASA)

Example ▼

Construct a triangle xyz so that $\|xy\| = 7$ cm, $\|\angle yxz\| = 40°$, and $\|\angle xyz\| = 70°$.

Solution:
A rough sketch, with the given information, is shown on the right.

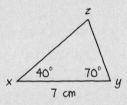

1. Using your ruler, draw a horizontal line segment 7 cm in length. Label the end points x and y. 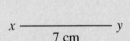	**2.** Use your protractor to draw an angle of $40°$ at x. 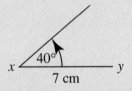
3. Use your protractor to draw an angle of $70°$ at y. 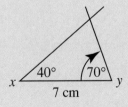	**4.** Where these two lines meet, label the point z. The triangle xyz is now drawn as required. 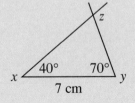

4. Given a right angle, the hypotenuse, and another side (RHS)

Example ▼

Construct the triangle *abc* so that $|\angle bac| = 90°$, $|ab| = 7$ cm, and $|bc| = 8$ cm.

Solution:
A rough sketch, with the given information, is shown on the right.

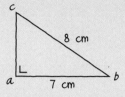

---

1. Using your ruler, draw a horizontal segment 7 cm in length. Label the end points *a* and *b*.

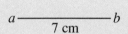

2. Using your protractor or set square, draw an angle of 90° at *a*.

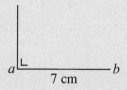

---

3. Set your compass to a radius of 8 cm. Place the compass point on *b*. Draw an arc to meet the vertical line. Label this point *c*.

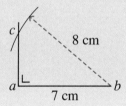

4. Using your ruler, join *b* to *c*. The triangle *abc* is now drawn as required.

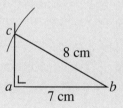

Exercise 25.4 ▼

Construct accurately each of the following triangles, with all dimensions in centimetres (the diagrams are not drawn to scale):

1.

2.

3.

4.

5.

8
40°
7

6.

5
60°
6

7.

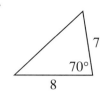

7
70°
8

8.

5
50°
4

9.

50° 45°
8

10.

75° 40°
6

11.

50° 70°
7

12.

60°
80°
9

13.

5
4

14.

6 7

15.

6
4

16.

8
7

17.

50° 60°
7

18.

7
4
6

19.

9
6

20.

75°
60°
8

Construct accurately each of the following triangles.
(It is good practice to draw a rough sketch first and to draw one side as a horizontal base at the beginning.)

21. $|ab| = 5$ cm, $|\angle bac| = 50°$, and $|ac| = 4$ cm.
22. $|ab| = 6$ cm, $|\angle bac| = 60°$, and $|\angle abc| = 40°$.
23. $|\angle bac| = 90°$, $|ab| = 6$ cm, and $|bc| = 7$ cm.
24. $|xy| = 7$ cm, $|xz| = 6$ cm, and $|yz| = 5$ cm.
25. $|pq| = 9$ cm, $|\angle qpr| = 30°$, and $|\angle pqr| = 30°$.
26. $|ab| = |ac| = |bc| = 6$ cm.
27. $|pq| = 7$ cm, $|\angle rpq| = 80°$, and $|pr| = 6$ cm.
28. $|rs| = 9$ cm, $|\angle srt| = 45°$, and $|\angle rst| = = 65°$.
29. $|pr| = 5$ cm, $|\angle rpq| = 90°$, and $|rq| = 6$ cm.
30. $|xy| = 5$ cm, $|xz| = 8$ cm, and $|yz| = 6$ cm.
31. $|\angle bac| = 70°$, $|ac| = 6$ cm, and $|\angle bca| = 60°$.
32. $|xy| = 6$ cm, $|\angle zxy| = 100°$, and $|xz| = 7$ cm.

Congruent triangles

Congruent means **identical**. Two triangles are said to be congruent if they are identical in every respect, i.e. they have **equal lengths of sides, equal angles, and equal areas**. In other words, they have the exact same size and shape. One could be placed on top of the other so as to cover it exactly.

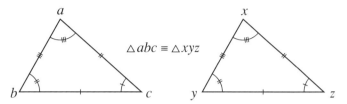

$$\triangle abc \equiv \triangle xyz$$

The symbol for congruence is $\equiv$. The fact that $\triangle abc$ is congruent to $\triangle xyz$ is written $\triangle abc \equiv \triangle xyz$. For two triangles to be congruent (identical), the three sides and three angles of one triangle must be equal to the three sides and three angles of the other triangle. However, it is not necessary to prove all six equalities to show that the two triangles are congruent. Any of the following four cases is sufficient to prove that two triangles are congruent. Notice that these are the same four types of triangle that can be constructed when you are given certain information.

Case 1

three sides of one triangle   =   **three sides of the other triangle**

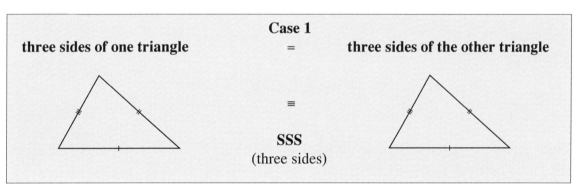

$\equiv$

SSS
(three sides)

Case 2

two sides and the included angle of one triangle   =   **two sides and the included angle of the other triangle**

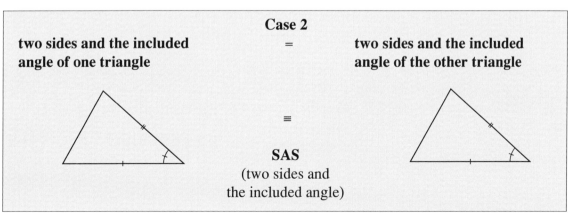

$\equiv$

SAS
(two sides and the included angle)

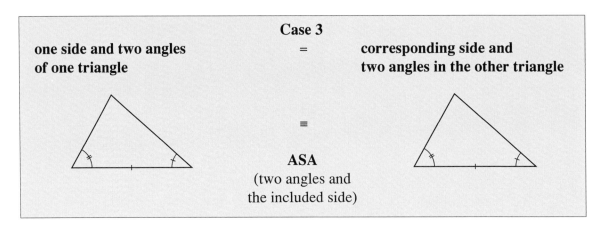

Case 3

one side and two angles   =   corresponding side and
of one triangle   two angles in the other triangle

≡

ASA
(two angles and
the included side)

Note: If any two pairs of angles are equal, the third pair of angles must also be equal.
It is essential that the equal sides correspond to each other.

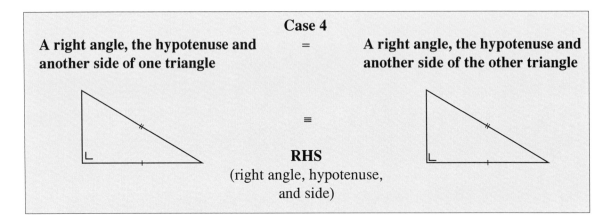

Case 4

A right angle, the hypotenuse and   =   A right angle, the hypotenuse and
another side of one triangle   another side of the other triangle

≡

RHS
(right angle, hypotenuse,
and side)

Note: For the study of congruent triangles it is important to understand the following:
   1. Corresponding angles are the angles opposite equal sides.
   2. Corresponding sides are the sides opposite equal angles.
   3. Three elements are necessary for each case of congruence. However, one of these
   elements must be the length of at least one of the sides.

Many geometrical properties can be proved using the four cases of congruent triangles and
the previous information on angles. Always state which case of congruence is used, i.e.
whether SSS, SAS, ASA, or RHS. State the reasons why the angles used are equal, e.g. alternate angles.

abcd is a parallelogram, with diagonals intersecting at *m*.
Prove that:

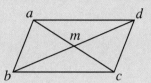

(i) △*abc* is congruent to △*adc*
(ii) △*amb* is congruent to △*cmd*
(iii) △*amd* is congruent to △*bmc*.

Solution:

(i) Redraw △*abc* and △*adc* separately.

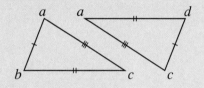

|*ab*| = |*cd*|	opp. sides
|*bc*| = |*ad*|	opp. sides
|*ac*| = |*ac*|	same side

Therefore △*abc* ≡ △*adc* (SSS)

(ii) Redraw △*amb* and △*cmd*; mark angles 1 and 2.

|∠1| = |∠2|	vertically opposite angles
|*am*| = |*md*|	diagonals bisect each other
|*bm*| = |*mc*|	diagonals bisect each other

Therefore △*amb* ≡ △*cmd* (SAS)

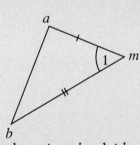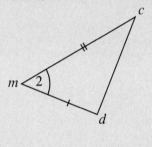

(iii) Redraw △*amd* and △*bmc*.
Mark angles 1, 2, 3 and 4.

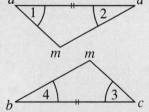

|*ad*| = |*bc*|	opp. sides
|∠1| = |∠3|	alternate angles
|∠2| = |∠4|	alternate angles

Therefore △*amd* ≡ △*bmc* (ASA)

Note: In each example, only one case of congruence was used. It should be noted that in
many situations more than one case of congruence can be used.

Under a translation, axial symmetry, or central symmetry, the shape and size of a figure
remain **exactly the same**. Therefore when these transformations are applied to a triangle, the
image is always a **congruent** triangle.

1. State the four cases in which triangles can be congruent.

Write down the type of congruence required for each of the following pairs of triangles. (All dimensions are in centimetres; diagrams are not drawn to scale.)

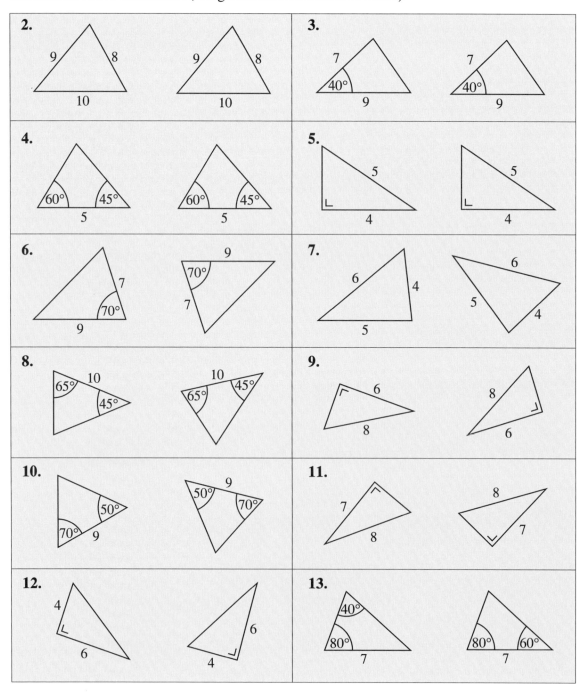

14. Explain why $\triangle xyw$ and $\triangle xzw$ are congruent.

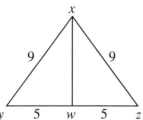

15. *abcd* is a rectangle. Explain why $\triangle abc$ and $\triangle adc$ are congruent.

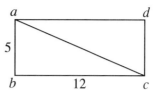

16. [*ps*] and [*qr*] are diameters of the circle with centre *o*.
Are $\triangle opq$ and $\triangle ors$ congruent?
Give a reason for your answer.

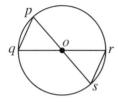

17. *vwxy* is a rhombus with diagonals intersecting at *o*.
(i) Explain why $\triangle owv \equiv \triangle oyv$.
(ii) Explain why $\triangle wvy \equiv \triangle wxy$.

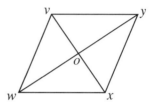

Exercise 25.6 ▼

Chapter test

(**Note:** This exercise revises all the geometry chapters, i.e. chapter 20, 21, and 25.)

1. Calculate the value of *x* in each of the following diagrams:

(i)

(ii)

(iii)

(iv)

(v) *abcd* is a parallelogram

(vi) $qp \,||\, sr$

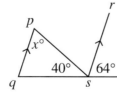

(vii) $L\,||\,M$

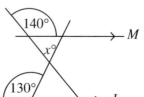

(viii) circle with centre *k*

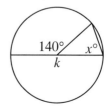

2. [*bd*] is a diagonal of the parallelogram *abcd*.
Calculate the value of *y*.

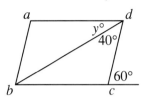

3. *wxyz* is a parallelogram.
$|\angle wxy| = 80°$ and $|wy| = |xy|$.
Calculate the value of $|\angle ywz|$.

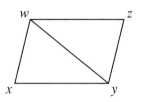

4. $ab \parallel cd$, $|\angle abc| = 35°$, and $|pc| = |pd|$.
Name another angle that measures 35°.
Hence, calculate $|\angle bpd|$.

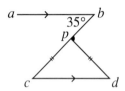

5. *L* and *M* are parallel lines.
Find the value of *x* and the value of *y*.

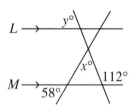

6. A circular clock shows the time to be half past one. What time would the hands show under an axial symmetry in the line joining twelve and six?

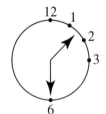

7. *prst* is a parallelogram with its diagonals intersecting at *v*. Name the image of the triangle *prt* under the central symmetry in *v*.

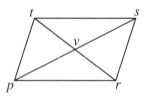

8. *k* is the centre of a circle. [*xz*] and [*yw*] are diameters, at right angles to each other.
What is the image of △*ykx* under axial symmetry in *xz*?

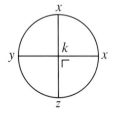

9. [*ps*] and [*qr*] are diameters of the circle with centre *o*.
Find the image of [*pq*] under the central symmetry in the point *o*.

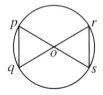

10. *pqrs* is a square, and *sqrt* is a parallelogram.
  (i) Write down the image of the triangle *pqs* under the translation $\overrightarrow{qr}$.
  (ii) Find the ratio:

  (a) $\dfrac{\text{area of } \triangle pqs}{\text{area of figure } pqrt}$

  (b) $\dfrac{\text{area of figure } pqrt}{\text{area of square } pqrs}$

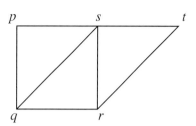

11. The area of $\triangle pxy$ is 12 cm^2.
Find the area of the rectangle *wxyz*.

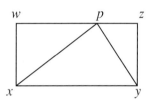

12. The area of the parallelogram *pqrs* is 16 cm^2.
Find the area of the triangle *qrt*.

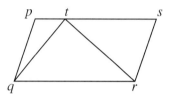

13. In a parallelogram *pqrs*, the area of the triangle *pqr* is 19 cm^2.
Find the area of the parallelogram.

14. Calculate the length of the missing side in each of the following right-angled triangles:

(i)   **(ii)**   **(iii)**   **(iv)**

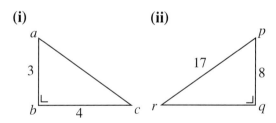
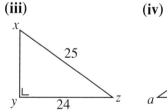
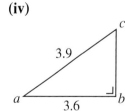

15. In a circle with centre *c* and radius 2.5 cm, $|pq| = 4$ cm.
Calculate $|pr|$.

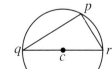

16. *abcd* is a parallelogram whose diagonals intersect at right angles at *o*.
If $|ac| = 6$ and $|bd| = 8$, show that $|ab| = |ad|$.

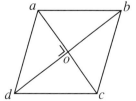

17. In $\triangle xyz$, $|xy| = |yz|$ and $|\angle xyz| = 90°$. If $|xy| = \sqrt{8}$, calculate $|xz|$.

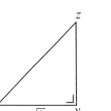

18. $abcd$ is a square, and $|ac| = \sqrt{18}$. Calculate the length of a side of the square.

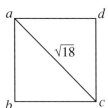

19. The side of a square is 5 cm long. Calculate the length of its diagonal. Write your answer in the form $\sqrt{k}$ (square root form).

20. $abcd$ is a parallelogram.
$ae \perp bc$, $|ab| = 5$ cm, $|ad| = 10$ cm, and $|ec| = 7$ cm.
Calculate:
(i) $|be|$ **(ii)** $|ae|$ **(iii)** the area of $abcd$
(iv) the length of the perpendicular from c to $[ab]$.

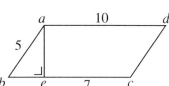

21. $abcd$ is a rectangle having diagonals intersecting at k.
$awbc$ and $pdbc$ are parallelograms.
$|bc| = 4$ and $|dc| = 3$.
(i) Name any two isosceles triangles not equal in area.
(ii) Find the image of $\triangle wbd$ under the translation $\overrightarrow{bc}$.
(iii) Name two angles each equal to $|\angle awb|$.
(iv) Calculate the area of the figure $wbcp$.
(v) Prove that $\triangle awb$ and $\triangle pdc$ are congruent.
(vi) Calculate $|bd|$.

22. $vwxy$ and $xrst$ are parallelograms. Their diagonals intersect at z and m, respectively.
x is the midpoint of $[wt]$ and of $[yr]$.
(i) Name two line segments each equal in length to $|vz|$.
(ii) What is the image of $[xs]$ under the translation $\overrightarrow{rx}$?
(iii) Say why $wrty$ is a parallelogram.
(iv) If $|\angle trs| = 25°$ and $|\angle wyx| = 42°$, find $|\angle wxy|$.
(v) Say why the triangle wxy is congruent to the triangle rtx.

23. $pqrs$ is a square and $pacs$ is a parallelogram, where
$|aq| = |qc| = |cr|$.
(i) Find the image of the triangle paq under the translation $\overrightarrow{ac}$.
(ii) Name two line segments each equal in length to $[ac]$.
(iii) If $|pq| = 4$, show that $|pa| = \sqrt{20}$.
(iv) Calculate the area of the figure $pqcs$.
(v) Prove that
$|\angle scq| = |\angle apq| + |\angle pqa|$.

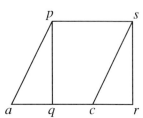

24. *abcm* and *mbcs* are parallelograms.

$|\angle crs| = 90°$.

$|am|$ and $|ab|$ are **not** equal.

(i) Name two line segments each equal in length to $|am|$.

(ii) Name two angles each equal to $|\angle mab|$.

(iii) Give a reason why the area of $\triangle abm$ equals the area of $\triangle mbc$.

(iv) Name a translation under which $\triangle mcs$ is the image of $\triangle abm$.

(v) The area of the figure *abrs* is 252 cm^2.
Calculate $|cr|$ if $|rs| = 14$ cm and $|bc| = 10$ cm.

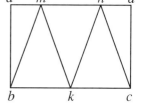

25. *abcd* is a rectangle. The midpoint of $[bc]$ is k.

$|bk| = |mn|$ and $|am| = |nd|$.

(i) Find the image of the triangle *mbk* under the translation $\vec{bk}$.

(ii) Name two parallelograms.

(iii) Name two angles each equal to $|\angle mbk|$.

(iv) If $|ab| = 6.8$ and $|mn| = 5$, calculate the area of the figure *mbcn*.

(v) If $|\angle mbk| = |\angle mkb|$, prove that $|\angle bmk| = 2|\angle abm|$.

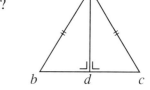

26. *abc* is an isosceles triangle where

$|ab| = |ac|$ and $ad \perp bc$.

(i) What is the image of $[ab]$ under the axial symmetry in *ad*?

(ii) If $|ab| = 5$ cm and $|ad| = 4$ cm, calculate $|bc|$.

(iii) Calculate the area of the triangle *abc*.

(iv) Say why the triangles *abd* and *adc* are congruent.

(v) Prove that
$|\angle abd| + |\angle acd| = 180° - 2|\angle dac|$.

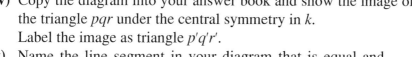

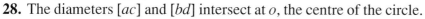

27. The diagram shows a circle with centre k, and a triangle *pqr* in which $|pq| = |qr| = |rp|$.

(i) Find $|\angle rpq|$.

(ii) If $|\angle kpq| = 30°$, find $|\angle pkq|$.

(iii) Say why the triangles *pkq* and *prk* are congruent.

(iv) Copy the diagram into your answer book and show the image of the triangle *pqr* under the central symmetry in k.
Label the image as triangle $p'q'r'$.

(v) Name the line segment in your diagram that is equal and parallel to $[pr]$.

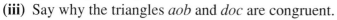

28. The diameters $[ac]$ and $[bd]$ intersect at o, the centre of the circle.

(i) Name two angles each equal to $|\angle dao|$.

(ii) Find the image of the triangle *abc* under the central symmetry in the point o.

(iii) Say why the triangles *aob* and *doc* are congruent.

(iv) If the area of the circle is 314, calculate its radius, assuming $\pi = 3.14$.

(v) If $|\angle bao| = 60°$, prove that $|ab| = |ob|$.

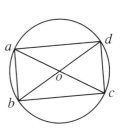

341

29. o is the centre of a circle. The diameters $[ac]$ and $[bd]$ intersect at right angles.

    (i) Find $|\angle bao|$.

    (ii) Name two angles each equal to $|\angle bao|$.

    (iii) Find the image of the triangle bao under the central symmetry in the point o.

    (iv) If the area of the triangle bao is 24.5 square units, calculate the radius of the circle.

    (v) Calculate

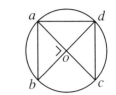

$$\frac{\text{area of triangle } abd}{\text{area of the circle}}$$

assuming $\pi = \dfrac{22}{7}$.

Give your answer as a fraction in its lowest terms.

30. c is the centre of a circle where $|\angle acy| = 60°$ and $|xb| = 7$.

    (i) Find the image of $\triangle xcb$ under the central symmetry in c.

    (ii) Find $|\angle axc|$.

    (iii) Name two angles each equal to $|\angle acy|$.

    (iv) Calculate $|ab|$.

    (v) Using angles, find the ratio

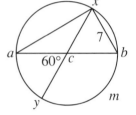

$$\frac{\text{area of region } cymb}{\text{area of circle}}$$

assuming $\pi = \frac{22}{7}$, if necessary.

Give your answer as a fraction in its lowest terms.

31. $[ab]$ is a diameter of a circle with centre c and h a point on the circle.

    (i) Name two isosceles triangles.

    (ii) Say why $\angle ahb$ is a right angle.

    (iii) The area of the triangle ahb is $96\sqrt{3}$ square units.

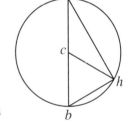

       If $|hb| = 8\sqrt{3}$ units, calculate $|ah|$.

    (iv) Prove that $|\angle ahc| + |\angle cbh| = 90°$.

    (v) If $|hb| = |bc|$, prove that $|\angle chb| = 60°$.

In the following construction questions, show all construction lines clearly.

32. Construct $\triangle abc$ so that $|ab| = 7$ cm, $|\angle bac| = 70°$, and $|ac| = 6$ cm.

33. Construct $\triangle xyz$ so that $|xy| = 8$ cm, $|xz| = 7$ cm, and $|yz| = 6$ cm.

34. Construct $\triangle pqr$ so that $|pq| = 6$ cm, $|\angle qpr| = 45°$, and $|\angle pqr| = 60°$.

35. Construct $\triangle abc$ so that $|\angle cab| = 90°$, $|bc| = 8$ cm, and $|ab| = 7$ cm.

36. Draw a line segment $[xy]$ so that $|xy| = 10$ cm.

Construct the perpendicular bisector of $[xy]$.

37. Using your protractor, draw $\angle abc$ so that $|\angle abc| = 80°$.

Construct the bisector of $\angle abc$.

38. Draw a line segment $[xy]$ so that $|xy| = 81$ mm.

Show by construction how to divide the line segment into three equal parts.

CHAPTER 26

TRIGONOMETRY

Trigonometric ratios and right-angled triangles

In a right-angled triangle, special ratios exist between the angles and the lengths of the sides. We look at three of these ratios.

Consider the right-angled triangle below with the acute angle P:

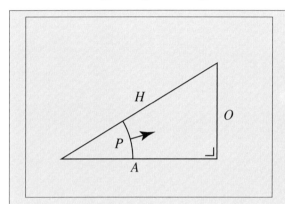

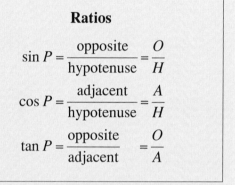

Ratios

$$\sin P = \frac{\text{opposite}}{\text{hypotenuse}} = \frac{O}{H}$$

$$\cos P = \frac{\text{adjacent}}{\text{hypotenuse}} = \frac{A}{H}$$

$$\tan P = \frac{\text{opposite}}{\text{adjacent}} = \frac{O}{A}$$

Memory Aid: <u>O</u>h, <u>h</u>ell, <u>a</u>nother <u>h</u>our <u>o</u>f <u>a</u>lgebra, sin, cos, and tan.
Each trigonometric ratio links two sides and an angle in a right-angled triangle.

Notes:
1. The side opposite the right angle is called the **hypotenuse, H**. The side opposite the angle P is called the **opposite, O**. The side near the angle P is called the **adjacent, A**.
2. If the lengths of any two sides are known, the third side can be found using Pythagoras's theorem: $A^2 + O^2 = H^2$, where A, O and H are the lengths of the sides.
3. The three angles of a triangle add up to $180°$.
4. Sin, cos and tan are short for sine, cosine, and tangent, respectively.
5. The arrow points to the side opposite the angle under consideration.

We can write trigonometric ratios for the two acute angles in a right-angled triangle. Make sure you know which angle you are using and which sides are the opposite and adjacent (the hypotenuse is always opposite the right angle). A good idea is to draw an arrow for the angle under consideration to indicate the opposite side to the angle.

Consider the right-angled triangle with sides of 5, 12 and 13 and angles P and Q, as shown:
Write down the ratios:

(i) $\sin P$ **(ii)** $\cos P$ **(iii)** $\tan P$

(iv) $\sin Q$ **(v)** $\cos Q$ **(vi)** $\tan Q$

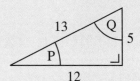

Solution:

Angle P

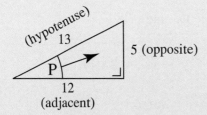

Angle Q

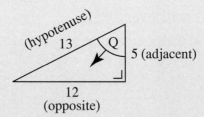

(i) $\sin P = \dfrac{O}{H} = \dfrac{5}{13}$

(ii) $\cos P = \dfrac{A}{H} = \dfrac{12}{13}$

(iii) $\tan P = \dfrac{O}{A} = \dfrac{5}{12}$

(iv) $\sin Q = \dfrac{O}{H} = \dfrac{12}{13}$

(v) $\cos Q = \dfrac{A}{H} = \dfrac{5}{13}$

(vi) $\tan Q = \dfrac{O}{A} = \dfrac{12}{5}$

Use Pythagoras's theorem to find the value of x.
Hence, write down the value of the ratio $\cos \theta$.

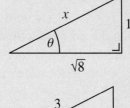

Solution:
$$x^2 = 1^2 + (\sqrt{8})^2$$
$$x^2 = 1 + 8$$
$$x^2 = 9$$
$$x = \sqrt{9} = 3$$
$$\cos \theta = \frac{A}{H} = \frac{\sqrt{8}}{3}$$

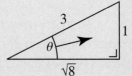

Note: It is good practice to leave the answer in surd (square root) form.

In each of the following right-angled triangles, write down the value of the ratios

(i) sin *P*   **(ii)** cos *P*   **(iii)** tan *P*.

1.
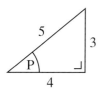

2.
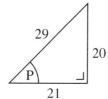

3.
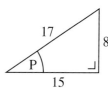

In each of the following right-angled triangles, write down the value of the ratios

(i) sin *A*   **(ii)** cos *A*   **(iii)** tan *A*   **(iv)** sin *B*   **(v)** cos *B*   **(vi)** tan *B*.

4.
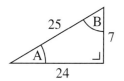

5.
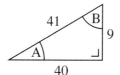

6.
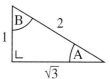

Evaluate each of the following:

7. $(\sqrt{5})^2 + 2^2$ **8.** $(\sqrt{2})^2 + 1^2$ **9.** $(\sqrt{3^2}) + (\sqrt{5})^2$ **10.** $(\sqrt{7})^2 + (\sqrt{8})^2$

Use Pythagoras's theorem to find *x*, the length of the missing side, in surd form where necessary, and express sin *Q*, cos *Q* and tan *Q* as a simple fraction or surd in each of the following:

11.
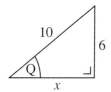

12.
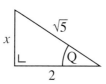

13.

14.

15.
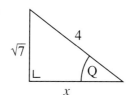

16.
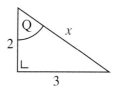

Use of a calculator

You can find values of sin, cos and tan for angles measured in degrees using a calculator. Before entering angles in degrees, make sure the calculator is in 'degree mode'. You will usually see DEG or D at the top of the display.

The sin, cos and tan keys

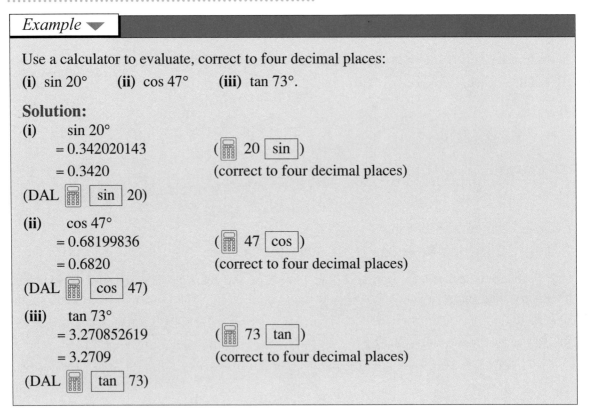

Example ▼

Use a calculator to evaluate, correct to four decimal places:

(i) sin 20°   **(ii)** cos 47°   **(iii)** tan 73°.

Solution:

(i)   sin 20°
        = 0.342020143   (▦ 20 sin)
        = 0.3420   (correct to four decimal places)
(DAL ▦ sin 20)

(ii)   cos 47°
        = 0.68199836   (▦ 47 cos)
        = 0.6820   (correct to four decimal places)
(DAL ▦ cos 47)

(iii)   tan 73°
        = 3.270852619   (▦ 73 tan)
        = 3.2709   (correct to four decimal places)
(DAL ▦ tan 73)

Note: DAL means 'direct algebraic logic'.

Exercise 26.2 ▼

Use your calculator to evaluate each of the following, correct to four decimal places:

1. sin 42°	**2.** cos 72°	**3.** tan 40°	**4.** sin 82°
5. cos 10°	**6.** tan 65°	**7.** cos 11°	**8.** tan 59°
9. sin 86°	**10.** tan 13°	**11.** sin 22°	**12.** cos 5°
13. 10 tan 53°	**14.** 20 cos 17°	**15.** 8 tan 34°	**16.** 4 sin 43°

Calculate exactly:

17. tan 45°	**18.** cos 60°	**19.** sin 30°	**20.** cos 90°

Show that:

21. $2 \tan 40° \neq \tan 80°$ **22.** $\cos 50 \neq 2 \cos 20°$ **23.** $\sin 90° = \tan 45°$

The $\boxed{\sin^{-1}}$, $\boxed{\cos^{-1}}$ and $\boxed{\tan^{-1}}$ keys

Given a value of $\sin \theta$, $\cos \theta$, or $\tan \theta$, we can find the value of the angle θ using the $\boxed{\sin^{-1}}$, $\boxed{\cos^{-1}}$ or $\boxed{\tan^{-1}}$ key, respectively. On most calculators, $\boxed{\sin^{-1}}$, $\boxed{\cos^{-1}}$ and $\boxed{\tan^{-1}}$ are obtained by first pressing $\boxed{\text{INV}}$ or $\boxed{\text{2nd F}}$ and then pressing $\boxed{\sin}$, $\boxed{\cos}$ or $\boxed{\tan}$, as the case may be.

Example ▼

Find the value of θ, to the nearest degree, given that

(i) $\sin \theta = 0.54$ **(ii)** $\cos \theta = \dfrac{2}{7}$ **(iii)** $\tan \theta = \dfrac{3.5}{4}$.

Solution:
(i) $\sin \theta = 0.54$
$\qquad \theta = 32.68363885°$ $\qquad$ ($\boxed{⌨}$ 0.54 $\boxed{\text{INV}}$ sin)
$\qquad \theta = 33°$ $\qquad$ (correct to the nearest degree)
(DAL $\boxed{⌨}$ $\boxed{\text{INV}}$ $\boxed{\sin}$ 0.54)

(ii) $\cos \theta = \dfrac{2}{7}$
$\qquad \theta = 73.3984504°$ $\qquad$ ($\boxed{⌨}$ 2 $\boxed{a\frac{b}{c}}$ 7 $\boxed{\text{INV}}$ $\boxed{\cos}$)
$\qquad \theta = 73°$ $\qquad$ (correct to the nearest degree)
(DAL $\boxed{⌨}$ $\boxed{\text{INV}}$ $\boxed{\cos}$ 2 $\boxed{a\frac{b}{c}}$ 7)

Note: 2 $\boxed{a\frac{b}{c}}$ 7 could also be keyed in: 2 $\boxed{÷}$ 7 $\boxed{=}$

(iii) $\tan \theta = \dfrac{3.5}{4}$ $\qquad$ (essential to press $\boxed{=}$)
$\qquad \theta = 41.18592517°$ $\qquad$ ($\boxed{⌨}$ 3.5 $\boxed{÷}$ 4 $\boxed{=}$ $\boxed{\text{INV}}$ $\boxed{\tan}$)
$\qquad \theta = 41°$ $\qquad$ (correct to the nearest degree)
(DAL $\boxed{⌨}$ $\boxed{\text{INV}}$ $\boxed{\tan}$ $\boxed{(}$ 3.5 $\boxed{÷}$ 4 $\boxed{)}$)

Note: $\dfrac{3.5}{4} = \dfrac{7}{8}$ (multiply top and bottom by 2)

$\qquad$ Therefore $\dfrac{3.5}{4}$ could be keyed in as 7 $\boxed{a\frac{b}{c}}$ 8 or 7 $\boxed{÷}$ 8 $\boxed{=}$

347

Use your calculator to find each of the following angles (correct to the nearest degree):

1. $\sin A = 0.4$

2. $\cos B = 0.25$

3. $\tan C = 1.22$

4. $\cos \theta = 0.843$

5. $\tan P = 0.2347$

6. $\sin Q = 0.3$

7. $\tan \theta = 2$

8. $\sin \theta = 0.5436$

9. $\cos \theta = 0.67$

10. $\tan A = \dfrac{1}{4}$

11. $\sin B = \dfrac{7}{8}$

12. $\tan C = \dfrac{2}{5}$

13. $\sin \theta = \dfrac{35}{100}$

14. $\cos A = \dfrac{1}{3}$

15. $\tan B = \dfrac{3}{2}$

16. $\cos A = \dfrac{3}{10}$

17. $\tan B = \dfrac{4.5}{8}$

18. $\sin C = \dfrac{2.5}{4}$

19. $\sin \angle abc = \dfrac{22.5}{30}$

20. $\cos \angle bac = \dfrac{8.1}{10}$

21. $\tan \angle cab = \dfrac{3.49}{5}$

Find each angle exactly:

22. $\cos A = 0.5$

23. $\sin B = 1$

24. $\tan \theta = \sqrt{3}$

25. $\sin \theta = \dfrac{1}{2}$

26. $\cos A = \dfrac{\sqrt{3}}{2}$

27. $\sin B = \dfrac{1}{\sqrt{2}}$

Calculating angles in a right-angled triangle

The three angles of a triangle add up to 180°.
In a right-angled triangle, one of the angles is 90°.
Therefore the other two angles must add up to 90°.

$A° + B° = 90$

We can find the size of an angle in a right-angled triangle if we know the length of two of its sides, with the following steps:

1. Draw a right-angled triangle (if not given).
2. Mark the angle under consideration.
3. Name the two sides you know: any two of the opposite, adjacent, or hypotenuse.
4. Choose the trigonometric ratio that links the angle required with the two known lengths.

(i)

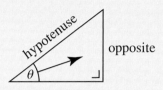

Hypotenuse and opposite known

Therefore use the sine ratio

$$\sin \theta = \frac{\text{opposite}}{\text{hypotenuse}}$$

(ii)

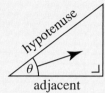

Hypotenuse and adjacent known

Therefore use the cosine ratio

$$\cos \theta = \frac{\text{adjacent}}{\text{hypotenuse}}$$

(iii)

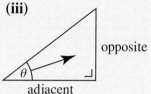

Opposite and adjacent known

Therefore use the tangent ratio

$$\tan \theta = \frac{\text{opposite}}{\text{adjacent}}$$

5. Use your calculator to find the angle.

Example ▼

In $\triangle pqr$, $|\angle pqr| = 90°$,
$|pq| = 6$ m, and $|pr| = 7$ m.
Find, to the nearest degree,
(i) $|\angle qpr|$ **(ii)** $|\angle prq|$.

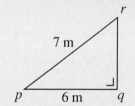

Solution:
(i) $\angle qpr$
  For $\angle qpr$,
  adjacent = 6 m, hypotenuse = 7 m.
  We know adjacent and hypotenuse,
  Therefore use the cosine ratio.

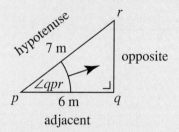

$$\cos \angle qpr = \frac{\text{adjacent}}{\text{hypotenuse}}$$

$$\cos \angle qpr = \frac{6}{7}$$

  $|\angle qpr| = 31.00271913°$ ($\boxed{}$ 6 $\boxed{a\frac{b}{c}}$ 7 $\boxed{\text{INV}}$ $\boxed{\cos}$)
  $|\angle qpr| = 31°$ (correct to the nearest degree)

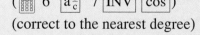

(ii) As $|\angle pqr| = 90°$,
  $|\angle qpr| + |\angle prq| = 90°$
  $\Rightarrow$ $31° + |\angle prq| = 90°$
       $|\angle prq| = 90° - 31° = 59°$

Calculate, to the nearest degree, the angles marked with a letter:

1.

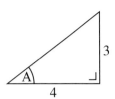

2.

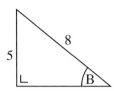

3.

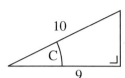

4.

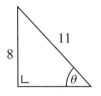

5.

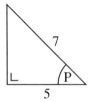

6.

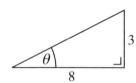

7.

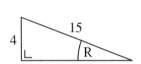

8.

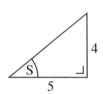

9.

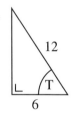

10.

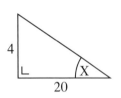

11.

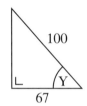

12.

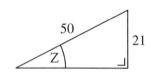

13.

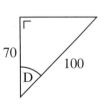

14.

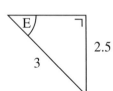

15.

16. In $\triangle abc$, $|\angle abc| = 90°$,
$|ab| = 18$, and $|bc| = 12$ cm.
Find, to the nearest degree,
(i) $|\angle bac|$ (ii) $|\angle bca|$.

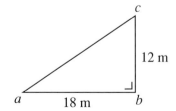

17. In $\triangle pqr$, $|\angle prq| = 90°$, $|pq| = 100$ m, and $|qr| = 72$ m. Find, to the nearest degree,
    (i) $|\angle pqr|$ **(ii)** $|\angle qpr|$.

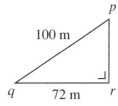

18. In $\triangle xyz$, $|\angle xyz| = 90°$, $|xz| = 200$ cm, and $|yz| = 150$ cm.
    (i) Write down the ratio sin $\angle yxz$, in its simplest form.
    (ii) Calculate, to the nearest degree,
        (a) $|\angle yxz|$ **(b)** $|\angle yzx|$.

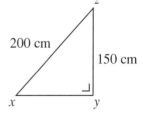

19. In $\triangle abc$, $|\angle abc| = 90°$, $|ab| = 4$ cm, $|bc| = 3$ cm, and $|ac| = 5$ cm. Draw a rough diagram of the triangle. Find, to the nearest degree,
    (i) $|\angle bac|$, using sin $\angle bac$
    (ii) $|\angle bac|$, using cos $\angle bac$
    (iii) $|\angle bac|$, using tan $\angle bac$.

20. Calculate, to the nearest degree, the angle θ in each of the following:
    (i) $10 \sin \theta = 7$ **(ii)** $3 \cos \theta = 2$ **(iii)** $4 \tan \theta = 5$.

Calculating the length of a side in a right-angled triangle

We can use a trigonometric ratio to calculate the length of a side in a right-angled triangle if we know the length of one side and one angle (other than the right angle), with the following steps:

1. Draw a right-angled triangle (if not given), indicating the known angle and known side.
2. Choose the trigonometric ratio that links the required side with the known angle and known side.
3. Write down this equation (the ratio).
4. Put in the known values.
5. Solve the equation to find the required length.

From the right-angled triangle, calculate the value of x, correct to two decimal places.

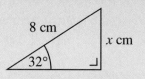

Solution:
We know the hypotenuse, and we require the length of the side **opposite** to the angle of 32°. Therefore use the sine ratio:

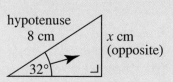

$$\sin \theta = \frac{\text{opposite}}{\text{hypotenuse}}$$

$$\sin 32° = \frac{x}{8} \qquad \text{(put in known values)}$$

$$8 \sin 32° = x \qquad \text{(multiply both sides by 8)}$$

$$8(0.529919264) = x \qquad (\sin 32° = 0.529919264)$$

$$4.239354114 = x \qquad \text{(remove brackets)}$$

$$4.24 = x \qquad \text{(correct to two decimal places).}$$

In $\triangle abc$, $|\angle bca| = 90°$, $|\angle abc| = 34°$, and $|ac| = 20$ m. Calculate $|bc|$, correct to two decimal places.

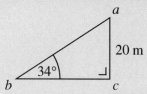

Solution:
Using the angle 34°, the opposite is 20 m and the adjacent is $|bc|$. Therefore use the tangent ratio:

$$\tan \theta = \frac{\text{opposite}}{\text{adjacent}}$$

$$\tan 34° = \frac{20}{|bc|}$$

This is awkward, as $|bc|$ is on the bottom of the fraction. Therefore we calculate $|\angle bac|$. Using the tangent ratio again,

$$\tan \theta = \frac{\text{opposite}}{\text{adjacent}}$$

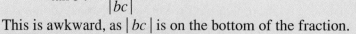

$$\begin{aligned}|\angle abc| + |\angle bac| &= 90° \\ 34° + |\angle bac| &= 90° \\ |\angle bac| &= 90° - 34° \\ |\angle bac| &= 56°\end{aligned}$$

$$\tan 56° = \frac{|bc|}{20}$$

$$20 \tan 56° = |bc| \qquad \text{(multiply both sides by 20)}$$

$$20(1.482560969) = |bc| \qquad (\tan 56° = 1.482560969)$$

$$29.65121937 = |bc| \qquad \text{(remove brackets)}$$

$$29.65 = |bc| \qquad \text{(correct to two decimal places)}$$

Where necessary, give your answers correct to two decimal places.
Calculate the length of the sides marked with a letter (all dimensions in centimetres):

1.

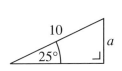

2.

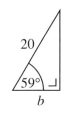

3.

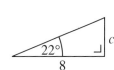

4.

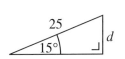

5.

6.

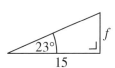

7.

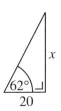

8.

9.

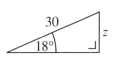

10.

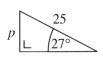

11.

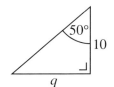

12.

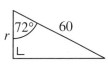

13.

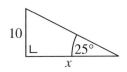

14.

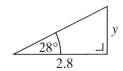

15.

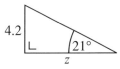

16.

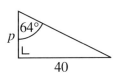

17.

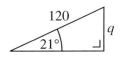

18.

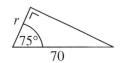

19. In $\triangle xyz$, $|\angle xzy| = 90°$, $|\angle xyz| = 27°$, and $|xy| = 5.8$ cm. Calculate $|yz|$.

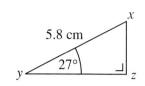

20. In $\triangle abc$, $|\angle abc| = 90°$, $|\angle bac| = 43°$, and $|ab| = 20$. Calculate **(i)** $|bc|$ **(ii)** $|ac|$.

21. In the diagram, $xw \perp yz$, $|xy| = 20$, $|\angle xyw| = 30°$, and $|\angle zxw| = 40°$. Calculate:
 (i) $|xw|$ (exactly)
 (ii) $|wz|$, correct to two decimal places.
 (Hint: Draw $\triangle xyw$ and $\triangle xzw$ separately.)

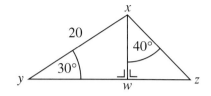

Finding the length of the hypotenuse

In some questions we are given the length of a side and an angle (other than the right angle) and asked to find the length of the hypotenuse. These questions are a little more difficult, as the length required, the hypotenuse, is on the bottom of the ratio, and a few extra steps are needed to find its value.

Example ▼

Calculate the value of x, the hypotenuse of the right-angled triangle shown.
(Give your answer correct to two decimal places.)

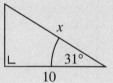

Solution:
We require the hypotenuse and know the adjacent.

Therefore we use the cosine ratio, $\cos \theta = \dfrac{\text{adjacent}}{\text{hypotenuse}}$

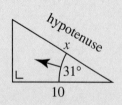

$$\text{Cos } 31° = \frac{10}{x} \qquad \text{(put in known values)}$$

$$x \cos 31° = 10 \qquad \text{(multiply both sides by } x\text{)}$$

$$x = \frac{10}{\cos 31°} \qquad \text{(divide both sides by cos 31°)}$$

$$x = \frac{10}{0·8571673} \qquad \text{(cos 31° = 0.8571673)}$$

$$x = 11.66633397 \quad \text{(divide the bottom into the top)}$$

$$x = 11.67 \qquad \text{(correct to two decimal places)}$$

Calculate the length of the hypotenuse, marked *x*, in each of the triangles (give all answers correct to two decimal places):

1.

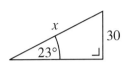

2.

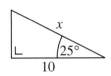

3.

4.

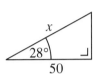

5.

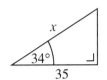

6.

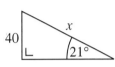

7.

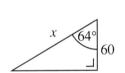

8.

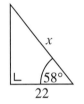

9.

10.

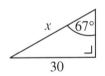

11.

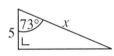

12.

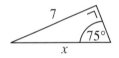

Practical applications

Many practical problems in navigation, surveying, engineering and geography involve solving a triangle. On our course all the problems can be represented with a right-angled triangle. Mark on your triangle the angles and lengths you know, and label what you need to calculate, using the correct ratio to link the angle or length required with the known angle or length. Angles of elevation and depression occur quite often in problems that can be solved with trigonometry.

Angle of elevation
The **angle of elevation** of an object as seen by an observer is the angle between the horizontal line from the object to the observer's eye (upwards from the horizontal).

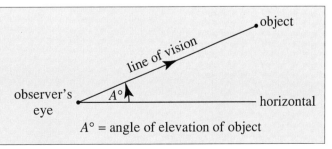

$A°$ = angle of elevation of object

Angle of depression

If the object is below the level of the observer, the angle between the horizontal and the observer's line of vision is called the **angle of depression** (downwards from the horizontal).

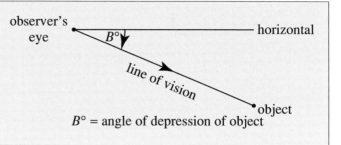

$B°$ = angle of depression of object

Note: An angle of elevation has an equal angle of depression. The angle of elevation from a to b is equal to the angle of depression from b to a.

The angles are alternate angles, as the horizontal lines are parallel.

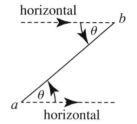

Example ▼

A ladder, of length 5 m, rests against a vertical wall so that the base of the ladder is 1.5 m from the foot of the wall.

Calculate the angle between the ladder and the ground, to the nearest degree.

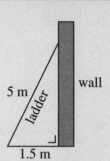

Solution:

Represent the situation with a right-angled triangle.
Let the angle between the ladder and the ground be $A°$.
We know the hypotenuse and the adjacent to angle $A°$.
Therefore use the cosine ratio:

$$\cos A = \frac{\text{adjacent}}{\text{hypotenuse}}$$

$$\cos A = \frac{1.5}{5}$$

$\cos A = 0.3$ (divide the bottom into the top)

$A = 72.54239688°$ (▦ 0.3 |INV| |cos|)

$A = 73°$ (nearest degree)

Therefore the angle between the ladder and the ground is 73° (correct to the nearest degree).

Example ▼

When the angle of elevation of the sun is 28°, an upright
flagpole casts a shadow of length 6 m.
Calculate the height of the pole, correct to one decimal
place.

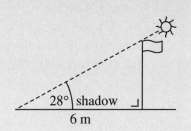

Solution:
Represent the situation with a right-angled triangle.
Let the height of the pole be h m.
We know the adjacent and require the opposite.
Therefore we use the tangent ratio:

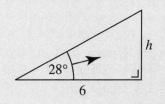

$$\tan 28° = \frac{h}{6} \qquad \left(\frac{\text{opposite}}{\text{adjacent}}\right)$$

$6 \tan 28° = h$ (multiply both sides by 6)

$6(0.531709431) = h$ ($\tan 28° = 0.531709431$)

$3.19025659 = h$ (remove brackets)

$3.2 = h$ (correct to one decimal place)

Therefore the height of the pole is 3.2 m (correct to one decimal place).

Exercise 26.7 ▼

1. The angle of elevation of the top of a flagpole, from a point on
   the ground 24 m from the foot of the pole, is 18°.
   Calculate the height of the flagpole, correct to one place of
   decimals.

2. A ladder of length 6 m rests against a vertical wall so that the
   base of the ladder is 2 m from the wall.
   Calculate, to the nearest degree, the angle between the ladder
   and the ground.

3. From a distance of 100 m, the angle of elevation of the top of
   a tower is 23°.
   Calculate the height of the tower, correct to one place of
   decimals.

4. The shadow of a building is 40 m long, measured on the horizontal ground, when the angle of elevation of the sun is 45°.
   (i)   Calculate the height of the building.
   (ii) How long will the shadow be when the angle of elevation of the sun becomes 38°, correct to the nearest
   metre?

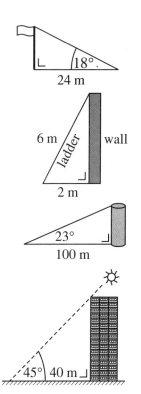

5. A wire is used to support an antenna 14.4 m tall, joining the top of the antenna to a point on the ground 6 m from the base, as shown. Calculate:

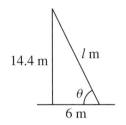

(i) the length, *l* m, of the wire

(i) the angle, θ, that the wire makes with the ground, correct to the nearest degree.

6. A girl standing on level ground casts a shadow 2.3 m long. The angle of elevation of the sun is 27°.

Calculate the girl's height, to the nearest centimetre.

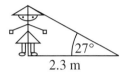

7. A vertical pole, [*pe*], is held on horizontal ground by two tight ropes, [*ap*] and [*bp*]. *a*, *e* and *b* lie in a straight line. $|pa| = 2.5$ m, $|pe| = 2$ m, and $|be| = 2.1$ m.

Calculate:

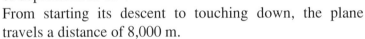

(i) $|ae|$ (ii) $|pb|$

(iii) $|\angle pae|$ (iv) $|\angle epb|$,

correct to the nearest degree.

8. When coming in to land, a light aeroplane starts its descent at a vertical height of *h* m above the ground.

The plane descends along a straight line at a constant angle of depression of 15°.

From starting its descent to touching down, the plane travels a distance of 8,000 m.

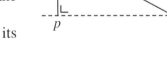

Calculate the vertical height, *h*, at which the plane starts its descent, correct to the nearest metre.

At the start of its descent, the plane is vertically above a point *p* on the ground.

It touches down at a point *q*.

Calculate $|pq|$, correct to the nearest metre.

9. The diagram represents a vertical television aerial, [*ta*].

The aerial casts a shadow [*sa*] on horizontal ground.

If $|ta| = 15$ m and $|sa| = 25$ m, calculate, to the nearest degree, the angle of elevation of the sun

(i.e. calculate $|\angle tsa|$).

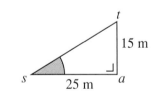

10. The diagram represents the frame *a*, *b*, *c*, *d* of a roof.

$|ab| = 7$ m, $|bc| = 5$ m, and $|bd| = 2.6$ m.

Calculate:

(i) $|ad|$, correct to one decimal place

(ii) $|cd|$, correct to two decimal places

(iii) $|\angle bad|$, correct to the nearest degree

(iv) $|\angle bdc|$, correct to one decimal place.

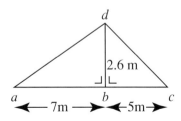

Exercise 26.8 ▼

Chapter test

1. (a) Given that $\sin A = \frac{4}{5}$,
write down the value of
  (i) $\cos A$
  (ii) $\tan A$
  (iii) $\sin B$.

(b) Find $\cos P$, and write your answer as a decimal.
Hence, or otherwise, find the angle P, correct to the
nearest degree.

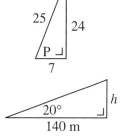

(c) The angle of elevation of the top of a television mast from
a point on the level ground 140 m from the foot of the
mast is 20°.
Find the height h of the mast, correct to two places of decimals.

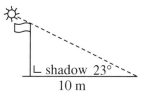

2. (a) If $\cos A = 0.525$, calculate A, to the nearest degree.

(b) When the angle of elevation of the sun is 23°, an upright
flagpole casts a shadow of length 10 m.
Calculate the height of the pole, correct to one place of
decimals.

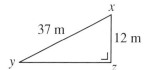

(c) $[xz]$ is a vertical television mast.
$[xy]$ is a supporting cable.
Calculate:
  (i) $|yz|$
  (ii) $|\angle xyz|$, correct to the nearest degree.

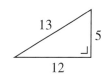

3. (a) Copy the diagram.
Indicate on it the angle A,
when $\tan A = \frac{12}{5}$
Calculate A, correct to the nearest degree.

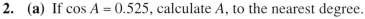

(b) In the triangle abc,
$|\angle acb| = 90°$, $|\angle abc| = 51°$, and
$|ab| = 7.8$.
Calculate:
  (i) $|\angle bac|$
  (ii) $|bc|$, correct to one decimal place.

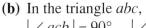

(c) An aeroplane takes off at an angle of 18° to the level ground. It travels a distance of 2,000 m in 25 seconds, as shown.

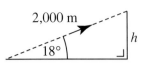

Calculate:
- **(i)** the average speed of the plane, in metres per second.
- **(ii)** the height, h, above the ground after 25 seconds, correct to the nearest metre.

4. (a) $\sin A = \frac{1}{5}$. Calculate the value of A, to the nearest degree.

(b) In $\triangle xyz$, $|\angle xzy| = 90°$, $|\angle xyz| = 55°$, and $|xy| = 8$ cm.
Calculate **(i)** $|xz|$ **(ii)** $|yz|$,
giving your answers correct to two places of decimals.

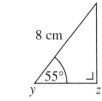

(c) The diagram shows a vertical cliff $[ac]$. A coastguard at a sees a boat b sailing away from the foot of the cliff, c.
If $|ac| = 150$ m and $|bc| = 100$ m,
- **(i)** calculate the angle of elevation, $\angle abc$, of the top of the cliff from the boat, to the nearest degree.
- **(ii)** After it has sailed for three more minutes, the angle of elevation of the top of the cliff from the boat is 45°. Calculate how far the boat has sailed in the three minutes.

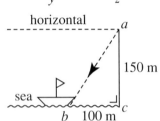

5. (a) (i) Calculate x in the diagram.
(ii) Write down the ratios $\sin A$, $\cos A$, and $\tan A$.
(iii) Calculate A°, correct to the nearest degree.

(b) In $\triangle abc$, $|\angle bca| = 90°$, $|ab| = 39$ m, and $|bc| = 36$ m.
- **(i)** Calculate $|ac|$.
- **(ii)** Write $\tan \angle bac$ in the form $\dfrac{a}{b}$.

Find, to the nearest degree,
- **(iii)** $|\angle bac|$ **(iv)** $|\angle abc|$.

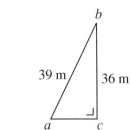

(c) $[qr]$ and $[mn]$ are two vertical poles standing on level ground pn.
$|\angle qpr| = 32°$ and $|pr| = 40$ m.
- **(i)** Calculate $|qr|$.
- **(ii)** If $|mn| = 31$ m, calculate $|rn|$.

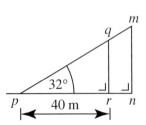

(Give your answers correct to the nearest metre.)

6. **(a)** If $\sin A = \frac{1}{2}$, find **(i)** A **(ii)** $\cos 2A$.

(b) In the triangle pqr, $|\angle prq| = 90°$, $|pq| = 100$ m, and $|qr| = 67$ m.

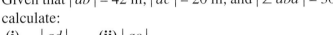

Calculate
(i) $|\angle pqr|$
(ii) $|\angle qpr|$.
(Give answers correct to the nearest degree.)

(c) $[ad]$ is a vertical mast standing on level ground. Wires join a to the ground at b and at c, as in the diagram.

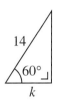

Given that $|ab| = 42$ m, $|dc| = 20$ m, and $|\angle abd| = 30°$, calculate:
(i) $|ad|$ **(ii)** $|ac|$
(iii) $|\angle acd|$, correct to the nearest degree.

7. **(a)** $\tan A = \frac{4}{5}$. Calculate A, correct to the nearest degree.

(b) Write down the value of $\cos 60°$.

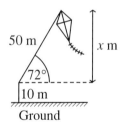

Hence, or otherwise, calculate the value of k in the right-angled triangle shown in the diagram.

(c) A kite is tied to a pole of length 10 m, which makes an angle of 72° with the horizontal. If the length of the string is 50 m, find the value of x, correct to the nearest metre. Hence, calculate the height of the kite above the ground.

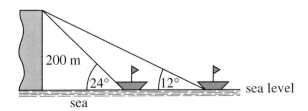

(d) From a boat at sea, the angle of elevation to the top of a vertical cliff, 200 m above sea level, is 12°. After the boat has sailed directly towards the cliff, the angle of elevation of the cliff is found to be 24°. How far did the boat sail towards the cliff, correct to the nearest metre?

USING EQUATIONS TO SOLVE PROBLEMS

Forming expressions

Statements in words can be translated into algebraic expressions. It is common to let x represent the unknown number, usually the smallest, in a problem given in words. However, any other letter would do.

For example, if x represents an unknown number, then:

Words	Expression
5 more than the number	$(x + 5)$
2 less than the number	$(x - 2)$
3 times the number	$3x$
4 times the number, less 1	$(4x - 1)$
a third of the number	$\frac{1}{3}x \ or \ \frac{x}{3}$
the number subtracted from 6	$6 - x$
the difference between two numbers is 8	x and $(x + 8)$
two numbers add up to 10	x and $(10 - x)$

Steps in constructing an equation in solving a practical problem

A numerical problem given in words can often be translated into an equation. The solution of this equation will give the answer to the problem. To solve a practical problem by constructing an equation, do the following:

Step 1:	Read the question carefully a few times.
Step 2:	Let x equal the unknown number that is required.
Step 3:	Write each statement in the problem in terms of x. Use a diagram if necessary.
Step 4:	Use the information in the problem to link the parts in step 3 to form an equation. Make sure both sides are measured in the same units.
Step 5:	Solve the equation (find the unknown number).
Step 6:	Test your solution in the problem itself—**not in your equation**, as your equation may be wrong.

Note: If the problem requires simultaneous equations to be solved, then step 2 becomes 'Let x and y equal the unknown numbers that are required.'

When an equation is constructed from a problem given in words, it may lead to any one of three types of equation:
1. simple linear equation   **2.** simultaneous linear equations   **3.** quadratic equation.

1. Using simple equations to solve problems

Example ▼

Alan has a number of marbles. His friend Brendan has 15 more than he has. Between them they have 39 marbles. How many marbles each have Alan and Brendan?

Solution:
Let x = the number of marbles Alan has.
Then $(x + 15)$ = the number of marbles Brendan has (15 more than Alan).
Link used to form the equation:
Given: (number of marbles Alan has) + (number of marbles Brendan has) = 39

$$\Rightarrow \qquad x \qquad + \qquad (x + 15) \qquad = 39$$
$$\Rightarrow \qquad x + x + 15 = 39$$
$$\Rightarrow \qquad 2x + 15\ = 39$$
$$\Rightarrow \qquad 2x = 39 - 15$$
$$\Rightarrow \qquad 2x = 24$$
$$\Rightarrow \qquad x = 12$$

Number of marbles Alan has = x = 12
Number of marbles Brendan has = $(x + 15) = (12 + 15) = 27$

Example ▼

The perimeter of a rectangle is 46 cm. One side is 5 cm longer than the other. Calculate the area of the rectangle.

Solution:
Let x cm = the length of the shorter side.
Then $(x + 5)$ cm = the length of the longer side (5 cm longer)

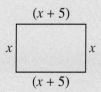

Link used to form the equation:

Given: Perimeter = 46 cm

$\Rightarrow$ $(x + 5) + x + (x + 5) + x = 46$

$\Rightarrow$ $x + 5 + x + x + 5 + x = 46$

$\Rightarrow$ $4x + 10 = 46$

$\Rightarrow$ $4x = 46 - 10$

$\Rightarrow$ $4x = 36$

$\Rightarrow$ $x = 9$

Width of the rectangle = x cm = 9 cm

Length of the rectangle = $(x + 5)$ cm = $(9 + 5)$ cm = 14 cm.

Area = length × breadth = $14 \times 9 = 126$ cm^2

Example ▼

This year, a woman is four times as old as her son. In five years' time she will be three times as old as him. What age is each of them now?

Solution:

Let x = the son's age now.

Then $4x$ = the mother's age now (four times as old).

In five years' time both mother and son will be five years older.

Therefore in five years' time,

son's age = $(x + 5)$ years and mother's age = $(4x + 5)$ years (add 5 to both ages).

Link used to form the equation:

Given, in five years time: mother's age = three times son's age

$\Rightarrow$ $(4x + 5) = 3(x + 5)$

$\Rightarrow$ $4x + 5 = 3x + 15$

$\Rightarrow$ $4x - 3x = 15 - 5$

$\Rightarrow$ $x = 10$

Son's age now = x years = 10 years

Mother's age now = $4x$ years = 4×10 years = 40 years

In questions 1 to 12, do the following:

1. Let x = the unknown number.
   (If there is a second unknown number, write this in terms of x.)
2. From the information in the question, look for a link to form an equation.
3. Solve the equation to find the unknown number, x.

1. A certain number is multiplied by 2, and then 5 is added on. The result is 11. Find the number.
2. A certain number is multiplied by 3, and then 2 is added on. The result is 14. Find the number.
3. A certain number is multiplied by 4, and then 3 is added on. The result is 27. Find the number.
4. A certain number is multiplied by 2, and then 5 is taken away. The result is 19. Find the number.
5. A certain number is multiplied by 3, and then 2 is taken away. The result is 13. Find the number.
6. When 6 is taken from four times a certain number, the answer is 22. Find the number.
7. A certain number is doubled, and then 7 is added on. The result is the same if 10 is added to the number. What is the number?
8. A certain number is multiplied by 3, and then 5 is taken away. The result is the same as multiplying the number by 2 and then adding on 4. Find the number.
9. One number is 3 more than another number. If the two numbers are added, the result is 23. Find the numbers.
10. One number is 7 more than another number. If the two numbers are added, the result is 29. Find the numbers.
11. One number is 4 more than another number. If five times the smaller number is equal to three times the larger number, find the numbers.
12. 5 is added to a certain number, and this new number is multiplied by 3. If the result is 21, find the original number.
13. The length of a rectangle is 4 cm greater than its breadth, as shown.
    (i)   Find, in terms of x, the perimeter of the rectangle.
    If the perimeter is 32 cm,
    (ii) use this information to form an equation
    (iii) solve the equation to find the value of x.

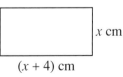

14. The length of a rectangle is 10 cm longer than the breadth. If the breadth is x cm,
    (i)   write down the length in terms of x
    (ii) draw a diagram of the rectangle
    (iii) write, in terms of x, the perimeter of the rectangle.

If the perimeter of the rectangle is 56 cm,

    (iv) use this information to form an equation.

    (v) solve the equation to find the value of x.

15. The perimeter of a rectangle is 42 cm. The length of the rectangle is twice its width. If the width is x cm,

    (i) write down the length in terms of x

    (ii) draw a diagram of the rectangle

    (iii) form an equation in x

    (iv) solve the equation to find the value of x

    (v) calculate the area of the rectangle.

16. This year, Catherine is x years old. Her brother Andrew is two years older. The sum of their ages is 38 years.

    (i) Write Andrew's age in terms of x.

    (ii) Form an equation in x.

    (iii) Solve the equation to find the value of x.

    (iv) How old is Andrew?

17. This year, Edward is x years of age. His sister Jane is six years older.

    (i) Write Jane's age in terms of x.

    (ii) Write down, in terms of x, both their ages two years from now.

In two years, Jane will be twice as old as Edward.

    (iii) Use this information to form an equation.

    (iv) Solve the equation to find the value of x.

18. A woman's age this year is four times that of her son. In four years' time she will be three times as old as her son.

    (i) If the son's age is x years this year, find, in terms of x, his mother's age now.

    (ii) Write, in terms of x, their ages in four years' time.

    (iii) Form an equation in x.

    (iv) Solve the equation to find the value of x.

19. A pen costs 40 cents more than a pencil. The cost of a pencil is x cents.

    (a) Write down, in terms of x, the cost of:

        (i) a pen **(ii)** 4 pencils **(iii)** 3 pens.

    (b) Four pencils and three pens cost €3.30.

        Using this information, write down an equation in terms of x.

    (c) Solve the equation to find x.

    (d) Calculate the cost of a pen.

20. The perimeter of the isosceles triangle shown is 64 cm.

    (i) Using this information, write down an equation in terms of x.

    (ii) Solve the equation to find x.

    (iii) What is the length of the base, $(5x - 1)$ cm?

21. Two cylindrical buckets hold 18 litres and 6 litres of liquid, respectively. To each bucket are now added another $2x$ litres of liquid, so that the first one now holds twice as much as the second one.

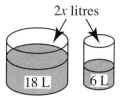

2x litres

18 L   6 L

(i) Express the volume of liquid in each bucket in terms of x.

(ii) Form an equation in x.

(iii) Solve the equation to find the value of x.

22. Three consecutive numbers (i.e. like $3, 4, 5$), are x, $x + 1$, and $x + 2$. When the three numbers are added together the result is 33.

(i) Use this information to form an equation.

(ii) Solve the equation to find the value of x.

(iii) What are the three numbers?

23. A girl bought a coat for $€\frac{x}{2}$ and a hat for $€\frac{x}{5}$.

The total amount of money she spent was €70.

(i) Use this information to form an equation.

(ii) Solve the equation to find the value of x.

(iii) Find the cost of her hat.

2. Using simultaneous equations to solve problems

Method:

1. Let x = one unknown number and y = the other unknown number.
2. Look for **two** facts that **link** x and y, and form two equations.
3. Solve these simultaneous equations.

Example ▼

The sum of two numbers is 8. Four times the first number less three times the second number is 11. Find the two numbers.

Solution:

Let x = the first number and y = the second number.

Two facts that link x and y:

1. The sum of the numbers is 8.
   Equation: $x + y = 8$ ①

2. Four times the first number less three times the second number is 11.
Equation: $4x - 3y = 11$ ②
Now solve the simultaneous equations ① and ②:

$$\begin{array}{ll} x + \ y = \ 8 & ① \\ 4x - 3y = 11 & ② \\ \hline 3x + 3y = 24 & ① \times 3 \\ 4x - 3y = 11 & ② \\ \hline 7x = 35 & \text{(add)} \\ x = 5 & \end{array}$$

$$\begin{array}{ll} x + y = 8 & ① \\ 5 + y = 8 & \\ y = 8 - 5 & \\ y = 3 & \end{array}$$

Put $x = 5$ into ① or ②

Therefore the first number is 5 and the second number is 3.

Example ▼

Five pens and two pencils cost €1.86. Three pens and four pencils cost €1.62.
Find the cost of a pen and the cost of a pencil.

Solution:

Let x cents = the cost of a pen and y cents = the cost of a pencil.
€1.86 = 186c and €1.62 = 162c. Change the euros into cents to avoid decimals.

Two facts that link x and y:

1. Five pens and two pencils cost €1.86.
Equation: $5x + 2y = 186$ ① (both sides in cents)
2. Three pens and four pencils cost €1.62.
Equation: $3x + 4y = 162$ ② (both sides in cents)
Now solve the simultaneous equations ① and ②

$$\begin{array}{ll} 5x + 2y = 186 & ① \\ 3x + 4y = 162 & ② \\ \hline 10x + 4y = 372 & ① \times 2 \\ 3x + 4y = 162 & ② \\ \hline 7x = 210 & \text{(subtract)} \\ x = 30 & \end{array}$$

$$\begin{array}{l} 5x + 2y = 186 \quad ① \\ 5(30) + 2y = 186 \\ 150 + 2y = 186 \\ 2y = 186 - 150 \\ 2y = 36 \\ y = 18 \end{array}$$

Put $x = 30$ into ① or ②

The cost of a pen is 30c and the cost of a pencil is 18c.

A concert was held in a hall that can hold 160 people. There are two prices of tickets, €5 and €3. On one evening when the hall was full, €600 was collected. Find how many of each ticket was sold on the night.

Solution:
Let x = the number of €5 tickets sold and y = the number of €3 tickets sold.
Two facts that link x and y:

1. There were 160 people in the hall.
    Equation: $x + y = 160$ ①
2. €600 was collected on the night.
    Equation: $5x + 3y = 600$ ②
    Now solve the simultaneous equations ① and ②

$$
\begin{array}{ll}
x + y = 160 & ① \\
5x + 3y = 600 & ② \\
\hline
3x + 3y = 480 & ① \times 3 \\
5x + 3y = 600 & ② \\
\hline
-2x = -120 & \text{(subtract)} \\
2x = 120 & \\
x = 60 &
\end{array}
$$

$$
\begin{array}{ll}
x + y = 160 & ① \\
60 + y = 160 & \\
y = 160 - 60 & \\
y = 100 &
\end{array}
$$

Put $x = 60$ in ① or ②:
Therefore the number of €5 tickets sold was 60 and the number of €3 sold was 100.

Exercise 27.2 ▼

In questions 1 to 8, let x = one number and y = the other number. Link x and y twice to form two equations, and solve these equations to find the unknown numbers.

1. The sum of two numbers is 14. The difference is 4. Find the numbers.
2. The difference between two numbers is 8. The sum of the two numbers is 20. Find the numbers.
3. The sum of two numbers is 9. Three times the first number less twice the second number is 7. Find the numbers.
4. The sum of four times one number and three times another number is 41. If twice the first number less three times the second number is 7, find the numbers.
5. Find two numbers such that three times the first number added to twice the second number is 29, while four times the first number less twice the second number is 20.
6. Three times a number added to a second number is 13. The first number added to three times the second number is 7. Find the two numbers.
7. Twice one number added to a second number is 7, while three times the first number added to twice the second number is 13. Find the two numbers.

8. The difference between two numbers is 4. Four times the first number less three times the second number is 18. Find the two numbers.

9. Two apples and a banana cost 70c. One apple and a banana cost 50c.
   Let x cents be the price of an apple and y cents the price of a banana.
   (a) Write down an equation in x and y to show the price of
       (i) two apples and a banana   **(ii)** one apple and a banana.
   (b) Solve your two equations simultaneously.
   (c) What is the price of **(i)** an apple   **(ii)** a banana?

10. Five pens and two pencils cost €2.50. Three pens and two pencils cost €1.70.
    (a) Write **(i)** €2.50 and **(ii)** €1.70 as cents.
        Let x cents be the price of a pen and y cents the price of a pencil.
    (b) Write down an equation in x and y to show the price of
        (i) five pens and two pencils   **(ii)** three pens and two pencils.
    (c) Solve your two equations simultaneously.
    (d) What is the price of **(i)** a pen **(ii)** a pencil?

11. Five packets of crisps and four bottles of lemonade cost €3.50.
    Two packets of crisps and two bottles of lemonade cost €1.60.
    (a) Write   **(i)** €3.50 and **(ii)** €1.60 as cents.
    Let x cents be the price of a packet of crisps and y cents the price of a bottle of lemonade.
    (b) Write down an equation in x and y to show the price, in cents, of:
        (i) five packets of crisps and four bottles of lemonade
        (ii) two packets of crisps and two bottles of lemonade.
    (c) Solve your two equations simultaneously.
    (d) What is the price of **(i)** a packet of crisps and **(ii)** a bottle of lemonade?

12. Seven books and three magazines cost €82.
    Two books and one magazine cost €24.
    Let €x be the price of a book and €y be the price of a magazine.
    (a) Write down an equation in x and y to show the price of:
        (i) seven books and three magazines   **(ii)** two books and one magazine.
    (b) Solve your two equations simultaneously.
    (c) What is the price of **(i)** a book **(ii)** a magazine?
    (d) Calculate the price of ten books and six magazines.

13. Eight cans of cola and two packets of peanuts cost €5.30.
    Six cans of cola and two packets of peanuts cost €4.10.
    (a) Write **(i)** €5.30 and **(ii)** €4.10 as cents.
    Let x cents be the price of a can of cola and y cents the price of a packet of peanuts.
    (b) Write down two equations in x and y to represent the data.
    (c) Calculate the price of **(i)** a can of cola and **(ii)** a packet of peanuts.

14. A school bought twenty tickets for a show. Some were teachers' tickets, costing €8 each, and some were pupils' tickets, costing €5 each. The total price of the tickets was €118. Let x be the number of teachers' tickets bought and y be the number of pupils' tickets bought.

(a) Write down an equation in x and y for the total **number** of tickets bought.
(b) Write down an equation in x and y for the total **price** of the tickets.
(c) Solve your two equations simultaneously.
(d) How many of each type of ticket did the school buy?

15. A theatre with seating accommodation for fifty people took in €600 on a night when all the seats were sold. Seats were priced as €15 and €10.
Let x be the number of €15 seats sold and y the number of €10 seats sold.
(a) Write down an equation in x and y for the **number** of seats sold.
(b) Write down an equation in x and y for the **price** of seats sold.
(c) Solve your two equations simultaneously.
(d) How many of each seat price were sold?

16. All eighty members of a club voted to elect the president of the club. There were only two candidates, Anne and Brian. Anne beat Brian by twenty votes.
Let x be the number of votes Anne received and y the number of votes Brian received.
(a) Write an equation in x and y for the **number** of members in the club who voted.
(b) Write an equation in x and y for the **difference** between the number of votes Anne received and the number of votes Brian received.
(c) Solve your two equations simultaneously.
(d) How many members of the club voted for Anne?

17. The opposite sides in a parallelogram are equal in length. Use this information to calculate the values of x and y for the following parallelograms (all dimensions in centimetres):

(a)

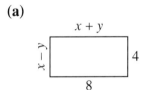

(b)

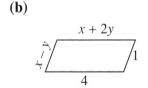

(c)

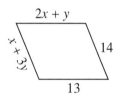

18. The opposite angles in a cyclic quadrilateral add up to 180°. Use this information to calculate the value of x and y from the cyclic quadrilateral shown on the right.

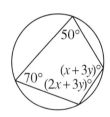

Using quadratic equations to solve problems

When we use an equation to solve a practical problem, the equation often turns out to be a quadratic equation. These equations usually have two solutions. If one of these makes no sense, for example producing a negative number of people, we reject it. Again, always look for the link in the question to set up the equation.

Note: The word 'product' means the result of multiplying.

When a number is added to its square, the total is 20.
Find the two possible numbers.

Solution:
Let x = the number; then its square is x^2.
Link used to form the equation:
Given: (the number) + (the number)^2 = 20

$$\Rightarrow \qquad x + x^2 = 20$$
$$\Rightarrow \qquad x^2 + x - 20 = 0$$
$$\Rightarrow \qquad (x + 5)(x - 4) = 0$$
$$\Rightarrow \qquad x + 5 = 0 \quad \text{or} \quad x - 4 = 0$$
$$\Rightarrow \qquad x = -5 \quad \text{or} \quad x = 4$$

Therefore the numbers are −5 and 4.

Example ▼

The area of a rectangle is 44 cm^2. If the length is 7 cm longer than the breadth, find the length and breadth of the rectangle.

Solution:
Draw a diagram of the rectangle.
Let x cm be the breadth.
Then $(x + 7)$ cm is the length (7 cm longer).
Link used to form the equation:
Given: area of the rectangle = 44 cm^2

$$\Rightarrow \text{(length)(breadth)} = 44$$
$$\Rightarrow \qquad (x + 7)(x) = 44$$
$$\Rightarrow \qquad x^2 + 7x = 44$$
$$\Rightarrow \qquad x^2 + 7x - 44 = 0$$
$$\Rightarrow \qquad (x + 11)(x - 4) = 0$$
$$\Rightarrow \qquad x + 11 = 0 \quad \text{or} \quad x - 4 = 0$$
$$\Rightarrow \qquad x = -11 \quad \text{or} \quad x = 4$$

The negative value, $x = -11$, is not possible, therefore $x = -11$ is rejected.
Therefore the breadth = x cm = 4 cm and length = $(x + 7)$ cm = $(4 + 7)$ cm = 11 cm.

1. When a number x is added to its square, the total is 12. Find the value of x.
2. When a number x is subtracted from its square, the result is 30. Find the value of x.
3. A rectangle has a width of x m. Its length is 2 m longer than this.

   $(x+2)$ m
   x m

   (i) Write an expression in x for the area of the rectangle.
   If the area of the rectangle is 15 m^2,
   (ii) use this information to form an equation
   (iii) solve the equation to find the value of x.
4. A rectangle has a width of x cm. Its length is 5 cm longer than this.

   (i) Write an expression in x for the area of the rectangle.

   $(x+5)$ m
   x m

   If the area of the rectangle is 36 cm^2,
   (ii) use this information to form an equation.
   (iii) solve the equation to find the value of x.
5. A rectangle has a width of x cm. Its length is 4 cm longer than this.
   (i) Sketch the rectangle, marking the length and width in terms of x.
   (ii) Write an expression in x for the area of the rectangle.
   If the area of the rectangle is 21 cm^2,
   (iii) use this information to form an equation
   (iv) solve the equation to find the value of x.
6. A man bought x articles at a price of €$(x + 3)$ each.
   (i) Write an expression in x for the price of the articles.
   If he spent €28 altogether,
   (ii) use this information to form an equation
   (iii) solve the equation to find the value of x.
7. A woman bought x articles at a price of €$(x - 2)$ each.
   (i) Write an expression in x for the price of the articles.
   If she spent €35 altogether,
   (ii) use this information to form an equation
   (iii) solve the equation to find the value of x.
8. One positive number is 2 greater than another positive number.
   (i) If the smaller number is x, write the larger number in terms of x.
   (ii) Write, in terms of x, an expression for the product of the two numbers.
   Note: 'product' means 'the result from multiplying'.
   If the product is 8,
   (iii) use this information to form an equation
   (iv) solve the equation to find x.
   What are the two numbers?
9. One positive number is 3 less than another number.
   (i) If the larger number is x, write the smaller number in terms of x.
   (ii) Write, in terms of x, an expression for the product of the two numbers.
   If the product is 18,

(iii) use this information to form an equation

(iv) solve the equation to find x.

What are the two numbers?

10. A square has a length of x cm.

A rectangle has a length of 4 cm and a width of x cm.

Write, in terms of x, an expression for the area of

(i) the square **(ii)** the rectangle.

If the area of the square added to the area of the rectangle is

12 cm^2,

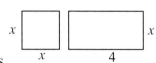

(iii) use this information to form an equation

(iv) solve the equation to find x.

11. A mug costs €$(x + 2)$ in a shop. A person bought x of these mugs at this price.

(i) Write, in terms of x, how much the person spent.

If the person spent €24,

(ii) use this information to form an equation

(iii) solve the equation to find x.

What is the price of a mug?

12. A girl walked at a speed of x km/h for $(x - 3)$ hours.

(i) Write, in terms of x, the distance walked by the girl.

(Hint: distance = speed × time.)

If the girl walked a distance of 10 km,

(ii) use this information to form an equation

(iii) solve the equation to find x.

Exercise 27.4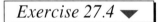

Chapter test

1. Peter is x years old. Mary is four years older than Peter.

(i) Write Mary's age in terms of x.

If the sum of their ages is 20 years,

(ii) use this information to form an equation

(iii) solve the equation to find the value of x

2. A compact disk costs €x. A minidisk costs €3 more than a compact disk.

(i) Write the price of a minidisk in terms of x

Five compact disks and four minidisks cost €201.

(ii) Use this information to form an equation.

(iii) Solve the equation to find the value of x.

(iv) What is the cost of a minidisk?

3. The admission price to a concert for two adults and six children is €48.

The admission price for six adults and two children is €64.

Let €x be the admission price for an adult and €y the admission price for a child.

(i) Write down two equations, each in x and y, to represent all the information given above.

    (ii) Solve the equations simultaneously to find the admission price for
        (a) an adult   **(b)** a child.

4. A rectangle has a width of x m. Its length is 4 m longer than this.

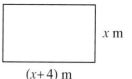

x m

    (i)   Write an expression in x for the area of the rectangle.
    If the area of the rectangle is 5 m^2,
    (ii) use this information to form an equation
    (iii) solve the equation to find the value of x.
    (iv) what is the perimeter of the rectangle?

$(x+4)$ m

5. Three consecutive odd numbers (i.e. like 5, 7, 9) are x, $x + 2$, and $x + 4$.
When the three numbers are added together the result is 45.
    (i)   Use this information to form an equation.
    (ii) Solve the equation to find the value of x.
    (iii) What are the three numbers?

6. At a supermarket, beans cost q cents per kilogram, potatoes cost $(q + 8)$ cents per kilogram, and tomatoes cost $(2q + 5)$ cents per kilogram. A customer bought 3 kg of beans, 10 kg of potatoes, and 2 kg of tomatoes. The bill came to €6.
Write €6 as cents.
    (i)   Form an equation in q.
    (ii) Solve the equation to find the value of q.

7. 1,500 tickets for a concert were sold. Tickets were priced at either €20 or €30. Ticket sales amounted to €38,000.
Let x be the quantity of €20 tickets sold and y the quantity of €30 tickets sold.
    (i)   Write down an equation in x and y for the number of tickets sold.
    (ii) Write down an equation in x and y for the total cost of the tickets.
    (iii) Solve your two equations simultaneously.
    (iv) How many of each type of ticket were sold?

8. On a Friday evening, 200 people attended a concert, when the price was €10 per person.
    (i)   How much money was taken at the door?
On a Saturday evening, $(200 - x)$ people attended the concert, when the price was €15 per person.
    (ii) Write, in terms of x, how much money was taken at the door on Saturday evening.
€400 more was taken in on Saturday evening than on Friday evening.
    (iii) Form an equation to show the difference between the takings for both nights.
    (iv) Solve the equation to find the value of x.

9. Five coats and six shirts cost €580.
Let €x be the price of a coat and €y the price of a shirt.
    (i)   Write an equation in x and y for the price of five coats and six shirts.
A coat costs €50 more than a shirt.
    (ii) Write an equation in x and y for the difference between the price of a coat and a shirt.
    (iii) Solve your two equations simultaneously.
    (iv) What is the price of **(a)** a coat and **(b)** a shirt?

10. Tom has x marbles. John has a third of the number of marbles that Tom has, and Simon has a quarter of the number that Tom has.
    (a) Write down, in terms of x, the number of marbles that (i) John has and (ii) Simon has.
    (b) Between them, John and Simon have 21 marbles.
        Write this statement as an equation in x.
    (c) Solve this equation to find the value of x.
    (d) How many marbles had (i) Tom, (ii) John, and (iii) Simon?
11. Five people shared equally the cost, €x, of a taxi to a concert.
    (i) Write, in terms of x, how much each of the five had to pay.
    Later, four of them shared equally the cost, €$(x - 3)$, of a taxi to another concert.
    (ii) Write, in terms of x, how much each of the four had to pay for the second journey.
        (The fifth person did not go with them to the second concert.)
    For the four who went to both concerts, the total cost was €15 each.
    (iii) Use this information to form an equation.
    (iv) Solve the equation to find the value of x.
12. This year a man is seven times as old as his daughter.
    (i) If his daughter is x years old now, how old is the father now in terms of x?
    (ii) Find, in terms of x, how old the father and daughter will be in five years' time.
    If in five years' time the father is four times as old as the daughter,
    (iii) use this information to form an equation
    (iv) solve the equation to find the value of x
    (v) how old is the father now?
13. Two numbers add up to 9. If one number is x,
    (i) write the other number in terms of x.
    When the two numbers are multiplied, the result is 20.
    (ii) Use this information to form an equation.
    (iii) Solve the equation to find the two numbers.

ANSWERS

Exercise 1.1 ▼

1. 17	**2.** 22	**3.** 15	**4.** 17	**5.** 8	**6.** 5
7. 4	**8.** 7	**9.** 14	**10.** 17	**11.** 20	**12.** 10
13. 25	**14.** 6	**15.** 8	**16.** 0	**17.** 15	**18.** 3
19. 19	**20.** 11	**21.** 14	**22.** 26	**23.** 13	**24.** 1
25. 2	**26.** 2	**27.** 8	**28.** 1	**29.** 7	**30.** 2

Exercise 1.2 ▼

1. 8	**2.** 34	**3.** 9	**4.** 16	**5.** 25	**6.** 5
7. 58	**8.** 12	**9.** 36	**10.** 4	**11.** 20	**12.** 4
13. 2	**14.** 16	**15.** 91	**16.** 24	**17.** 47	**18.** 176
19. 7	**20.** 1	**21.** 30	**22.** 8	**23.** 19	**24.** 48
25. 11	**26.** 2	**27.** 27	**28.** 32	**29.** 69	**30.** 67
31. 4	**32.** 2	**33.** 5	**34.** 3	**35.** 4	**36.** 2
37. 3	**38.** 6	**39.** 5	**40.** 4	**41.** 5	**42.** 1
43. 2	**44.** 3	**45.** 1			

Exercise 2.1 ▼

1. 1, 2, 3, 6
2. 1, 2, 4, 8
3. 1, 2, 5, 10
4. 1, 2, 3, 4, 6, 12
5. 1, 3, 5, 15
6. 1, 2, 3, 6, 9, 18
7. 1, 2, 4, 5, 10, 20
8. 1, 2, 3, 4, 6, 8, 12, 24
9. 1, 2, 4, 7, 14, 28
10. 1, 2, 4, 8, 16, 32
11. 1, 2, 4, 5, 8, 10, 20, 40
12. 1, 2, 3, 4, 6, 8, 12, 16, 24, 48
13. 1, 2, 3, 4, 5, 6, 10, 12, 15, 20, 30, 60
14. 1, 2, 4, 5, 8, 10, 16, 20, 40, 80
15. 1, 2, 3, 5, 6, 9, 10, 15, 18, 30, 45, 90
16. 1, 2, 3, 4, 5, 6, 8, 10, 12, 15, 20, 24, 30, 40, 60, 120
17. 1, 2, 4
18. 1, 3, 9
19. 1, 2, 4, 8, 16
20. 1, 5, 25
21. 1, 2, 4, 8, 16, 32, 64
22. 1, 2, 4, 5, 10, 20, 25, 50, 100

1. 5	**2.** 3	**3.** 2	**4.** −2	**5.** −3	**6.** 0
7. 5	**8.** 3	**9.** 5	**10.** 2	**11.** 5	**12.** −2
13. −2	**14.** −3	**15.** 2	**16.** −2	**17.** −8	**18.** 0
19. 7	**20.** 9				

1. −4	**2.** −15	**3.** 18	**4.** −20	**5.** −6	**6.** 16
7. −24	**8.** 15	**9.** −2	**10.** −5	**11.** −3	**12.** −5
13. −2	**14.** 4	**15.** −3	**16.** 2	**17.** 1	**18.** 9
19. 4	**20.** −8	**21.** −22	**22.** −3	**23.** −7	**24.** 5

1. 9	**2.** 25	**3.** 49	**4.** 1	**5.** 8	**6.** 27
7. 64	**8.** 4	**9.** 16	**10.** 25	**11.** 36	**12.** 1
13. −1	**14.** 1	**15.** 49	**16.** −27	**17.** −8	**18.** 100
19. 64	**20.** 144				

1. 17	**2.** 10	**3.** 14	**4.** 8	**5.** 5	**6.** 7
7. 5	**8.** 3	**9.** 14	**10.** 21	**11.** 1	**12.** 14
13. 2	**14.** 6	**15.** 2	**16.** 8	**17.** 7	**18.** 32
19. 3	**20.** 0	**21.** −8	**22.** 4	**23.** −2	**24.** −5
25. 5	**26.** −4	**27.** 2	**28.** 3	**29.** 0	**30.** 40

1. 18	**2.** 20	**3.** 6	**4.** 4	**5.** 2	**6.** 3
7. 3	**8.** 2	**9.** 1	**10.** 4	**11.** 10	**12.** 4
13. 10	**14.** 24	**15.** 28	**16.** −12	**17.** 15	**18.** −4
19. 6	**20.** 8	**21.** 6	**22.** 2	**23.** 24	**24.** 0
25. 9	**26.** 18	**27.** 16	**28.** 12	**29.** 32	**30.** 48
31. 20	**32.** 61	**33.** 2	**34.** 9	**35.** 9	**36.** 16
37. 80	**38.** 12	**39.** 32	**40.** 3	**41.** 2	**42.** 1
43. 3	**44.** 2	**45.** 9			

1. 2	**2.** 3	**3.** −5	**4.** −6	**5.** −5	**6.** 3
7. −10	**8.** 6	**9.** 4	**10.** 20	**11.** 7	**12.** −1
13. 1	**14.** 5	**15.** 8	**16.** 66	**17.** 16	**18.** 7
19. 10	**20.** 28	**21.** 50	**22.** 2	**23.** 3	**24.** 2
25. −2	**26.** 2	**27.** −4			

1. $\frac{5}{4}$ or $1\frac{1}{4}$ **2.** $\frac{7}{6}$ or $1\frac{1}{6}$ **3.** $\frac{11}{8}$ or $1\frac{3}{8}$ **4.** $\frac{17}{12}$ or $1\frac{5}{12}$

5. $\frac{3}{2}$ or $1\frac{1}{2}$ **6.** $\frac{19}{15}$ or $1\frac{4}{15}$ **7.** $\frac{9}{4}$ or $2\frac{1}{4}$ **8.** $\frac{3}{8}$

9. $\frac{1}{6}$ **10.** $\frac{7}{20}$ **11.** $\frac{1}{10}$ **12.** $-\frac{1}{8}$

13. $-\frac{1}{4}$ **14.** $-\frac{1}{24}$ **15.** $-\frac{11}{35}$ **16.** $\frac{67}{12}$ or $5\frac{7}{12}$

17. $\frac{39}{8}$ or $4\frac{7}{8}$ **18.** $\frac{109}{20}$ or $5\frac{9}{20}$ **19.** $\frac{45}{8}$ or $5\frac{5}{8}$ **20.** $\frac{67}{10}$ or $6\frac{7}{10}$

21. $\frac{92}{15}$ or $6\frac{2}{15}$ **22.** $\frac{5}{6}$ **23.** $\frac{14}{15}$ **24.** $\frac{1}{2}$

25. $\frac{23}{12}$ or $1\frac{11}{12}$ **26.** $-\frac{11}{10}$ or $-1\frac{1}{10}$ **27.** $-\frac{41}{12}$ or $-3\frac{5}{12}$ **28.** 2

29. $\frac{27}{8}$ or $3\frac{3}{8}$ **30.** $\frac{29}{8}$ or $3\frac{5}{8}$ **31.** 3 **32.** $-\frac{21}{20}$ or $-2\frac{1}{20}$

33. $-\frac{77}{30}$ or $-2\frac{17}{30}$ **34.** $\frac{41}{24}$ or $1\frac{17}{24}$ **35.** $\frac{43}{20}$ or $2\frac{3}{20}$ **36.** $\frac{1}{3}$

37. $\frac{7}{6}$ or $1\frac{1}{16}$ **38.** $\frac{1}{4}$ **39.** $\frac{14}{5}$ or $2\frac{4}{5}$ **40.** $\frac{8}{9}$

41. $-\frac{1}{16}$ **42.** $-\frac{21}{8}$ or $-2\frac{5}{8}$ **43.** $\frac{61}{36}$ or $1\frac{25}{36}$

1. $\frac{10}{21}$ **2.** $\frac{3}{20}$ **3.** $\frac{15}{28}$ **4.** $\frac{1}{3}$

5. $\frac{8}{21}$ **6.** $\frac{3}{4}$ **7.** $\frac{15}{16}$ **8.** 3

9. $\frac{5}{6}$ **10.** $\frac{49}{12}$ or $4\frac{1}{12}$ **11.** $\frac{3}{2}$ or $1\frac{1}{2}$ **12.** $\frac{7}{2}$ or $3\frac{1}{2}$

13. 10 **14.** $\frac{5}{16}$ **15.** $\frac{54}{11}$ or $4\frac{10}{11}$ **16.** $\frac{35}{36}$

Exercise 4.7

1. $\frac{21}{20}$ or $1\frac{1}{20}$ **2.** $\frac{6}{5}$ or $1\frac{1}{5}$ **3.** $\frac{2}{5}$ **4.** $\frac{4}{3}$ or $1\frac{1}{3}$

5. $\frac{3}{2}$ or $1\frac{1}{2}$ **6.** $\frac{1}{6}$ **7.** 2 **8.** 4

9. $\frac{1}{3}$ **10.** $\frac{5}{8}$ **11.** $\frac{2}{5}$ **12.** $\frac{6}{7}$

13. $\frac{2}{3}$ **14.** 3 **15.** $\frac{1}{2}$ **16.** $\frac{7}{2}$ or $3\frac{1}{2}$

17. $\frac{21}{5}$ or $4\frac{1}{5}$ **18.** $\frac{7}{3}$ or $2\frac{1}{3}$ **19.** $\frac{15}{2}$ or $7\frac{1}{2}$ **20.** $\frac{16}{5}$ or $3\frac{1}{5}$

21. 20 **22.** $\frac{7}{20}$ **23.** 10 **24.** $\frac{10}{3}$ or $3\frac{1}{3}$

Exercise 4.8

1. $\frac{1}{4}$ **2.** $\frac{4}{9}$ **3.** $\frac{9}{16}$ **4.** $\frac{16}{25}$

5. $\frac{1}{16}$ **6.** $\frac{1}{9}$ **7.** $\frac{1}{27}$ **8.** $\frac{1}{125}$

9. $\frac{27}{125}$ **10.** $\frac{25}{16}$ or $1\frac{9}{16}$ **11.** $\frac{16}{9}$ or $1\frac{7}{9}$ **12.** $\frac{49}{16}$ or $3\frac{1}{16}$

13. $\frac{100}{9}$ or $11\frac{1}{9}$ **14.** $\frac{144}{25}$ or $5\frac{19}{25}$ **15.** $\frac{27}{8}$ or $3\frac{3}{8}$ **16.** $\frac{81}{25}$ or $3\frac{6}{25}$

17. $\frac{8}{27}$ **18.** $\frac{125}{8}$ or $15\frac{5}{8}$ **19.** $\frac{1}{4}$ **20.** $\frac{4}{9}$

Exercise 4.9

1. $\frac{17}{20}$ **2.** $\frac{3}{5}$ **3.** $\frac{7}{4}$ or $1\frac{3}{4}$ **4.** $\frac{1}{4}$

5. $\frac{5}{8}$ **6.** $\frac{4}{3}$ or $1\frac{1}{3}$ **7.** 2 **8.** $\frac{7}{8}$

9. $\frac{31}{16}$ or $1\frac{15}{16}$ **10.** $\frac{5}{4}$ or $1\frac{1}{4}$ **11.** $\frac{1}{4}$ **12.** 1

13. 6 **14.** $\frac{1}{2}$ **15.** $\frac{1}{5}$ **16.** $\frac{31}{9}$ or $3\frac{4}{9}$

17. $\frac{29}{6}$ or $4\frac{5}{6}$ **18.** $\frac{8}{3}$ or $2\frac{2}{3}$ **19.** $\frac{25}{36}$ **20.** $\frac{13}{36}$

21. 2 **22.** $\frac{15}{7}$ or $2\frac{1}{7}$ **23.** $\frac{1}{3}$ **24.** $\frac{7}{5}$ or $1\frac{2}{5}$

25. $\frac{1}{10}$ **26.** 2 **27.** $\frac{2}{5}$ **28.** €12.60

29. 12 **30.** 200 **31.** 210 **32.** 100

33. *A* received 48, *B* received 45, and *C* received 54.

34. $4\frac{1}{4}$ m or $\frac{17}{4}$ m **35.** 450 **36.** $\frac{4}{15}$

1. $\frac{3}{4}$ **2.** $\frac{3}{5}$ **3.** $\frac{2}{3}$ **4.** $\frac{1}{5}$ **5.** $\frac{5}{8}$ **6.** $\frac{1}{3}$

7. $\frac{1}{6}$ **8.** $\frac{1}{4}$ **9.** $\frac{1}{3}$ **10.** $\frac{2}{7}$ **11.** $\frac{1}{2}$ **12.** $\frac{3}{4}$

13. $\frac{3}{10}$ **14.** $\frac{1}{3}$ **15.** $\frac{4}{5}$ **16.** $\frac{5}{16}$ **17.** $\frac{1}{5}$ **18.** $\frac{2}{5}$

19. $\frac{3}{7}$ **20.** $\frac{1}{3}$

21. (i) $\frac{2}{5}$ (ii) $\frac{1}{3}$ (iii) $\frac{4}{15}$

22. (i) $\frac{1}{3}$ (ii) $\frac{3}{10}$ (iii) $\frac{1}{5}$ (iv) $\frac{1}{6}$

1. $\frac{19}{12}$ or $1\frac{7}{12}$ **2.** $\frac{11}{30}$ **3.** $\frac{17}{8}$ or $2\frac{1}{8}$ **4.** $\frac{5}{2}$ or $2\frac{1}{2}$

5. 9   **6.** $\frac{3}{2}$ or $1\frac{1}{2}$ **7.** $\frac{5}{8}$ **8.** $\frac{11}{4}$ or $2\frac{3}{4}$

9. $\frac{7}{24}$ **10.** $\frac{1}{6}$ **11.** 2   **12.** $\frac{4}{3}$ or $1\frac{1}{3}$

13. $\frac{1}{4}$ **14.** $\frac{2}{3}$ **15.** $\frac{9}{16}$ **16.** $\frac{1}{2}$

17. $\frac{3}{2}$ or $1\frac{1}{2}$ **18.** 4   **19.** $\frac{4}{5}$ **20.** $\frac{7}{9}$

21. $\frac{7}{20}$ **22.** (i) €9,000   (ii) €15,000   **23.** 375

1. 9.5   **2.** 6.2   **3.** 21.9   **4.** 11.1   **5.** 2.6   **6.** 4

7. 12.3   **8.** 24.2   **9.** 35.4   **10.** 19.7   **11.** 25.6   **12.** 5.94

13. 4.5   **14.** 0   **15.** 27   **16.** 12.348   **17.** −11.16   **18.** 5.8

19. 1.5   **20.** 30.33   **21.** 4.5   **22.** 15.5   **23.** 4.07   **24.** 5.85

25. 1.92   **26.** 1.12   **27.** 40   **28.** 60   **29.** 32.5   **30.** 4

31. 3   **32.** 2   **33.** 5   **34.** 2.8   **35.** 5.8   **36.** 2.9

37. 3   **38.** 0.5   **39.** 2.3   **40.** 0.75   **41.** 0.4   **42.** 0.75

43. 4   **44.** 5.2   **45.** 6.25

46. (i) 0.5   (ii) 2   (iii) 2.4

Exercise 5.4 ▼

1. 12; 12.06   **2.** 3; 2.91   **3.** 20; 20.14   **4.** 6; 6.2
5. 28; 28.22   **6.** 15; 14.93   **7.** 6; 5.995   **8.** 13; 13.24
9. 19; 19.39   **10.** 4; 4.1   **11.** 2; 2.02   **12.** 5; 5.2
13. 4; 4.2   **14.** 5; 4.98   **15.** 6; 6.1

Exercise 5.5 ▼

1. $\frac{2}{5}$ **2.** $\frac{7}{10}$ **3.** $\frac{3}{5}$ **4.** $\frac{1}{5}$ **5.** $\frac{9}{10}$

6. $\frac{1}{4}$ **7.** $\frac{3}{4}$ **8.** $\frac{3}{20}$ **9.** $\frac{7}{20}$ **10.** $\frac{11}{20}$

11. $\frac{1}{8}$ **12.** $\frac{3}{8}$ **13.** $\frac{11}{10}$ or $1\frac{1}{10}$ **14.** $\frac{23}{10}$ or $2\frac{3}{10}$ **15.** $\frac{19}{5}$ or $3\frac{4}{5}$

16. $\frac{1}{20}$ **17.** $\frac{49}{20}$ or $2\frac{9}{20}$ **18.** $\frac{81}{25}$ or $3\frac{6}{25}$ **19.** $\frac{14}{5}$ or $2\frac{4}{5}$ **20.** $\frac{1}{16}$

21. $\frac{29}{25}$ or $1\frac{4}{25}$ **22.** $\frac{29}{8}$ or $3\frac{5}{8}$ **23.** $\frac{61}{25}$ or $2\frac{11}{25}$ **24.** $\frac{27}{25}$ or $1\frac{2}{25}$ **25.** $\frac{41}{20}$ or $2\frac{1}{20}$

Exercise 5.6 ▼

1. 10   **2.** 2.51   **3.** 9.1   **4.** 6   **5.** 460
6. 7.2   **7.** 25.6   **8.** 4.95   **9.** 35.84   **10.** 4.4
11. 0.8   **12.** 0.04   **13.** 0.9   **14.** 34   **15.** 2.5
16. 2   **17.** 5.6   **18.** 2.9
19. (i) 25   (ii) 20.55   (iii) 4.5
20. (i) 0.36   (ii) 0.64   (iii) 6.25   (iv) 2.5
21. (i) 16   (ii) 64   (iii) 12
22. (i) 4.8   (ii) 2.4   (iii) 2   (iv) 5.4
23. 9; 8.9   **24.** 8; 7.8   **25.** 3; 3.15   **26.** 7; 6.8   **27.** $\frac{1}{2}$

28. $\frac{1}{10}$ **29.** $\frac{3}{10}$ **30.** $\frac{3}{2}$ or $1\frac{1}{2}$ **31.** $\frac{6}{5}$ or $1\frac{1}{5}$ **32.** $\frac{9}{5}$ or $1\frac{4}{5}$

33. $\frac{9}{4}$ or $2\frac{1}{4}$ **34.** $\frac{16}{5}$ or $3\frac{1}{5}$ **35.** $\frac{69}{20}$ or $3\frac{9}{20}$ **36.** $\frac{15}{8}$ or $1\frac{7}{8}$ **37.** 11.92

38. 222.61   **39.** 11.03   **40.** 16.45   **41.** 0.86

Exercise 6.1 ▼

1. $4a$ **2.** $5x$ **3.** $8x$ **4.** $9a$
5. $6m$ **6.** $10p$ **7.** $7ab$ **8.** $6pq$
9. $3x^2$ **10.** $6x^2$ **11.** $11x + 7$ **12.** $9a + 6$
13. $9y + 8$ **14.** $9a + 7$ **15.** $7x + 10$ **16.** $10x + 18$
17. $11x + 15$ **18.** $9x + 22$ **19.** $5x^2 + 7x + 6$ **20.** $7x^2 + 9x + 18$

21. $x^3 + 6x^2 + 11x + 3$ **22.** $2x^3 + 7x^2 + 11x + 4$ **23.** $3x^3 + 14x^2 + 11x + 2$

24. $6x^3 + 13x^2 + 18x + 8$ **25.** $7x + 4y$ **26.** $4x + 7y$

27. $4x + 3y + 7$ **28.** $6x + 5y + 9$ **29.** $3x$

30. a **31.** $-2x$ **32.** $-4y$

33. $5a$ **34.** $5x$ **35.** $3x$

36. $-x$ **37.** $7x + 6$ **38.** $5x + 4$

39. $4x - 2$ **40.** $4x + 15$ **41.** $2x - 3$

42. $3x - 1$ **43.** $-2x + 3$ **44.** $-x + 4$

45. $x^2 + 2x - 6$ **46.** $2x^2 - 5x - 12$ **47.** $5x^2 - 7x - 6$

48. $4x^2 - 26x + 5$ **49.** $x^3 + 2x^2 - x - 2$ **50.** $x^3 - 4x^2 + 2x + 8$

51. $2x^3 - 5x^2 - 14x - 3$ **52.** $6x^3 - 13x^2 + 18x - 8$ **53.** $-6x^3 + 8x^2 - 11x + 2$

54. $-4x^3 + 5x^2 - 6x + 1$ **55.** $2x + 11y + 3$ **56.** $4x - 7y - 1$

57. xy **58.** $4ab + 3bc$ **59.** $9abc$

60. $7x + 5xy$ **61.** $3p^2 + 2pq$ **62.** $2a^2b$

63. $8a^2b - 3ab^2$ **64.** 0

Exercise 6.2 ▼

1. $2x + 8$ **2.** $6x + 15$ **3.** $4x^2 + 12x$ **4.** $10x^2 + 15x + 20$

5. $-6x - 10$ **6.** $10x - 40$ **7.** $-3x + 12$ **8.** $-x + 3$

9. $6x^2 - 9x + 6$ **10.** $-4x^2 + 12x - 16$ **11.** $12x + 8y$ **12.** $-6p + 9q + 12$

13. $16x + 18$ **14.** $11x + 20$ **15.** $16x + 24$ **16.** $8x + 30$

17. x **18.** 2 **19.** $4x$ **20.** $x + 2$

21. $x + 4$ **22.** $5x + 3$ **23.** $2p - 1$ **24.** $2q + 2$

25. $5q$ **26.** 3 **27.** $x^2 + 3x + 4$ **28.** x^2

29. $2x^2$ **30.** 4 **31.** $8x + 11y$ **32.** $5x - 3y + 6$

33. $6x - 2y - 3$ **34.** $2y$ **35.** $4x - 4$ **36.** 1

Exercise 6.3 ▼

1. $10x^2$ **2.** $12x^2$ **3.** $7x^2$ **4.** x^3 **5.** $15x^3$ **6.** $6a^3$

7. $8x^3$ **8.** $21x^3$ **9.** $-20a^3$ **10.** $-15a^3$ **11.** $30x^3$ **12.** $8x^3$

13. $8p^3$ **14.** $10x^3$ **15.** $-20x^3$ **16.** x^2 **17.** $60x^3$ **18.** $30a^3$

19. $12a^3b^3$ **20.** $30x^2$ **21.** $10p^2q^2$ **22.** $3x^2y^2$ **23.** $30x^3y^3$ **24.** $-x^3$

25. $-9p^4$ **26.** $24x^2y^2$ **27.** $-30x^3y^3$ **28.** $32x^3y^2$ **29.** $6x^2y^2$ **30.** $20x^3y^3$

31. 24

Exercise 6.4 ▼

1. $x^2 + 5x + 6$ **2.** $x^2 + 6x + 9$ **3.** $2x^2 + 13x + 15$

4. $3x^2 + 11x + 10$ **5.** $x^2 + 2x - 8$ **6.** $2x^2 - 5x + 3$

7. $3x^2 - 19x + 20$ **8.** $10x^2 - 23x + 12$ **9.** $4x^2 + 12x + 9$

10. $9x^2 - 4$ **11.** $x^3 + 5x^2 + 10x + 8$ **12.** $2x^3 + 13x^2 + 21x + 9$

13. $x^3 - 5x^2 + 7x - 3$ **14.** $6x^3 - 13x^2 - 9x + 10$ **15.** $8x^3$

16. $5x^2$ **17.** 0 **18.** a

19. $2x^2 + 5xy + 3y^2$ **20.** $6x^2 + 7xy + 2y^2$ **21.** $10x^2 - 9xy + 2y^2$

22. x^2 **23.** $3y^2$ **24.** $6x^2 + 6xy$

25. $2a$ **26.** $2a^2$ **27.** $2ab$

28. 0 **29.** a^2 **30.** $2a^2 + 2b^2$

Exercise 6.5 ▼

1. $x^2 + 3x + 2$ **2.** $x^2 + 7x + 12$ **3.** $x^2 + 11x + 30$

4. $x^2 + 9x + 14$ **5.** $x^2 + 12x + 32$ **6.** $2x^2 + 11x + 12$

7. $15x^2 + 13x + 2$ **8.** $8x^2 - 10x + 3$ **9.** $2x^2 - x - 15$

10. $6x^2 + 7x - 3$ **11.** $2x^2 - 9x + 4$ **12.** $12x^2 - 11x - 15$

13. $2x^2 + 3x - 20$ **14.** $10x^2 - 9x + 2$ **15.** $4x^2 - 13x - 12$

16. $x^3 + 6x^2 + 11x + 12$ **17.** $2x^3 + 9x^2 + 11x + 6$ **18.** $3x^3 + 8x^2 + 8x + 8$

19. $2x^3 + 9x^2 + 9x + 20$ **20.** $3x^3 + 4x^2 + 2x + 1$ **21.** $2x^3 + 15x^2 + 28x + 15$

22. $2x^3 + 7x^2 + 12x + 9$ **23.** $6x^3 + 5x^2 + 13x + 4$ **24.** $x^3 - 6x^2 + 11x - 6$

25. $2x^3 - 7x^2 - 6x + 4$ **26.** $2x^3 - 5x^2 - 8x + 5$ **27.** $6x^3 - 7x^2 + 11x - 6$

28. $4x^3 - 6x^2 - 16x + 15$ **29.** $2x^3 + 3x^2 - 6x + 2$ **30.** $x^2 + 4x + 4$

31. $4x^2 + 12x + 9$ **32.** $4x^2 - 20x + 25$ **33.** $9x^2 - 6x + 1$

34. 7 **35.** 2 **36.** $x^3 + 6x^2 + 11x + 6$

Exercise 6.6 ▼

1. $\dfrac{29}{6}$ **2.** $\dfrac{29}{12}$ **3.** $\dfrac{19}{20}$ **4.** $\dfrac{19}{18}$ **5.** $\dfrac{3}{8}$

6. $\dfrac{37}{30}$ **7.** $\dfrac{5x}{6}$ **8.** $\dfrac{7x}{12}$ **9.** $\dfrac{9x}{20}$ **10.** $\dfrac{7x}{18}$

11. $\dfrac{x}{8}$ **12.** $-\dfrac{5x}{12}$ **13.** $\dfrac{5x + 17}{6}$ **14.** $\dfrac{7x + 31}{12}$ **15.** $\dfrac{3x + 11}{10}$

16. $\dfrac{3x + 13}{4}$ **17.** $\dfrac{7x + 9}{12}$ **18.** $\dfrac{13x + 16}{21}$ **19.** $\dfrac{33x - 17}{20}$ **20.** $\dfrac{8x + 9}{4}$

21. $\dfrac{9x - 1}{6}$ **22.** $\dfrac{4x + 11}{12}$ **23.** $\dfrac{7x - 17}{15}$ **24.** $\dfrac{-8x + 19}{6}$ **25.** $\dfrac{10x + 47}{12}$

26. $\dfrac{5x + 6}{8}$ **27.** $\dfrac{19x - 13}{12}$ **28.** $\dfrac{x + 16}{21}$ **29.** $\dfrac{7x - 10}{6}$ **30.** $\dfrac{x + 5}{6}$

Exercise 6.7

1. $4a$	**2.** $5x$	**3.** $3p$	**4.** $2b$	**5.** $2a$	**6.** $4p$
7. $3x$	**8.** 2	**9.** x	**10.** x	**11.** 1	**12.** 1
13. 1	**14.** $2a$	**15.** $2x$	**16.** $3a$	**17.** $3b$	**18.** $2q$
19. $2a^2$	**20.** $5x$				

Exercise 6.8

1. 6	**2.** 15	**3.** 20	**4.** 28	**5.** 14	**6.** 6
7. 120	**8.** 64	**9.** 112	**10.** 70	**11.** 45	**12.** 59
13. 41	**14.** 50	**15.** 9	**16.** 2	**17.** 3	**18.** 8
19. 2	**20.** 1	**21.** 2	**22.** 88	**23.** 31	**24.** 60

Exercise 6.9

1. 1	**2.** 4	**3.** 29	**4.** 19	**5.** 18	**6.** 0
7. 18	**8.** 20	**9.** 17	**10.** 22	**11.** 30	**12.** 25
13. -6	**14.** 14	**15.** 29	**16.** 14	**17.** 59	**18.** 25
19. 1	**20.** 20	**21.** 30	**22.** 2	**23.** 4	**24.** 1
25. 4	**26.** 5	**27.** 16	**28.** 1	**29.** 6	

Exercise 6.10

1. **(a)** 4 **(b)** q **(c)** $x^3 - 9x^2 + 24x - 16$

2. **(a)** $2x^3 - x + 1$ **(b)** $3x - 15;\ 0$

3. **(b)** $2x^3 - 9x^2 + 13x - 12$ **(c)** 6 **(d)** $\dfrac{7x + 29}{12}$

4. **(a) (i)** 9 **(ii)** 5 **(b) (i)** x^2 **(ii)** 6 **(c)** $x^3 - 7x^2 + 7x + 6$ **(d)** $\dfrac{3x - 5}{10}$

5. **(a)** -2 **(b)** $6b$ **(c)** $x^3 - 8x^2 + 21x + 18$

(d) $\dfrac{2x - 1}{8}$ **(e)** 32

6. **(a)** 18 **(b)** $6x^3 + 3x^2 - 26x + 10$ **(c)** $6x^2$

(d) $\dfrac{13x + 4}{20}$ **(e)** 30 km

Exercise 7.1 ▼

1. 2	**2.** 4	**3.** 3	**4.** 5	**5.** 3	**6.** 5
7. 3	**8.** 2	**9.** 6	**10.** 11	**11.** −2	**12.** −3
13. −6	**14.** −5	**15.** 0	**16.** 0	**17.** 3	**18.** 5
19. 4	**20.** 6	**21.** −2	**22.** 3	**23.** 4	**24.** −4
25. 2	**26.** 2	**27.** −10	**28.** −6	**29.** 4	**30.** 2

Exercise 7.2 ▼

1. 2	**2.** 4	**3.** 4	**4.** 1	**5.** 6	**6.** −5
7. 1	**8.** 4	**9.** 2	**10.** 4	**11.** 4	**12.** −1
13. 3	**14.** 3	**15.** −6	**16.** 2	**17.** 1	**18.** 3
19. 3	**20.** 1	**21.** 9	**22.** −4	**23.** 2	**24.** 5
25. 7	**26.** 2	**27.** 6	**28.** 1	**29.** 2	**30.** −3

Exercise 7.3 ▼

1. 3	**2.** 5	**3.** 1	**4.** 3	**5.** 1	**6.** 5
7. 2	**8.** 5	**9.** 10	**10.** −12	**11.** 2	**12.** −11
13. −6	**14.** 3	**15.** 4	**16.** 5	**17.** 4	**18.** 9
19. 4	**20.** 7	**21.** 3	**22.** 3	**23.** 1	**24.** 2
25. −6	**26.** 15	**27.** 8	**29.** 1	**29.** 5	**30.** 7

Exercise 7.4 ▼

1. 4	**2.** 3	**3.** 5	**4.** 0	**5.** 3	**6.** 5
7. 6	**8.** 1	**9.** 2	**10.** 2	**11.** 2	**12.** 1
13. 8	**14.** 4	**15.** 3	**16.** −1	**17.** 0	**18.** 6
19. 1	**20.** 4	**21.** 5	**22.** 2	**23.** 2	**24.** 6
25. 1	**26.** 3	**27.** −4	**28.** 4	**29.** 2	**30.** 3

Exercise 8.1 ▼

2. 2 hours 35 mins   **3.** 3 hours 40 mins   **4.** 18:02

5. 15:15   **6. (a)** 1 hour 35 mins   **(b)** 2 hours 25 mins

7. 13:55   **8.** 03:05   **9.** 35 mins   **11.** 11:15

Exercise 8.2 ▼

3. (i) 4 hours 25 mins; 4 hours 5 mins; 3 hours 45 mins   **(ii)** 40 mins   **(iii)** 08:53
4. (i) 3 hours 40 mins   **(ii)** 17:40   **(iii)** 40 mins
5. (i) 43 mins; 12:04   **(ii)** 18:40   **(iii)** 11:15   **(iv)** 18 mins   **(v)** 07:39; 40 mins
6. (i) 13 mins   **(iii)** 08:08   **(iv)** 08:20   **(v)** 12 mins; 07:48
7. (a) 5   **(b)** 4 hours and 25 mins   **(c)** 07:40   **(d)** 10:50   **(e)** 10:50
   (f) 1 hour and 16 minutes   **(g)** 10:20   **(h)** 8 minutes

Exercise 9.1 ▼

2. 5 hours   **3.** 15 km/h   **4.** 300 km

5. (a) $2\frac{1}{2}$ hours   **(b)** 72 km/h   **6.** 150 km   **7.** 64 km/h   **8.** 4 m/s

9. 18:30   **10. (a)** $4\frac{1}{4}$ **(b)** 60 km/h   **11.** 72 km/h   **12.** 91 km

13. 60 km/h   **14.** 1 hour 45 mins; 84 kh/h

15. (i) 2 hours 45 mins   **(ii)** 11:50   **(iii)** 94 km/h

Exercise 9.2 ▼

1. 590 km   **2.** 51 km   **3.** 1,800 km; 300 km/h
4. (i) 280 km   **(ii)** 5 hours   **(iii)** 56 km/h
5. (a) 6 hours   **(b)** 462 km   **(c)** 77 km/h
6. (a) 4 hours   **(b)** 260 km   **(c)** 65 km/h
7. (i) 560 km   **(ii)** 10 hours   **(iii)** 56 km/h
8. (i) 430 km   **(ii)** 5 hours   **(iii)** 86 km/h
9. (i) 3 hours   **(ii)** 244 km   **(iii)** 364 km   **(iv)** 7 hours   **(v)** 52 km/h
10. 90 km/h   **11. (a)** 504 km   **(b)** 8 hours   **(c)** 63 km/h
12. (a) 55 km/h   **(b)** 66 km/h   **(c)** 11 hours; 660 km   **(d)** 60 km/h

Exercise 10.1 ▼

1. $\frac{1}{5}$; 0.2	**2.** $\frac{3}{10}$; 0.3	**3.** $\frac{1}{2}$; 0.5	**4.** $\frac{1}{4}$; 0.25	**5.** $\frac{1}{10}$; 0.1
6. $\frac{1}{20}$; 0.05	**7.** $\frac{2}{5}$; 0.4	**8.** $\frac{3}{4}$; 0.75	**9.** $\frac{4}{5}$; 0.8	**10.** $\frac{3}{5}$; 0.6
11. $\frac{7}{20}$; 0.35	**12.** $\frac{9}{20}$; 0.45	**13.** $\frac{13}{20}$; 0.65	**14.** $\frac{19}{20}$; 0.95	**15.** $\frac{11}{20}$; 0.55
16. $\frac{3}{25}$; 0.12	**17.** $\frac{1}{25}$; 0.04	**18.** $\frac{3}{20}$; 0.15	**19.** $\frac{1}{50}$; 0.02	**20.** $\frac{22}{25}$; 0.88
21. $\frac{6}{5}$; 1.20	**22.** $\frac{3}{2}$; 1.5	**23.** $\frac{11}{10}$; 1.1	**24.** $\frac{9}{5}$; 1.8	**25.** $\frac{9}{4}$; 2.25
26. $\frac{1}{8}$; 0.125	**27.** $\frac{5}{8}$; 0.625	**28.** $\frac{3}{40}$; 0.075	**29.** $\frac{7}{40}$; 0.175	**30.** $\frac{23}{125}$; 0.184
31. $\frac{1}{3}$	**32.** $\frac{2}{3}$	**33.** $\frac{1}{6}$	**34.** $\frac{5}{6}$	**35.** $\frac{1}{200}$

Exercise 10.2 ▼

1. 23%	**2.** 37%	**3.** 18%	**4.** 6%	**5.** 240%
6. 50%	**7.** 25%	**8.** 75%	**9.** 40%	**10.** 90%
11. 85%	**12.** 66%	**13.** 36%	**14.** 150%	**15.** 120%
16. 8%	**17.** 125%	**18.** 108%	**19.** $17\frac{1}{2}$%	**20.** $12\frac{1}{2}$%
21. $33\frac{1}{3}$%	**22.** $87\frac{1}{2}$%	**23.** $8\frac{1}{3}$%	**24.** $66\frac{2}{3}$%	**25.** $56\frac{1}{4}$%

Exercise 10.3 ▼

1. 75%	**2.** 40%	**3.** 60%	**4.** 20%	**5.** 80%
6. 12%	**7.** 250%	**8.** 150%	**9.** 25%	**10.** 30%
11. 20%	**12.** 45%	**13.** 40%	**14.** 15%	**15.** 20%
16. 25%	**17.** $33\frac{1}{3}$%	**18.** 15%	**19.** 120%	**20.** 75%
21. 35%	**22.** 32%	**23.** 35%	**24.** 16%	**25.** 60%; 40%

26. 71%   **27.** 16%; 24%; 40%; 20%

28. 20 wins in 25 is 80%, 30 wins in 40 is 75%   **29.** $2\frac{1}{2}$%

30. **(i)** 25%   **(ii)** 20%

Exercise 10.4 ▼

1. 20%	**2.** 50%	**3.** 25%	**4.** 10%	**5.** 5%	**6.** 12%
7. 7%	**8.** 9%	**9.** 14%	**10.** 8%	**11.** $12\frac{1}{2}$%	**12.** 5%
13. 7%	**14.** 15%	**15.** $12\frac{1}{2}$%	**16.** $13\frac{1}{2}$%	**17.** $33\frac{1}{3}$%	**18.** $66\frac{2}{3}$%
19. 6%	**20.** 2%	**21.** 7%	**22. (i)** 201.6 kg **(ii)** 12%	**23.** 5.5%	

Exercise 10.5

1. €38 **2.** €30 **3.** 84c **4.** 54.30 **5.** €6 **6.** 92 m
7. 50 m **8.** €81.15 **9.** €182.07 **10.** 75.96 **11.** €38.50 **12.** 325 m
13. €37.20 **14.** €120 **15.** €4 **16.** €23.80 **17.** 462 **18.** €2.01
19. 300 m **20.** €120 **21.** €496; €620; €992; €372 **22.** €9.52

Exercise 10.6

1. (i) 336 (ii) 44.8 (iii) 134.4 (iv) 67.2 (v) 4,480
2. (i) 188 (ii) 45.12 (iii) 14.1 (iv) 4,888 (v) 225.6
3. 115 kg **4.** €454.75 **5.** €31.36 **6.** 57c **7.** 615 kg
8. (a) €102 (b) €212.50 (c) €467.50 (d) €667.25 **9.** 325
10. €18,000; €16,560; €15,732

Exercise 10.7

1. 25% **2.** 10% **3.** 20% **4.** 15% **5.** 8% **6.** 10%
7. $12\frac{1}{2}$ % **8.** 27% **9.** $33\frac{1}{3}$% **10.** $66\frac{2}{3}$% **11.** 20% **12.** 8%
13. 15% **14.** 5% **15.** 12% **16.** 24% **17.** 55% **18.** $12\frac{1}{2}$%
19. 18% **20.** 3% **21.** (i) 25% (ii) 20% **22.** 15% **23.** 21%
24. 12% **25.** €75; 50%; $33\frac{1}{3}$ % **26.** 30% **27.** 12% **28.** 10%
29. 8% **30.** 20% **31.** 25% **32.** 40% **33.** 17% **34.** 20%
35. 5% **36.** €126 **37.** €17 **38.** €176 **39.** €33 **40.** €132
41. €110.40 **42.** €22.80 **43.** €63 **44.** €40 **45.** €297 **46.** €4.50

Exercise 10.8

1. 1,000 **2.** €300 **3.** 600 **4.** 50 **5.** 3,100; 248
6. €576 **7.** €410 **8.** €33 **9.** €48 **10.** €250
11. €2,200 **12.** €320; €48 **13.** €540 **14.** €210 **15.** 14 cm
16. 160 kg **17.** €750 **18.** €13,600 **19.** €174,000
20. (i) 280 (ii) 70 (iii) 56 **21.** B paid €22; A paid €20.

Exercise 10.9

2. (i) 80% (ii) 13% **3.** Maths **4.** 20%; 25%; 40%; 15%
5. (i) 13% (ii) 12 **6.** 12% **7.** 338 **8.** €6.30
9. €2.03 **10.** €62.10 **11.** €5,400; €4,968; €4,719.60 **12.** 96
13. €14.20 **14.** €288; (a) €273.60 (b) 14% **15.** $12\frac{1}{2}$%

16. 5% **17.** 575 **18.** 700 **19.** €350 **20.** €60

21. 21; €2.40 **22.** (i) €19 (ii) €1.90 (iii) €2.85

Exercise 11.1 ▼

1. €14; €154 **2.** €31.50; €241.50 **3.** €16.32; €152.32 **4.** €15.34; €133.34
5. €8.10; €53.10 **6.** €124.20; €664.20 **7.** €6.72; €38.72 **8.** €75; €675
9. €189; €1269 **10.** €12.75; €162.75 **11.** 15%; €12 **12.** 18%; €27
13. 23%; €575 **14.** 8%; €156.60 **15.** $12\frac{1}{2}$%; €130 **16.** 21%; €22.05
17. €152.52 **18.** €68.40 **19.** €4.83 **20.** €108
21. €264.80 **22.** 12% **23.** 23%
24. (i) 4,200 (ii) €1,722 (iii) 21%

Exercise 11.2 ▼

1. €250; €25 **2.** €120; €18 **3.** €240; €12 **4.** €800; €168
5. €4,500; €1,035 **6.** €80; €9.60 **7.** €350; €73.50 **8.** €54; €9.72
9. €52; €4.16 **10.** €180; €22.50 **11.** €40 **12.** €650
13. €82 **14.** €240 **15.** (i) €970 (ii) €116.40
16. €850; €1,045.50 **17.** €495.60 **18.** €69 **19.** €12,075
20. €984

Exercise 11.3 ▼

1. €10,000; €2,000; €16,000 **2.** €33,300; €13,320; €32,180
3. €15,350; €3,684; €21,116 **4.** €11,200; €5,152; €11,328
5. €16,890; €4,222.50; €20,017.50 **6.** €25,310; €8,099.20; €26,660.80
7. €19,238; €6,733.30; €22,046.70 **8.** €25,265; €4,737.60; €20,527.40
9. €25,200; €4,065.60; €21,134.40 **10.** €19,509; €2,546.95; €16,962.05
11. (i) €20,400 (ii) €4080 (iii) €23,120 (iv) 15%
12. (i) €30,800 (ii) €12,320 (iii) €26,180 (iv) 32%
13. (i) €19,040 (ii) €4,188.80 (iii) €20,451.20 (iv) 83%
14. (i) €17,920 (ii) €5,734.40 (iii) €22,937.60 (iv) 80%
15. (i) €16,625 (ii) €4,156.25 (iii) €17,718.75 (iv) 19%
16. €9,150 **17.** €10,700; €27,300 **18.** €5,620 **19.** €6,464; 32%
20. €7,200; 24% **21.** €12,000; 40% **22.** €11,000; 20% **23.** €37,000; 35%
24. €14,000; 18% **25.** €22,100; 25% **26.** €25,790; 22% **27.** €18,810; 24%
28. €11,170; 38% **29.** €17,580; 32% **30.** €18,999; 27% **31.** €30,750; 32%
32. €27,760; 40% **33.** 23% **34.** 38%

Exercise 11.4 ▼

1. €20,500	**2.** €23,950	**3.** €14,920	**4.** €25,580
5. €6,850	**6.** €5,972	**7.** €6,541	**8.** €5,427
9. €22,828	**10.** €6,990	**11.** €18,400	**12.** €23,880
13. €7,500	**14.** €3,780	**15.** €52,980	

Exercise 11.5 ▼

1. €60.50   **2.** 12%   **3.** €172.20   **4.** €18   **5.** €18.90
6. €70   **7.** €88   **8.** 850; €78.20; €96.60   **9.** €202.50
10. (i) €24,480   (ii) €4,896   (iii) €27,744   (iv) 85%
11. (i) €26,180   (ii) €10,472   (iii) €22,253   (iv) 68%
12. (i) €23,800   (ii) €5,236   (iii) €25,564   (iv) 17%
13. (i) €26,880   (ii) €8,601.60   (iii) €34,406.40   (iv) 20%
14. €8,018.50   **15.** €10,528; €31,772   **16.** €27,200; 36%   **17.** €18,600; 40%
18. €29,700   **19.** €11,400   **20.** €37,600

Exercise 12.1 ▼

11. €60   **12.** €32.40   **13.** €73.60   **14.** €30   **15.** €600.30
16. €668.80   **17.** €2,532   **18.** €5,200   **19.** €2,682.50

Exercise 12.2 ▼

17. €15,000   **18.** 7%   **19.** €450   **20.** 4.5%

Exercise 12.3 ▼

17. €4,200; €168   **18.** €6,800

Exercise 12.4 ▼

1. €61.80	**2.** €410	**3.** €416	**4.** €521.64
5. €65.28	**6.** €73.08	**7.** €168	**8.** €499.20
9. €115.85	**10.** €649.28	**11.** €630.50	**12.** €1910.16
13. €12.61	**14.** €2,497.28	**15.** €6,073.92	**16.** €4,775.40

17. (i) €13,206   (ii) €14,064.39   **18.** €9,447.84
19. (i) €750   (ii) €795   (iii) €842.70; €14,887.70
20. €400; €11,248.64   **21.** €21,854.54   **22.** 5%; €630.50

1. €736 **2.** €432.25 **3.** €11,448 **4.** €5,356
5. €1,755.52 **6.** €1,515.30 **7.** €19,776.96 **8.** €2,744.95

1. €4,720 **2.** €2,712 **3.** €5,337 **4.** €5,549 **5.** €2,085.60

1. **(a)** €120 **(b)** €945 **(c)** €200; €200
2. **(a)** €60 **(b)** €430.50 **(c)** €5,400
3. **(a)** €2,568 **(b)** €2,865.24 **(c)** 9%
4. **(a)** €18.75 **(b)** €936.48 **(c)** **(i)** €390 **(ii)** 6%
5. **(a)** €2,090 **(b)** €2,160.64 **(c)** €840
6. **(a)** €2,332 **(b)** €26,369.28 **(c)** **(i)** €850 **(ii)** €34
  (d) **(i)** €66,550 **(ii)** €16,550 **(iii)** €6,620; 13.24% **(e)** €6,554

1. 1 : 2 **2.** 3 : 4 **3.** 1 : 3 **4.** 2 : 5 **5.** 3 : 5 **6.** 2 : 3
7. 5 : 4 **8.** 5 : 3 **9.** 6 : 5 **10.** 3 : 2 **11.** 4 : 5 **12.** 1 : 5
13. 3 : 2 **14.** 4 : 3 **15.** 8 : 7 **16.** 5 : 8 **17.** 2 : 3 : 5 **18.** 3 : 4 : 5
19. 1 : 4 : 5 **20.** 3 : 4 : 7 **21.** 2 : 5 **22.** 3 : 4 **23.** 2 : 3 **24.** 1 : 3
25. 1 : 5 **26.** 3 : 8 **27.** 3 : 10 **28.** 9 : 10 **29.** 2 : 7 **30.** 3 : 1
31. 3 : 8 **32.** 1 : 5 **33.** 1 : 10 **34.** 8 : 15
35. **(i)** 1 : 3 **(ii)** 1 : 1 **(iii)** 2 : 3 **(iv)** 1 : 2
36. **(i)** 1 : 2 **(ii)** 1 : 3 **37.** **(i)** 1 : 3 **(ii)** 2 : 5 **(iii)** 7 : 2
38. 6 : 5 **39.** **(i)** 3 : 2 **(ii)** 3 : 10 **(iii)** 5 : 1
40. 5 : 4 **41.** 1 : 2 **42.** 5 : 8 **43.** 1 : 3 **44.** 3 : 1 **45.** 7 : 9
46. 1 : 3 **47.** 4 : 5 **48.** 1 : 3 **49.** 5 : 7 **50.** 1 : 3 **51.** 1 : 5
52. 3 : 4

Exercise 13.2 ▼

1. €6; €12
2. €12; €18
3. €6; €18
4. 15 kg; 25 kg
5. 12 mins; 16 mins
6. 30 cm; 20cm
7. 6 months; 3 months
8. 20; 16
9. 56; 32
10. €75; €45
11. 200 students; 250 students
12. 120 g; 140 g
13. 90; 60
14. €16.24; €8.12
15. €6.12; €9.18
16. €24; €96; €60
17. 200 g; 160 g; 120 g
18. €1,000; €1,400; €1,600
19. 30 kg; 60 kg; 80 kg
20. 72 cm; 54 cm; 36 cm
21. €8; €16
22. €35; €15
23. €10; €20
24. €560
25. 180
26. €15
27. Boy €160; girl €240.
28. 15 cm; 20 cm; 25 cm
29. Copper 42 kg; zinc 24 kg; tin 18 kg
30. €21,600; €34,560
31. A €3,000; B €2,000; C €1,500
32. 20; 10
33. 12 kg; 16 kg
34. €100; €200
35. 10; 30
36. 4 kg; 20 kg
37. 60 g; 140 g
38. 15 cm; 21 cm
39. €16; €28
40. 5 g; 10 g; 20 g
41. €48; €24; €6
42. 12; 20; 28
43. €75; €95

Exercise 13.3 ▼

1. (i) €60; €60   (ii) €80; €40   (iii) €90; €30   (iv) €75; €45
2. A €160; B €80; C €40   **3.** P €60; Q €30; R €30
4. €12   **5.** (i) B   (ii) A €20; B €10; C €40
6. (i) X   (ii) X €30, Y €90, Z €180

Exercise 13.4 ▼

1. €60   **2.** (i) €42   (ii) €18   **3.** €200
4. (a) 819   (b) 455   **5.** 64 km/h   **6.** 18 years   **7.** 25,000
8. (i) 56   (ii) 20   **9.** 75 cm   **10.** 63 cm   **11.** 162 cm
12. (a) €108   (b) €24; €36   **13.** €400; €160   **14.** 91   **15.** €31.92

Exercise 13.5 ▼

1. (i) €80   (ii) €560   **2.** (i) €0.25   (ii) €0.75   (iii) €3
3. €240   **4.** (i) 40   (ii) 320   (iii) 20   **5.** €300.80
6. €20.30   **7.** (a) 20   (b) 1,400   (c) 1,200   (d) 1,100
8. (a) 0.2 kg or 200 g   (b) 0.6 kg or 600 g   (c) 8 kg
9. (i) €96   (ii) €24   (iii) €136   (iv) €152
10. 960 g   **11.** €588   **12.** $13\frac{1}{2}$ cm   **13.** 480
14. (a) 20 km   (b) 80 km   (c) 5 km   (d) 15 km   (e) 3.5 km
      (f) 4 cm   (g) 6 cm   (h) 7.5 cm   (i) 15 cm   (j) 1.25 cm

15. (a) 288 cm or 2.88 m **(b)** 36 cm or 0.36 m **(c)** 234 cm or 2.34 m; 3 cm
16. €270 **17. (a)** €6 **(b)** €180 **18.** €30

Exercise 13.6 ▼

1. (i) $150 **(ii)** €120 **2.** $90 **3.** $40 **4.** €320
5. €85 **6. (i)** $48 **(ii)** $966 **(iii)** ¥59,616 **(iv)** €75
 (v) €500 **(vi)** €720 **(vii) (a)** $p = 2.3$ **(b)** $q = 276$ **(c)** $r = 120$
7. (i) €1 = $1.40 **(ii)** €1 = $2.20 **8.** Cheaper in Ireland by €1.50
9. Cheaper in Canada by €5 **10.** R1,920; R64

Exercise 13.7 ▼

1. (i) 24 days **(ii)** 6 days **(iii)** 2 days
2. (i) 40 days **(ii)** 5 days **(iii)** 20 days
3. 25 days **4.** 4 sweets **5.** 25 minutes **6.** 9 hours
7. (i) 120 people **(ii)** 3 people **(iii)** 2 people **8.** 6 days
9. 27 people **10.** 16 check-outs **11.** 30 pupils; 50 classrooms
12. 15 days **13.** 14 days **14.** 18 pieces **15.** 20 sewing machines

---

Exercise 13.8 ▼

1. 1 : 3 **2. (i)** 96; 48 **(ii)** 54; 90 **(iii)** 112; 32
3. €100; €140; €180 **4. (a)** 1 : 3 **(b)** 1 : 4 **(c)** 2 : 5
5. Copper 180 g; tin 240 g; lead 180 g **6.** €32 **7. (a)** €9.60
 (b) €12 **(c)** €6.40 **8. A** €480; **B** €240; **C** €120 **9.** 12
10. €4 **11.** 20 c **12. (a) (i)** €6.75 **(ii)** €11.25 **(b)** €8.40
13. €192 **14. (i)** 2 : 3 **(ii)** 5 : 4 **(iii)** 3 : 4 **(iv)** 5 : 6 **(v)** 1 : 1
15. 180 m **16. (i)** €6 **(ii)** €72 **17.** $1,215 **18.** $98

Exercise 14.1 ▼

1. (ii) (a) train **(b)** walking **(iii)** 24 **(iv)** 25%
2. (ii) green **(iii)** 40 **(iv)** 20%
3. (ii) 50 **(iii)** 24% **4. (ii)** soccer **(iii)** 48 **(iv)** $12\frac{1}{2}\%$ **(v)** 40%
5. (ii) 360 **6. (iii)** 10 **(iv)** 48 **(v)** 25%
7. (ii) 0 **(iii)** 9 **(iv)** 36 **(v)** $66\frac{2}{3}\%$

1. (ii) 48   (iii) 25%   (iv) €1,920   **2.** (ii) €600   (iii) 10%

3. (ii) €144,000   (iii) $12\frac{1}{2}\%$ **4.** (ii) 30 cm   (iii) $33\frac{1}{3}\%$

5. (ii) 10°C at 15:00   (iii) 7°C   (iv) 12:00 and 17:00

6. (i) 18   (ii) 10   (iii) 12:00   (iv) 10

7. (ii) 145 cm   (iii) 1999   (iv) (a) 40%   (b) 6%

Exercise 14.3 ▼

3. $33\frac{1}{3}\%$ **4.** (ii) 30%   **5.** (ii) 80%

6. (i) 180   (ii) D; 30%   **7.** (ii) 15%

Exercise 14.4 ▼

1. 300

2.

Work	Sports	Hospital	School	Home
270	180	108	225	297

3.

Spain	Britain	France	United States	Ireland
480	72	288	240	360

4. (i) 20°   (ii)

A	B	C	D	E
40	50	60	20	10

5. (i) 90°   (ii)

Bus	Walking	Train	Bicycle
81	216	108	135

(iii) 540

6. (a) 18°

	Leisure	Mortgage	Power and fuel	Other	Clothes	Bank	Food
(b)	€90	€180	€135	€67.50	€112.50	€45	€270
(c)	10%	20%	15%	$7\frac{1}{2}\%$	$12\frac{1}{2}\%$	5%	30%

7. (a) 40°   (b)

Orange	Blue	Red	Green	Purple
126	84	56	98	140

1. 4   **2.** 5   **3.** 2   **4.** 6   **5.** 50   **6.** 5
7. 4   **8.** 4   **9.** 37   **10.** 5   **11.** 0   **12.** 1.1
13. 4; 2   **14.** 7; 6   **15.** 3; 3   **16.** 3; 2   **17.** 3; 0   **18.** 8.2; 8.4
19. 3.5; 4.1   **20.** $\frac{1}{2}$; $\frac{1}{3}$ **21.** $2\frac{2}{5}$; $1\frac{1}{2}$ **22.** €5.06   **23.** €105.85   **24.** €16.02
25. (i) 56 mm   **(ii)** 8 mm   **26.** 12 mins 26 secs   **27.** 54; 56

1. 32   **2.** 30   **3.** 24   **4.** 21   **5.** 5
6. 3   **7.** 7   **8.** 5   **9.** 16   **10.** 2
11. 6   **12.** 4   **13.** 3   **14.** 3   **15.** 2
16. 3   **17.** 15; 9   **18.** 10   **19.** 2   **20.** 8
21. 4   **22.** 21   **23.** 4

1. 1; 2   **2.** 1; 3   **3.** 3; 3   **4.** 5; 5   **5.** 1; 3   **6.** 4; 3
7. (i) 3; 3   **(ii)** 11   **8. (a)** 6   **(b)** 6   **9. (a)** 30   **(b)** 0   **(c)** 2
10. (i) 3   **(ii)** 0   **(iii)** 2   **(iv)** 9   **11. (b)** 6   **(c)** 4   **(d)** 20
12. (ii) 2   **(iii)** 3   **(iv)** 9   **(v)** 35%   **13. (ii)** 1   **(iii)** 3   **(iv)** 30%

2. (i) €6   **(ii)** 65%   **(iii)** €5.70   **3. (a)** 4   **(b)** 15; 16; 31

4. (ii) 48   **(iii)** 200   **(iv)** 6.5   **5. (ii)** 2.5   **(iii)** 3; 7

6. (ii) 40   **(iii)** €6   **(iv)** 89   **7. (i)** 3   **(ii) (a)** 6   **(b)** 6

8. (a) 1.9   **(b) (i)** 150   **(ii)** 2.5   **(iii)** 500; 108°

9. (a) 9   **(b) (i)** B

(ii)

Grade	A (93)	B (77)	C (62)	D (47)	E (32)
Number of pupils	4	10	4	4	3

(iii) 66.96

10. (i) 1   **(iii)** 60   **(iv)** 4   **(v)** 135   **(vi)** 2.25

11. (a) 7   **(b)**

Youth club	Sweets	Cinema	Savings	Pitch and putt
€2.70	€0.90	€3.24	€2.16	€1.80

12. **(a)** 10

(b)

	Mortgage	Clothes	Food	Electricity and gas	Savings	Entertainment	Other
	€180	€60	€120	€90	€45	€75	€30

13. **(a)** 3   **14.** **(a)** 2   **(b) (i)** 3   **(ii)** 6
   (c) 36%   **(d)** 23   **(e)** 2

Exercise 15.1 ▼

1. $\{2, 4, 6, 8\}$ **2.** $\{1, 3, 5, 7, 9\}$ **3.** $\{1, 2, 3, 4, 6, 12\}$
4. $\{S, U, C, E\}$ **5.** $\{2, 3, 5, 7, 11, 13\}$ **6.** $\{A, R, N, G, E, M, T\}$
7. $\{A, O, U, I, E\}$ **8.** $\{A, E, I\}$ **9.** $\{3, 6, 9, 12, 15, 18, 21\}$
10. $\{5, 10, 15, 20, 25, 30\}$
11. {Monday, Tuesday, Wednesday, Thursday, Friday, Saturday, Sunday}
12. {Saturday, Sunday}   **13.** {January, June, July}   **14.** $\{1, 2, 3, 4, 5, 6, 7, 8, 9\}$
15. $\{0, 1, 4, 9, 16, 25\}$

Exercise 15.2 ▼

1. **(i)** 7   **(ii)** 16   **3.** **(ii)** 8   **5.** **(i)** $P = \{a, e, i\}, Q = \{a, e\}$
   (ii) no   **(iii)** 1   **6.** **(i)** 9   **(ii)** 34   **(iii)** 29   **(iv)** 25
   7. **(i)** the null set, { } or ∅   **(ii)** 0
8. **(i)** $A = \{r, e, a, n, g\}$,   **(ii)** $B = \{r, a, n, g, e\}$ **(iii)** yes   **(iv)** 0

Exercise 15.3 ▼

1. $\{6, 8, 10, 12, 14\}$ **2.** $\{3, 5, 7, 9, 11\}$ **3.** $\{T, E, N, S\}$
4. $\{T, O, M, R, W\}$ **5.** $\{1, 2, 4, 7, 14, 28\}$ **6.** $\{1, 2, 3, 4, 6, 9, 12, 18, 36\}$
7. $\{4, 8, 12, 16, 20, 24\}$ **8.** $\{2, 3, 5, 7, 11, 13, 17, 19\}$ **9.** $\{A, O, U, I, E\}$
10. $\{O, I, U\}$ **11.** {Tuesday, Thursday}   **12.** { } or ∅
13. { } or ∅   **14.** { } or ∅

Exercise 15.4 ▼

2. **(i)** $\{2, 4, 6, 8, 10\}$ **(ii)** $\{1, 3, 5, 7, 9\}$ **(iii)** $\{3, 6, 9\}$ **(iv)** $\{2, 3, 5, 7\}$
   (v) $\{5, 10\}$ **(vi)** $\{1, 2, 3, 4, 6, 8\}$ **(vii)** $\{1, 4, 9\}$ **(viii)** $\{1, 8\}$ **(ix)** { } or ∅
4. $\{231, 141, 600, 501\}$
5. **(i)** { }, $\{p\}$, $\{q\}$, $\{r\}$, $\{p, q\}$, $\{p, r\}$, $\{q, r\}$, $\{p, q, r\}$

(ii) { }, {1}, {2}, {3}, {4}, {1, 2}, {1, 3}, {1, 4}, {2, 3}, {2, 4}, {3, 4}, {1, 2, 3}, {1, 2, 4}, {1, 3, 4), {2, 3, 4}, {1, 2, 3, 4}.

6. {a, b, c}, {a, b, d}, {a, c, d}, {b, c, d}

Exercise 15.5 ▼

1. **(ii)** {4, 5}; {1, 2, 3, 4, 5, 6, 7}   **(iii)** 5   **(iv)** yes
2. **(ii)** {b, d}; {a, b, c, d, e, f, g, h}   **(iii)** 4
3. **(ii)** {e, f}; {c, d, e, f, g, h}   **(iii)** 4
4. **(ii)** {2, 4, 5, 6, 8}; {2, 5}   **(iv)** 3
6. **(iii)** 2   **(iv)** {7, 8}

Exercise 15.6 ▼

1. **(i)** {1, 2, 3}   **(ii)** {7, 8}   **2.** **(i)** {b, d}   **(ii)** {e, f, g}; 1
3. **(i)** {r, s}   **(ii)** {u, v, w}   **(iii)** {r, s, u, v, w}   **(iv)** { } or ∅
5. **(i)** {3, 4, 5}   **(ii)** {1, 3, 4}   **(iii)** {6, 7, 8}   **(iv)** {1, 6, 8}   **(v)** {1, 2, 3, 4, 5, 6, 7, 8}
   (vi) {1, 3, 4, 6, 8}   **(vii)** {2, 7}   **(viii)** {1, 3, 4, 5}   **(ix)** {1, 2, 5, 6, 7, 8, 9}
   (x) {1, 5, 6, 8, 9}   **(xi)** {7}

Exercise 15.7 ▼

1. {a, b}   **2.** {4, 6, 8}   **3.** **(i)** {2, 3, 4, 7}   **(ii)** {2, 3, 6, 7, 8}
4. **(i)** {b, c, e}   **(ii)** {c, d, e, f}   **(iii)** {c, e}   **(iv)** {c, e}; 5
5. **(i)** {a, b, g, t, k, m, n, r, s, v, p, q}   **(ii)** {k, m, n, g, h, t}
   (iii) {g, h, t, r, s, v}   **(iv)** {g, h, t}
   (v) {k, m, n, g, h, t, r, s, v}   **(vi)** {k, m, n}
   (vii) {r, s, v}   **(viii)** {r, s, v, a, b, p, q}
   (ix) {k, m, n, a, b, p, q}   **(x)** {a, b, p, q}
   (xi) {a, b, p, q}   **(xii)** {r, s, v}
   (xiii) {k, m, n}   **(xiv)** {a, b, k, m, n, g, h, t, p, q}

Exercise 15.8 ▼

7. **(i)** {1, 2, 4, 5, 7}   **(ii)** {1, 3, 5, 6}   **(iii)** {1, 4, 6, 8, 9}   **(iv)** {2, 4, 7}
   (v) {1, 2, 3, 4, 5, 6, 7}   **(vi)** {1, 5}   **(vii)** {2, 3, 5, 7}   **(viii)** {5}
   (ix) {1, 4, 6}   **(x)** {1, 2, 4, 5, 6, 7}
8. **(i)** {3}   **(ii)** {1, 2}   **(iii)** {1, 2, 3, 4, 5}   **(iv)** {2, 4}   **(v)** {3}
   (vi) { } or ∅   **(vii)** {2, 4, 7}   **(viii)** {7}   **(ix)** {2}   **(x)** {2, 7}
   (xi) {6, 7}   **(xii)** {1, 3, 5}; 3   **10.** **(a)** **(i)** {3, 4, 5}   **(ii)** {1, 7}
   (iii) {6}   **(iv)** {2}   **(b)** **(i)** 6   **(ii)** 1   **(iii)** 1

1. **(i)** 15 **(ii)** 45 **(iii)** 27 **(iv)** 9 **(v)** 42
2. **(i)** 22 **(ii)** 34 **(iii)** 33 **(iv)** 5 **(v)** 23
3. **(i)** 4 **(ii)** 24 **(iii)** 28
4. **(i)** 11 **(ii)** 12 **(iii)** 2 **5. (i)** 28 **(ii)** 15 **(iii)** 7
6. 9 **7.** 35 **8.** 150 **9. (i)** 46 **(ii)** 10
   (iii) 11 **(iv)** 18 **(v)** 39 **(vi)** 7 **(vii)** 25 **(viii)** 18
   (ix) 36 **10** 27 **11.** 10 **12.** 25
13. **(i)** 10 **(ii)** 8 **14.** 6 **15 (i)** 8 **(ii)** 15 **(iii)** 7
16. $28 - x = 22; 6$

1. **(i)** 10 **(ii)** 18 **(iii)** 61 **(iv)** 8 **(v)** 5 **(vi)** 20 **(vii)** 45
   (viii) 4 **(ix)** 35 **(x)** 20
2. **(i)** 5 **(ii)** 32 **(iii)** 9 **(iv)** 47 **(v)** 7 **(vi)** 3 **(vii)** 6
   (viii) 22 **(ix)** 27 **(x)** 22 **(xi)** 54
3. 12 **4.** 2 **5. (a)** 2 **(b)** 3 **(c)** 5
6. **(i)** 13 **(ii)** 6 **(iii)** 23 **(iv)** 32 **(v)** 23 **(vi)** 1
7. **(i)** 37 **(ii)** 18 **(iii)** 20 **(iv)** 21 **(v)** 5 **(vi)** 28
   (vii) 35 **(viii)** 2 **(ix)** 3 **(x)** 17 **(xi)** 4 **(xii)** 22
8. **(i)** 4 **(ii)** 15 **(iii)** 7 **(iv)** 10
9. **(a)** 3 **(b)** 8 **(c)** 4 **(d)** 19 **(e)** 26 **(f)** 8
10. 30 **11. (a) (i)** 4 **(ii)** 6 **(iii)** 18

1. **(i)** $\{B, A, N\}$ **(ii)** $\{B, O, K, E, P, R\}$ **(iii)** $\{T, E, N, S\}$ **(iv)** $\{T, H, I, R, E\}$
2. **(i)** $\{2, 3, 6, 7, 8\}$ **(ii)** $\{2, 4, 6, 9\}$ **(iii)** $\{1, 2, 3, 4, 5, 6, 7, 8, 9, 10\}$ **(iv)** $\{2, 6\}$
   (v) $\{1, 4, 5, 9, 10\}$ **(vi)** $\{2, 3, 4, 6, 7, 8, 9\}$ **(vii)** $\{1, 5, 10\}$
   (viii) $\{1, 3, 4, 5, 7, 8, 9, 10\}$
4. **(i)** $\{1, 4, 7, 8, 9\}$ **(ii)** $\{1, 4\}$ **(iii)** $\{2, 3, 8\}$ **(iv)** $\{4, 5, 6, 7, 9\}$
   (v) $\{1, 2, 3, 4, 5, 6, 7, 8, 9\}$ **(vi)** $\{10\}$ **(vii)** $\{1\}$ **(viii)** $\{4\}$ **(ix)** $\{1, 8\}$
5. **(a) (i)** 30 **(ii)** 5 **(b) (i)** 5 **(ii)** 4 **(c) (i)** 4 **(ii)** 17
6. **(i)** $\{3, 7\}$ **(ii)** $\{6\}$ **(iii)** $\{1, 2, 3, 9\}$ **(iv)** $\{3\}$ **(v)** $\{3, 5\}$
7. **(i)** 10 **(ii)** 3 **(iii)** 5 **(iv)** 8 **(v)** 27
8. **(i)** 10 **(ii)** 29 **(iii)** 19 **(iv)** 23 **(v)** 4
9. **(i)** 3 **(ii)** 7
10. **(i)** 21 **(ii)** 16 **(iii)** 5 **(iv)** 2
12. 11 **13. (i)** 5 **(ii)** 24

1. $4a$ **2.** $2p$ **3.** $2y$ **4.** 1

5. $3a$ **6.** $-2p$ **7.** x **8.** $-2p$

9. $3x$ **10.** $3r$ **11.** b **12.** 2

13. 1 **14.** $4a$ **15.** $2a$ **24.** $4(x + 2)$

25. $a(b + c)$ **26.** $3(a + b)$ **27.** $p(2 + q)$ **28.** $4(3a + 2b)$

29. $3(m + 2n)$ **30.** $x(x + 1)$ **31.** $x(x - 3)$ **32.** $2x(1 + 2x)$

33. $a(a + 5)$ **34.** $2p(2 + p)$ **35.** $5x(x + 2)$ **36.** $3x(a + 2b)$

37. $4a(b - 2)$ **38.** $2p(q - 3r)$ **39.** $6x(p - q)$ **40.** $5a(b + 2c)$

41. $7x(1 - 4y)$ **42.** $2a(1 - 2a)$ **43.** $3a(1 + 2b + 3c)$ **44.** $4a(a - 5b)$

45. $p(q + r - 1)$ **46.** $3x(2y - 3z)$ **47.** $q(r - 2s)$ **48.** $b(4a - 3b)$

49. $3x(x - 3y)$ **50.** $6pq(3p - 1)$ **51.** $4xy(x + 2y)$ **52.** $2ab(a + 3b)$

53. $5ab(2c - 3d)$ **54.** $a^2 + 3a$; $a(a + 3a)$ **55. (i)** $4a(2b + 3)$ **(ii)** $2(2b + 3)$; $2a$

1. $(a + b)(c + d)$ **2.** $(p + q)(r + s)$ **3.** $(x + a)(p + q)$

4. $(x - y)(m + n)$ **5.** $(y - 3)(2x + 5)$ **6.** $(c - 3d)(2a - b)$

7. $(a + b)(x + y)$ **8.** $(q + r)(p + x)$ **9.** $(m + n)(x + y)$

10. $(a + b)(5 + x)$ **11.** $(x + y)(4 + z)$ **12.** $(b + c)(a + d)$

13. $(p + q)(3 + r)$ **14.** $(x + 4)(a + p)$ **15.** $(x + y)(5 + a)$

16. $(p + q)(a + b)$ **17.** $(x - y)(a + 2)$ **18.** $(p - q)(3 + r)$

19. $(m - n)(a + 4)$ **20.** $(a - b)(c + d)$ **21.** $(a + b)(3 - c)$

22. $(q + r)(p - 5)$ **23.** $(p + q)(x - y)$ **24.** $(p + q)(r - 2s)$

25. $(a + b)(a + 2)$ **26.** $(x - y)(x + z)$ **27.** $(x + 2p)(x + q)$

28. $(2 - x)(x + y)$ **29.** $(m + n)(m + 4)$ **30.** $(p - 3)(p + q)$

31. $(b + c)(a + 1)$ **32.** $(q + r)(p + 1)$ **33.** $(a + b)(x - 1)$

34. $(y + z)(x - 1)$

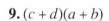

9. $(c + d)(a + b)$ **10.** $(q + r)(p + 3)$ **11.** $(x + 2)(a + b)$

12. $(x + y)(3 + z)$ **13.** $(p - q)(x + y)$ **14.** $(b + c)(2a - 5)$

15. $(a + d)(b - c)$ **16.** $(p - q)(2a - b)$ **17.** $(x - 4)(a - p)$

18. $(a - b)(3 - q)$ **19.** $(q - r)(p + s)$ **20.** $(a - b)(p - q)$

21. $(a + b)(x - 1)$ **22.** $(p - q)(1 - 3a)$ **23.** $(a - b)(p - 1)$

24. $(1 + c)(a - b)$

1. $(x + 1)(x + 2)$
2. $(x + 1)(x + 3)$
3. $(x + 1)(x + 5)$
4. $(x + 1)(x + 7)$
5. $(x + 1)(x + 11)$
6. $(x + 2)(x + 4)$
7. $(x + 1)(x + 4)$
8. $(x + 3)(x + 4)$
9. $(x + 2)(x + 5)$
10. $(x + 1)(x + 10)$
11. $(x + 2)(x + 6)$
12. $(x + 1)(x + 12)$
13. $(x - 2)(x - 7)$
14. $(x - 3)(x - 7)$
15. $(x - 2)(x - 6)$
16. $(x + 2)(x - 4)$
17. $(x - 2)(x + 10)$
18. $(x + 2)(x - 6)$
19. $(x - 3)(x + 5)$
20. $(x + 3)(x - 4)$
21. $(x - 5)(x + 6)$
22. $(x + 3)(x + 3)$
23. $(x + 2)(x + 2)$
24. $(x + 4)(x + 6)$
25. $(x - 1)(x + 2)$
26. $(x + 2)(x - 3)$
27. $(x + 3)(x - 8)$
28. $(x + 1)(x - 3)$
29. $(x - 1)(x + 6)$
30. $(x - 4)(x - 25)$
31. $(x + 3)(x + 16)$
32. $(x - 1)(x + 4)$
33. $(x - 4)(x + 5)$
34. $(x + 4)(x - 6)$
35. $(x + 2)(x - 5)$
36. $(x - 3)(x + 20)$
37. $(x + 5)(x - 7)$
38. $(x - 4)(x - 5)$
39. $(x + 6)(x - 7)$
40. $(x - 3)(x + 6)$
41. $(x + 5)(x + 9)$
42. $(x + 4)(x - 7)$
43. $(x + 2)(x - 7)$
44. $(x - 5)(x + 8)$
45. $(x + 3)(x - 9)$
46. $(x + 4)(x - 18)$
47. $(x - 2)(x + 30)$
48. $(x + 5)(x - 16)$
49. $x^2 + 9x + 20; (x + 4)(x + 5)$
50. $x^2 - 2x - 15; (x + 3)(x - 5)$

10. $(3a - 2b)(3a + 2b)$
11. $(4x - 5y)(4x + 5y)$
12. $(6p - 5)(6p + 5)$
13. $(2 - 3y)(2 + 3y)$
14. $(5 - 2b)(5 + 2b)$
15. $(4 - 3a)(4 + 3a)$
16. $(2 - x)(2 + x)$
17. $(x - 5)(x + 5)$
18. $(x - 6)(x + 6)$
19. $(x - y)(x + y)$
20. $(a - b)(a + b)$
21. $(p - 4)(p + 4)$
22. $(q - 3)(q + 3)$
23. $(7p - 9q)(7p + 9q)$
24. $(5x - 2)(5x + 2)$
25. $(10 - a)(10 + a)$
26. $(2a - 5)(2a + 5)$
27. $(3 - 2a)(3 + 2a)$
28. $(8p - 1)(8p + 1)$
29. $(1 - 3x)(1 + 3x)$
30. $(4x - 1)(4x + 1)$
31. $(a - 5b)(a + 5b)$
32. $(4a - b)(4a + b)$
33. $(10 - 3p)(10 + 3p)$
34. $(1 - 11a)(1 + 11a)$
35. $(6 - 5x)(6 + 5x)$
36. $(5p - 7)(5p + 7)$
37. $(11 - 3x)(11 + 3x)$
38. $(5a - 8)(5a + 8)$
39. $(8a - 1)(8a + 1)$
40. $(4p - 9q)(4p + 9q)$
41. $(10a - 7b)(10a + 7b)$
42. $(12x - 11y)(12x + 11y)$
43. 16
44. 48
45. 51
46. 21
47. 200
48. 17
49. 1,200
50. 1,002,000
51. 4
52. 6
53. 10
54. 0.4

1. $5(x + 4)$
2. $a(b + c)$
3. $3p(1 + 2q)$
4. $p(q - 2)$
5. $p(p - 3)$
6. $2a(2a - 1)$
7. $(a + b)(c + d)$
8. $(q - r)(p + s)$
9. $(x + y)(3 - a)$
10. $(x + 1)(x + y)$
11. $(p + q)(p + 3)$
12. $(q + r)(2p - 5)$
13. $(x + 1)(x + 6)$
14. $(x - 3)(x - 5)$
15. $(x + 2)(x + 3)$
16. $(x - 2)(x + 4)$
17. $(x - 2)(x + 3)$
18. $(x - 3)(x + 4)$
19. $(x - 4)(x + 7)$
20. $(x - 2)(x + 7)$
21. $(x - 8)(x + 10)$
22. $(4 - a)(4 + a)$
23. $(x - 3)(x + 3)$
24. $(3x - 5)(3x + 5)$
25. $(1 - 5p)(1 + 5p)$
26. $(6a - 1)(6a + 1)$
27. $(5a - 4b)(5a + 4b)$
28. 11
29. 32
30. 19
31. 24
32. 70
33. 4
34. $4(2a + 3b)$
35. $(p + q)(a + 3)$
36. $(x + 3)(x + 6)$
37. $(2a - 5b)(2a + 5b)$
38. $(x - y)(a + b)$
39. $(x + 3)(x - 5)$
40. $(p - 6)(p + 6)$
41. $a(a - 5)$
42. $(x + 8)(x - 1)$
43. $(2 - 3a)(2 + 3a)$
44. $6p(q + r)$
45. $(a + c)(a + b)$
46. $(x + 4)(a + p)$
47. $(x - 3)(x + 3)$
48. $3x(x - 4)$
49. $(x - 3)(x - 9)$
50. $(x + 2p)(x + q)$
51. $4ab(2a + 3 + b)$
52. $(x + 3)(x - 10)$
53. $(5a + x)(p - q)$
54. $3y(2x + 3y)$
55. $(x - 5)(x + 8)$
56. $(4a - 9b)(4a + 9b)$
57. $(p + q)(r - 2s)$

1. $x = 2, y = 1$
2. $x = 3, y = 2$
3. $x = 1, y = 4$
4. $x = 5, y = 2$
5. $x = 3, y = 1$
6. $x = 2, y = 4$
7. $x = 3, y = 4$
8. $x = 1, y = 2$
9. $x = 5, y = 2$
10. $x = 4, y = 2$
11. $x = 2, y = 2$
12. $x = 2, y = 1$
13. $x = 1, y = 3$
14. $x = 9, y = 4$
15. $x = 3, y = 1$
16. $x = 9, y = 2$
17. $x = -1, y = 3$
18. $x = -2, y = -3$
19. $x = -2, y = 3$
20. $x = -1, y = -4$
21. $x = 1, y = 1$
22. $x = 4, y = 3$
23. $x = -2, y = -3$
24. $x = -2, y = 0$
25. $x = 0, y = 3$
26. $x = 6, y = 3$
27. $x = 2, y = 1$
28. $x = 3, y = -4$
29. $x = -1, y = -1$
30. $x = -2, y = -2$
31. $x = 2, y = 3$
32. $x = 1, y = -4$
33. $x = -2, y = 5$
34. $x = 7, y = 3$
35. $x = 1, y = 2$
36. $x = -2, y = 3$
37. $x = 2, y = 4$
38. $x = 0, y = -2$
39. $x = 2, y = 2$

Exercise 17.2

1. $-3, 1$	**2.** $3, 8$	**3.** $-5, -4$	**4.** $0, 1$	**5.** $-4, 0$
6. $0, 2$	**7.** $-4, 4$	**8.** $-2, 2$	**9.** $-12, 12$	**10.** $1, 4$
11. $-4, -2$	**12.** $3, 5$	**13.** $-4, 2$	**14.** $-2, 1$	**15.** $-3, 5$
16. $-7, -5$	**17.** $-4, 5$	**18.** $2, 3$	**19.** $0, 5$	**20.** $-2, 0$
21. $0, 4$	**22.** $-3, 3$	**23.** $-8, 8$	**24.** $-10, 10$	**25.** $-1, 1$
26. $-9, 9$	**27.** $-7, 7$	**28.** $0, 7$	**29.** $-1, 8$	**30.** $-11, 11$
31. $4, 5$	**32.** $-1, 4$	**33.** $-8, 0$	**34.** $-1, 9$	**35.** $-6, 6$
36. $3, 7$	**37.** $2, 10$	**38.** $-2, 6$	**39.** $3, 4$	**40.** $-5, 3$
41. $2, 6$	**42.** $-2, 8$	**43.** $-3, 7$	**44.** $-4, 4$	**45.** $-4, 6$

Exercise 17.3

1. $x \geqslant 4$	**2.** $x \leqslant 3$	**3.** $x > 2$	**4.** $x < 3$	**5.** $x \geqslant -1$
6. $x \leqslant -2$	**7.** $x \geqslant -2$	**8.** $x \leqslant 2$	**9.** $x \geqslant 3$	**10.** $x \leqslant 5$
11. $x \leqslant 3$	**12.** $x \geqslant 5$	**13.** $x \geqslant 2$	**14.** $x \leqslant 1$	**15.** $x < 2$
16. $x > -3$	**17.** $x > 3$	**18.** $x > 1$	**19.** $x \geqslant -4$	**20.** $x \leqslant 4$
21. $x > -2$	**22.** $x \leqslant 3$	**23.** $x > -3$	**24.** $x < 2$	**25.** $x \geqslant 2$
26. $x \leqslant -3$	**27.** $x \leqslant 2$	**28.** $x \geqslant 2$	**29.** $x \leqslant 5$	**30.** $x \leqslant -1$
31. $x \leqslant 4$	**32.** $x \geqslant 4$	**33.** $x > -4$	**34.** $x \geqslant 4$	**35.** $0, 1, 2, 3$

36. $0, 1, 2, 3, 4$ **37.** $0, 1, 2, 3, 4, 5$ **38.** $0, 1, 2$

39. **(i)** $0, 1, 2, 3, 4$ **(ii)** $0, 1$ **(iii)** $0, 1, 2$ **40.** 6

Exercise 17.4

1. **(a)** $x = 2, y = 4$ **(b)** $3, 4$ **(c)** $0, 1, 2, 3, 4$
2. **(a)** $-9, 3$ **(b)** $x \geqslant -1$ **(c)** $x = 1, y = 3$
3. **(a)** $x \leqslant 4$ **(b)** $x = 1, y = 2$ **(c)** $-2, 8$
4. **(a)** $x = 2, y = -3$ **(b)** $-7, 3$ **(c)** $0, 1, 2, 3, 4, 5, 6$
5. **(a)** $x = 1, y = -4$ **(b)** $0, 5$ **(c)** $x \geqslant 2$
6. **(a)** $-10, 10$ **(b)** $x = -1, y = -1$ **(c)** $x > 2$

Exercise 18.1

1. 2^3	**2.** 3^4	**3.** 4^6	**4.** 6^7	**5.** 10^5	**6.** 16
7. 81	**8.** 125	**9.** $100{,}000$	**10.** $32{,}768$	**11.** $1{,}024$	**12.** $531{,}441$

Exercise 18.2 ▼

1. 2^7 **2.** 3^8 **3.** 4^5 **4.** 5^6 **5.** 6^9 **6.** 5^7

7. 3^6 **8.** 2^7 **9.** 3^3 **10.** 4^4 **11.** 2^3 **12.** 10^2

13. 9^2 **14.** 5^4 **15.** 6^4 **16.** 7^2 **17.** 2^6 **18.** 3^{12}

19. 5^8 **20.** 8^{10} **21.** 7^{15} **22.** 6^{20} **23.** 4^{14} **24.** 9^{18}

25. 6 **26.** 7 **27.** 5 **28.** 3 **29.** 2 **30.** 4

31. 10 **32.** 6 **33.** 20 **34.** 4^2 **35.** 3^4 **36.** 2^3

37. 3^2

Exercise 18.3 ▼

1. 4×10^3 **2.** 5×10^4 **3.** 2×10^5 **4.** 3×10^6 **5.** 3×10^2

6. 7.5×10^3 **7.** 3.6×10^4 **8.** 6.5×10^5 **9.** 2.3×10^6 **10.** 2.08×10^3

11. 6.07×10^3 **12.** 3.05×10^4 **13.** 1.58×10^6 **14.** 2.04×10^4 **15.** 5.03×10^5

16. 8.532×10^6 **17.** 1.4×10^3 **18.** 1.44×10^4 **19.** 4.2×10^3 **20.** 1.45×10^5

21. 1.2×10^5 **22.** 3.5×10^4 **23.** 2.5×10^3 **24.** 4.5×10^3 **25.** 3.2×10^4

26. 5.4×10^4 **27.** 2.28×10^5 **28.** 2.6×10^6 **29.** 1.7×10^5 **30.** 2.7×10^4

31. 4.3×10^4 **32.** $a = 3.6; n = 4$ **33.** $a = 1.9; n = 5$

Exercise 18.4 ▼

1. 6.2×10^3 **2.** 6×10^4 **3.** 4.6×10^5 **4.** 3.8×10^6 **5.** 7×10^6

6. 6.5×10^5 **7.** 7.6×10^4 **8.** 5×10^5 **9.** 6×10^3 **10.** 7×10^4

11. 2.3×10^5 **12.** 5.2×10^4 **13.** 2.8×10^4 **14.** 2.4×10^4 **15.** 3.2×10^6

16. 2.3×10^6 **17.** 2.6×10^4 **18.** 3×10^5

19. **(i)** $a = 5.6; n = 4$ **(ii)** $a = 6.2; n = 5$

Exercise 18.5 ▼

1. 6×10^6 **2.** 8×10^8 **3.** 5.2×10^5 **4.** 8.4×10^6 **5.** 1.8×10^6

6. 4.5×10^7 **7.** 7.68×10^8 **8.** 9.45×10^6 **9.** 4×10^2 **10.** 2×10^2

11. 4×10^4 **12.** 2.5×10^3 **13.** 1.4×10^5 **14.** 2.4×10^3 **15.** 5.8×10^3

16. 1.2×10^2 **17.** 3×10^3

18. **(i)** $a = 9.5; n = 6$ **(ii)** $a = 1.6; n = 3$

Exercise 18.6 ▼

1. **(a)** 8 **(b)** 12,500 **(c)** 7.4×10^2 **(d)** $a = 4; n = 3$

2. **(a)** 4 **(b)** 2,800 **(c)** 1.44×10^2 **(d)** 3.6×10^8

3. **(a)** 6 **(b)** 1,740 **(c)** 1.5×10^4 **(d)** 2.5×10^4

4. **(a)** 5^2 **(b)** **(i)** 5.4×10^4 **(ii)** 6×10^3 **(c)** 3×10^3

7. (i) 25 cm^2 **(ii)** 20 cm   **8. (i)** 64 m^2 **(ii)** 32 m
9. (i) 100 cm^2 **(ii)** 40 cm   **10. (i)** 144 m^2 **(ii)** 48 m
11. (i) 6.25 cm^2 **(ii)** 10 cm   **12. (i)** 20.25 m^2 **(ii)** 18 m
13. (i) 64 cm **(ii)** 195 cm^2 **14. (i)** 86 cm **(ii)** 262 cm^2
15. (i) 56 cm **(ii)** 95 cm^2 **16. (i)** 64 cm **(ii)** 217 cm^2
17. (i) 120 cm **(ii)** 288 cm^2 **18. (i)** 70 cm **(ii)** 228 cm^2
19. 40 cm^2 **20.** 48 cm^2 **21.** 30 cm^2 **22.** 22.5 cm^2
23. 31.5 cm^2 **24.** 75 cm^2 **25.** 18.36 cm^2 **26.** 10 cm^2
27. 70 cm^2 **28. (i)** 36 cm **(ii)** 72 cm^2
29. 136 cm^2 **30.** 1360 cm^2 **31.** 240 cm^2

7. (i) 12 cm **(ii)** 40 cm   **8. (i)** 10 m **(ii)** 42 m   **9.** 45 cm^2
10. (i) 5 cm **(ii)** 25 cm^2 **11. (i)** 6 m **(ii)** 24 m   **12.** 32 mm
13. 10 cm   **14.** 12 cm   **15.** 18 cm
16. 6 cm   **17.** 12 cm   **18.** 6 m
19. (i) 36 cm^2 **(ii)** 6 cm

1. (i) 6,000 m^2 **(ii)** 1,216 m^2 **(iii)** 304; €1,520   **2.** 1,500; €750
3. 200   **4. (i)** 800 m^2 **(ii)** 124 m^2 **(iii)** 496
5. (a) 4,500 **(b)** €1,260 **(c)** €2,160   **6.** 20 litres; €308   **7.** €885

1. 31.4 cm; 78.5 cm^2 **2.** 62.8 m^2; 314 m^2 **3.** 125.6 mm; 1,256 mm^2
4. 75.36 cm; 452.16 cm^2 **5.** 37.68 m; 113.04 m^2 **6.** 25.12 mm; 50.24 mm^2
7. 81.64 cm; 530.66 cm^2 **8.** 188.4 cm; 2826 cm^2 **9.** 53.38 m; 226.865 m^2
10. 15.7 cm; 19.625 cm^2 **11.** 88 cm; 616 cm^2 **12.** 44 cm; 154 cm^2
13. 132 mm; 1386 mm^2 **14.** 176 cm; 2,464 cm^2 **15.** 220 mm; 3,850 mm^2
16. 13.2 m; 13.86 m^2 **17.** 66 cm; 346.5 cm^2 **18.** 8.8 m; 6.16 m^2
19. 22 cm; 38.5 cm^2 **20.** 30.8 cm; 75.46 cm^2 **21.** 56.52 cm; 254.34 cm^2
22. 12.56 m; 12.56 m^2 **23.** 18.84 cm; 28.26 cm^2 **24.** 3.14 m; 0.785 m^2
25. 47.1 cm; 176.625 cm^2 **26.** 6π cm; 9π cm^2 **27.** 4π m; 4π m^2
28. 22π mm; 121π mm^2 **29.** 9π cm; 20.25π cm^2 **30.** 3π m; 2.25 m^2

31. **(i)** 113.04 cm^2 **(ii)** 18.84 cm **(iii)** 42.84 cm
32. **(i)** 50.24 cm^2 **(ii)** 12.56 cm **(iii)** 20.56 cm
33. **(i)** 235.5 cm^2 **(ii)** 47.1 cm **(iii)** 67.1 cm
34. **(i)** 18.84 cm^2 **(ii)** 6.28 cm **(iii)** 18.28 cm
35. **(i)** 25.12 cm^2 **(ii)** 6.28 cm **(iii)** 22.28 cm
36. **(i)** 84.78 cm^2 **(ii)** 18.84 cm **(iii)** 36.84 cm
37. 3,706.5 cm^2 **38.** 299.97 cm^2 **39.** 197.82 cm^2 **40.** 21.5 cm^2
41. 30.96 cm^2 **42.** 657 cm^2 **43.** 2016 cm^2 **44.** 1,438.5 cm^2
45. 504 cm^2 **46.** 616 cm^2

Exercise 19.5 ▼

17. 44 cm   **18.** 25π m^2 **19.** 12.56 cm   **20.** 4.5 m

Exercise 19.6 ▼

1. **(i)** 21 cm **(ii)** 132 cm **(iii)** 330 m **(iv)** 200   **2.** 8,225 cm^2 **3.** 116 cm
4. **(i)** 49 m **(ii)** 308 m **(iii)** 600 m **(iv)** 9 **(v)** 14.4 km/h
5. 154 cm^2; l = 70 cm; 210 cm^2 **6.** 28 cm

Exercise 19.7 ▼

1. **(i)** 480 cm^3 **(ii)** 376 cm^2 **2.** **(i)** 225 cm^3 **(ii)** 230 cm^2
3. **(i)** 64 cm^3 **(ii)** 96 cm^2 **14.** **(i)** 8 cm^3 **(ii)** 18
15. 13   **16.** 3000   **17.** 144   **18.** 36   **19.** 6450 cm^3
20. 7,632 cm^3 **21.** 2,400 cm^3 **22.** **(i)** 36 litres **(ii)** 12 minutes
23. 54 minutes   **24.** 350 cm^3; 3632 g   **25.** 24 litres

Exercise 19.8 ▼

1. **(i)** 8 cm **(ii)** 1,160 cm^2 **2.** **(i)** 4 cm **(ii)** 96 cm^2 **3.** **(i)** 2 cm **(ii)** 8 cm^3
4. **(i)** 10 cm **(ii)** 484 cm^2 **5.** 150 cm^2 **6.** 40 cm

Exercise 19.9 ▼

11. **(i)** 13,860 cm^3 **(ii)** 1,320 cm^2 **12.** **(i)(a)** 5,760π cm^3 **(b)** 90π cm^3 **(ii)** 64
13. 58,875 cm^3 **14.** **(a)** 1,100 cm^3 **(b)(i)** 20 cm by 10 cm by 14 cm
(ii) 2,800 cm^3 **(iii)** 600 cm^3 **15.** 23,550 m^3

11. 4,186.67 cm³; 1256 cm²   **12** 33.49 m³; 50.24 m²   **13.** 267.95 cm³; 200.96 cm²
14. 523.33 mm³; 314 mm²   **15.** 65.42 cm³; 78.5 cm²   **16. (i)** 36π cm³ **(ii)** 36π cm²
18. 113.04 mm³ **(i)** 18 mm   **(ii)** 3 mm   **(iii)** 508.68 mm³   **(iv)** 169.56 mm³
19. 388,080 g   **20. (i)** 4 : 1   **(ii)** 8 : 1

Exercise 19.11 ▼

1. 8 cm   **2.** 5 cm   **3.** 3 cm   **4. (i)** 20 cm   **(ii)** 1570 cm³   **5.** 9 cm
6. 6 mm   **7. (i)** 6 cm   **(ii)** 288π cm³   **8.** 14 cm   **9.** 3 m
10. 14 cm   **11. (i)** 21 cm   **(ii)** 1650 cm³   **12.** 9   **13.** 9 cm
14. 2 cm   **15.** 4 cm   **16.** 3 cm   **17.** 8 cm   **18.** 36π cm³; 6 cm
19. 36 cm   **20. (i)** 7 cm   **(ii)** 80%

Exercise 19.12 ▼

1. (i) 60 cm   **(ii)** 155 cm²   **2. (i)** 72 cm   **(ii)** 128 cm²
3. (i) 44 cm   **(ii)** 154 cm²   **4. (i)** 194 cm   **(ii)** 1246 cm²   **5.** $94\frac{1}{2}$ cm²
6. 3,674 cm²   **7.** 504 cm²   **8. (a)** 576   **(b)** €691.20   **(c)** €901.20
9. 400 cm²;   **(i)** 314 cm² **(ii)** 21.5%   **10.** 38.5 cm²;   **(i)** 21 cm² **(ii)** 21.43%
11. (i) 440 cm² **(ii)** 748 cm² **(iii)** 502 cm²   **12.** $1,500\pi$ cm³; 160
13. (i) 19,800 cm³   **(ii)** 4,851 cm³   **(iii)** 14,949 cm³
14. 88,000 cm³;   88 litres;   1.76 litres;   4 cm
15. 550 cm³;   40;   10 cm   **16. (i)** 121.5π cm³ **(ii)** 36 cm   **(iii)** 729π cm³ **(iv)** $\frac{2}{3}$
17. (i) 1,100 cm² **(ii)** 3 litres
18. (i) 198 cm³ **(ii)** 49,500 cm³ **(iii)** 9,900 cm³ **(iv)** 11 cm
19. 400   **20.** 8 cm; 4 cm; 192 cm³   **21.** 8 cm   **22.** 4 cm
23. 4 cm   **24. (i)** 10 cm   **(ii)** 384.65 cm³   **25.** 48 cm²

Exercise 20.1 ▼

1. $x = 40$ **2.** $y = 50$ **3.** $a = 70$ **4.** $b = 60$ **5.** $x = 30$
6. $x = 50$ **7.** $y = 40$ **8.** $x = 20$ **9.** $a = 130; b = 50; c = 50$
10. $p = 70; q = 110; r = 110$ **11** $x = 125; y = 55; z = 55$
12. $x = 32, y = 148, z = 148$ **13.** $a = 110$ **14.** $b = 120$ **15.** $a = 40$
16. $x = 30$ **17.** $x = 20$ **18.** $x = 130; y = 110$
19. $x = 40; y = 60; z = 80; w = 80$ **20.** $x = 36$ **21. (i)** 130°   **(ii)** 80°
22. (i) 90°   **(ii)** 110°

Exercise 20.2 ▼

1. $a = 65$; $b = 115$; $c = 115$ 2. $x = 130$; $y = 130$; $z = 50$
3. $p = 120$; $q = 60$; $r = 60$; $s = 120$ 4. $a = 110$; $b = 110$; $c = 70$
5. $a = 100$; $b = 80$ 6. $p = 105$ 7. $a = 55$; $b = 55$; $c = 125$
8. $x = 132$; $y = 132$; $z = 48$ 9. $x = 80$; $y = 100$; $z = 110$; $w = 70$
10. $a = 80$; $b = 85$; $c = 100$ 11. $a = 72$; $b = 45$; $c = 63$
12. $x = 70$; $y = 80$; $z = 100$

Exercise 20.3 ▼

1. $x = 75$ 2. $y = 30$ 3. $z = 50$
4. $a = 50$ 5. $x = 55; y = 70$ 6. $a = 70; b = 70$
7. $x = 65; y = 50$ 8. $p = 63; q = 54$ 9. $a = 60, b = 120$
10. $x = 55; y = 70$ 11. $a = 78; b = 136$ 12. $a = 70; b = 55, c = 55$
13. $a = 112; b = 62$ 14. $x = 60$ 15. $x = 62$
16. $x = 50$; $y = 50$; $z = 80$; $w = 100$ 17. $x = 18$
18. $x = 35$; $y = 110$; $z = 70$ 19. $a = 130$; $b = 90$; $c = 40$
20. $a = 40$; $b = 140$; $c = 80$ 21. $x = 50$; $y = 130$; $z = 25$
22. $a = 42$; $b = 96$; $c = 42$; $d = 69$ 23. (i) $45°$ (ii) $75°$ (iii) $45°$
24. (i) $50°$ (ii) $80°$ (iii) $100°$ 25. 34 cm

Exercise 20.4 ▼

1. $x = 90$; $y = 90$ 2. $a = 70$; $b = 110$; $c = 110$
3. $a = 105$; $b = 75$; $c = 105$ 4. $a = 60$; $b = 60$; $c = 120$
5. $x = 50$; $y = 80$; $z = 50$ 6. $a = 25$; $b = 25$ 7. $x = 120$; $y = 120$; $z = 32$
8. $a = 100$; $b = 35$; $c = 45$; $d = 35$ 9. $x = 30$; $y = 50$; $z = 100$
10. $a = 30$; $b = 25$; $c = 25$ 11. $a = 115$ 12. $x = 40$; $y = 55$
13. $x = 30$; $y = 40$ 14. (i) $30°$ (ii) $90°$ (iii) $60°$ (iv) $60°$

Exercise 20.5 ▼

1. $a = 90; b = 30$ 2. $x = 90; y = 40$ 3. $p = 90; q = 35$
4. $a = 50$ 5. $x = 25$ 6. $y = 45$
7. $a = 34; b = 90; c = 70$ 8. $p = 110; q = 85$ 9. $a = 100; b = 62$
10. $a = 37; b = 90; c = 53$ 11. $p = 90; q = 26; r = 64$ 12. $x = 52; y = 52$
13. $a = 25$ 14. $p = 55; q = 70$ 15. $x = 50$
16. $p = 50; q = 80$ 17. $a = 60; b = 30$ 18. $a = 90; b = 50; c = 50$
19. (i) $x = 32$ (ii) $y = 58$ 20. (i) $90°$ (ii) $36°$ (iii) $36°$ (iv) $180°$

1. (i) $x = 70$ (ii) 110 **2.** (i) $a = 125$ (ii) $b = 70$
3. (i) $x = 100$ (ii) $y = 30$ (iii) $z = 100$ (iv) $w = 30$
4. (i) $p = 46$ (ii) $q = 72$ (iii) $r = 72$ **5.** (i) $a = 52$ (ii) $b = 128$
6. $80°$ **7.** $x = 60$ **8.** $y = 20$
9. $30°$ **10.** (i) $40°$ (ii) $70°$ **11.** $x = 65$; $y = 65$
12. $p = 90$ **13.** $23°$ **15.** (i) $70°$ (ii) $105°$
16. $60°$ **17.** $80°$ **18.** (i) $a = 110$ (ii) $b = 70$
19. $30°$; $60°$; $90°$ **20.** (i) $112°$ (ii) $68°$ (iii) $34°$ (iv) $56°$ (v) $90°$

1. (i) $\triangle srt$ (ii) $[rt]$ (iii) $\angle rst$; $\overrightarrow{qr}$; $\overrightarrow{rt}$; p
2. (i) $\triangle utv$ (ii) $[tv]$ (iii) $\angle tuv$ (iv) $\triangle rus$ (v) $[rs]$ (vi) $\angle sur$ (vii) $\overrightarrow{tv}$
   (viii) $\overrightarrow{us}$ (ix) $\overrightarrow{sr}$
3. (i) $\triangle yzr$ (ii) $[yr]$ (iii) $\angle zyr$; $xqzy$; $xzry$; $\angle yzr$; $\angle zxy$; $40\ \text{cm}^2$
4. (i) e (ii) $[dc]$ (iii) $\triangle dyf$ (iv) $[cy]$ (v) $[yf]$ (vi) $\angle ydf$; $dxcy$
   (vii) $8\ \text{cm}^2$ (viii) $16\ \text{cm}^2$ (ix) $32\ \text{cm}^2$
5. (i) v (ii) $[rs]$ (iii) $\triangle svu$ (iv) $\angle usv$; $\overrightarrow{vs}$ or $\overrightarrow{sp}$ or $\overrightarrow{ur}$ or $\overrightarrow{rq}$; $10\ \text{cm}^2$; $120°$

1. 2 **2.** 1 **3.** 3 **4.** 1 **5.** 0 **6.** 2
7. 6 **8.** infinite **9.** 0 **10.** 1 **11.** 8 **12.** 1
13. 0 **14.** 4 **15.** 0 **16.** 6

1. (a) (i) f (ii) e (iii) b (iv) a (v) d (vi) c (vii) y (viii) x (ix) $[fe]$
   (x) $\triangle dax$ (xi) $\angle yfd$ (xii) $\angle xcd$ (b) (i) d (ii) b (iii) a (iv) c (v) x
   (vi) $\triangle adx$ (vii) $\angle dxc$ (viii) $[xb]$
2. (i) s (ii) q (iii) $\triangle poq$ (iv) $\angle pqo$
3. (i) r (ii) $[ts]$ (iii) $\triangle psr$ (iv) $\angle tsv$
4. (i) q (ii) $[qo]$ (iii) $\triangle qos$
5. (i) $\triangle bak$ (ii) $adcb$ (iii) $\triangle abd$; $\triangle cbd$; $\triangle abc$; $\triangle adc$ (iv) $[dc]$
6. (a) (i) d (ii) c (iii) q (iv) $\triangle bzq$ (v) $\angle zpa$ (b) (i) a (ii) r (iii) d
   (iv) $\triangle qap$ (v) rectangle $pzsd$ (c) $[br]$ (d) $32\ \text{cm}^2$

Exercise 21.5 ▼

1. **(i)** c **(ii)** d **(iii)** $[ba]$ **(iv)** $[cb]$ **(v)** $\triangle cdm$ **(vi)** $\angle dam$
2. **(i)** r **(ii)** w **(iii)** s **(iv)** p **(v)** $[qy]$ **(vi)** $\triangle szo$ **(vii)** $\triangle zws$ **(viii)** square $yqxo$
3. **(i)** r **(ii)** v **(iii)** q **(iv)** y **(v)** s **(vi)** $[vu]$
   (vii) $[vs]$ **(viii)** $\triangle vys$ **(ix)** $\triangle qpx$ **(x)** $\angle tys$
4. **(i)** $[st]$; $[qr]$; $[pq]$; $[sr]$ **(ii)** p **(iii)** s **(iv)** $[rs]$ **(v)** $\triangle rxq$ **(vi)** s
   (vii) t **(viii)** $[rt]$ **(ix)** $\triangle rqy$ **(x)** $\angle tsq$; $[st]$; t; 40 cm^2
5. **(i)** $[xd]$; $[ab]$; $[by]$ **(ii)** $\triangle dax$ **(iii)** $\triangle acd$ **(iv)** $[bd]$ **(v)** $50°$ **(vi)** 64 cm^2 **(vii)** z

Exercise 21.6 ▼

1. **(i)** $[ad]$ **(ii)** $\triangle aob$ **(iii)** $\triangle adc$ **(iv)** 40 cm^2
2. **(i)** y **(ii)** $\triangle yox$ **(iii)** $[xw]$; 6 cm^2
3. **(i)** $\triangle fge$ **(ii)** $[ed]$ **(iii)** c **(iv)** $[bc]$
4. **(i)** $xqky$; $xkry$ **(ii)** $\angle ykr$; $\angle kyx$; $\angle qxp$ **(iii)** $\triangle ykr$ **(iv)** y **(v)** $\triangle xpq$; 48 cm^2
5. **(i)** f **(ii)** e **(iii)** $[cg]$ **(iv)** $[xj]$ **(v)** rectangle $cefg$ **(vi)** $\triangle fgc$
   (vii) rectangle $fgce$ **(viii)** d **(ix)** $\triangle ijg$
   (x) rectangle $dcba$; 30 cm^2; $\overrightarrow{be}$ or $\overrightarrow{cf}$ or $\overrightarrow{dg}$ or $\overrightarrow{ac}$ or $\overrightarrow{hj}$
6. **(iv)** g **(v)** $[fg]$ **(vi)** $\triangle gdy$ **(vii)** $\triangle gdy$ **(viii)** $[ey]$ **(ix)** $\overrightarrow{ad}$ or $\overrightarrow{bc}$ or $\overrightarrow{dg}$ or $\overrightarrow{ef}$
   (x) $\overrightarrow{ea}$ or $\overrightarrow{db}$ or $\overrightarrow{fd}$ or $\overrightarrow{gc}$ or $\overrightarrow{yx}$ **(xi)** central symmetry in y
   (xii) central symmetry in x; 10 cm^2

Exercise 22.1 ▼

7. **(i)** $k = 5$ **(ii)** $t = 4$

Exercise 22.2 ▼

1. $(8, 7)$ **2.** $(5, 6)$ **3.** $(5, 1)$ **4.** $(2, 0)$ **5.** $(-4, 9)$
6. **(i)** $(8, 1)$ **(ii)** $(5, -2)$ **(iii)** $(-2, -4)$ **(iv)** $(-4, -1)$
7. **(i)** $(7, -3)$ **(ii)** $(1, 4)$ **(iii)** $(-2, -4)$ **(iv)** $(12, 3)$; $(-2, 3)$
8. $(3, 7)$ **9.** $(2, 3)$ **10.** $(3, 3)$

Exercise 22.3 ▼

11. **(i)** $(-3, -4)$ **(ii)** $(3, 4)$ **(iii)** $(3, -4)$ **12.** $a(1, 1)$, $b(4, 2)$, $c(3, 4)$

1. $2x - y - 7 = 0$　　**2.** $3x - y - 3 = 0$　　**3.** $4x - y + 1 = 0$　　**4.** $x - y - 1 = 0$
5. $2x + y - 7 = 0$　　**6.** $x + y - 3 = 0$　　**7.** $3x + y + 11 = 0$　　**8.** $4x + y + 5 = 0$
9. $5x - y - 2 = 0$　　**10.** $5x + y = 0$　　**11.** $x - 2y - 9 = 0$　　**12.** $2x - 3y - 7 = 0$
13. $4x + 5y - 18 = 0$　　**14.** $x + 2y - 3 = 0$　　**15.** $x + 4y = 0$　　**16.** $2x + 5y + 26 = 0$
17. $x + y - 1 = 0$　　**18.** $x + 2y + 1 = 0$

1. $x - y + 3 = 0$　　**2.** $2x + y - 10 = 0$　　**3.** $3x - y - 8 = 0$　　**4.** $x + y - 11 = 0$
5. $2x - y - 6 = 0$　　**6.** $4x + y - 17 = 0$　　**7.** $3x + y - 9 = 0$　　**8.** $4x - y + 6 = 0$
9. $x - y - 2 = 0$　　**10.** $2x - y = 0$　　**11.** $x - 2y + 7 = 0$　　**12.** $x + 3y + 7 = 0$
13. $2x - 5y + 27 = 0$　　**14.** $x + 2y - 16 = 0$　　**15.** $2x - 3y + 8 = 0$
16. (i) 2 **(ii)** $2x - y + 6 = 0$　　**17. (i)** -2 **(ii)** $2x + y - 11 = 0$
18. (i) $\sqrt{8}$ **(ii)** $(2, 6)$ **(iii)** -1 **(iv)** $x + y - 8 = 0$ **(vi)** -2 **(vii)** $p(8, 0); q(0, 8)$

1. $(5, 6)$　　**2.** $(-3, 4)$　　**3.** $(2, 3)$　　**4.** $(-1, -3)$　　**6.** $p(10, 0)$　　**7.** $q(0, 2)$
8. $k = 2$　　**9.** $(4, -3)$　　**10.** $3x - y - 7 = 0$　　**11.** $p(3, 0),\ q(0, 5);\ 7\frac{1}{2}$
12. $a(4, 0),\ b(0, -3);\ 5$　　**13. (i)** $(3, 2)$ **(ii)** $(3, 2)$
14. (ii) $k(1, 3)$ **(iii)** $\sqrt{10}$ **(iv)** $-\frac{1}{3}$ **(v)** $x + 3y - 10 = 0$
15. (iii) $\frac{1}{2}$ **(iv)** $x - 2y + 6 = 0$ **(v)** $y = 3;\ 4$
16. (ii) $(\frac{3}{2}, 1)$ **(iii)** 6 **(iv)** $6x - y - 8 = 0$ **(v)** $(0, -8)$ **(vi)** $k = 3$
17. (iii) 1 **(iv)** $x - y + 3 = 0$ **(v)** $q(-3, 0)$
18. (iii) $q(2, 1)$ **(iv)** -1 **(v)** $x + y - 3 = 0$ **(vi)** $c(0, 3)$ **(vii)** 3
19. (ii) $\frac{3}{4}$ **(iii)** $3x - 4y + 13 = 0$ **(iv)** $k(0, \frac{13}{4})$ **(v)** $\frac{3}{4}$
20. (ii) $m(4, 2)$ **(iii)** -1 **(iv)** $x + y - 6 = 0$ **(v)** $p(6, 0), q(0, 6)$

1. $\{(1, 5), (2, 8), (3, 11), (4, 14), (5, 17)\}$
2. $\{(0, 1), (2, 9), (4, 17), (6, 25), (8, 33)\}$
3. $\{(-3, -5), (-2, -3), (-1, -1), (0, 1), (1, 3), (2, 5)\}$
4. $\{(-2, 1), (-1, 2), (0, 3), (1, 4), (2, 5), (3, 6)\}$
5. $\{(-5, -22), (-4, -17), (-3, -12), (-2, -7), (-1, -2), (0, 3), (1, 8), (2, 13)\}$
6. $\{(-2, -10), (-1, -7), (0, -4), (1, -1), (2, 2), (3, 5), (4, 8), (5, 11)\}$
7. $\{(-3, -11), (-2, -9), (-1, -7), (0, -5), (1, -3), (2, -1)\}$

8. $\{(-1, -4), (0, -3), (1, -2), (2, -1), (3, 0), (4, 1)\}$

9. $\{(0, 3), (1, 4), (2, 7), (3, 12), (4, 19), (5, 28), (6, 39)\}$

10. $\{(-2, -2), (-1, -2), (0, 0), (1, 4), (2, 10), (3, 18), (4, 28)\}$

Exercise 23.2 ▼

1. (i) 7 (ii) 9 (iii) 11 (iv) 13   **2.** (i) 4 (ii) 10 (iii) 16 (iv) 22

3. (i) 23 (ii) 7 (iii) 15 (iv) 11   **4.** (i) 1 (ii) −3 (iii) 3 (iv) 9

5. (i) −1 (ii) −4 (iii) 2 (iv) −7   **6.** (i) 3 (ii) 8 (iii) −7 (iv) −12

7. (i) 5 (ii) 7 (iii) 2 (iv) 12   **8.** (i) −6 (ii) −3 (iii) 9 (iv) 30

9. (i) 0 (ii) 2 (iii) 3 (iv) 12; $-2 < 0$ **10.** (i) 3 (ii) 1 (iii) −1 (iv) 2; $7 > 0$

11. (i) 7 (ii) 13 (iii) 7 (iv) 13; $23 = 23$

12. (i) 2 (ii) 3 (iii) 4 (iv) 1 (v) 0; $6 > 5$

13. (i) 3 (ii) 8 (iii) −1 (iv) 3; −4, 2   **14.** (i) −6 (ii) −6 (iii) −4; −1, 4

Exercise 23.3 ▼

1. Range = $\{7, 9, 11, 13, 15\}$. $f = \{(1, 7), (2, 9), (3, 11), (4, 13), (5, 15)\}$

2. Range = $\{8, 14, 20, 26\}$. $f = \{(2, 8), (4, 14), (6, 20), (8, 26)\}$

3. Range = $\{-3, 1, 5, 9, 13\}$. $f = \{(0, -3), (1, 1), (2, 5), (3, 9), (4, 13)\}$

4. Range = $\{-5, -3, -1, 1, 3, 5\}$. $f = \{(-2, -5), (-1, -3), (0, -1), (1, 1), (2, 3), (3, 5)\}$

5. Range = $\{1, 2, 3, 4, 5, 6\}$. $f = \{(-3, 1), (-2, 2), (-1, 3), (0, 4), (1, 5), (2, 6)\}$

6. Range = $\{7, 10, 13\}$ **7.** Range = $\{-2, 3, 8\}$ **8.** Range = $\{1, 3, 5, 7, 9\}$

9. Range = $\{-8, -5, -2, 1\}$ **10.** Range = $\{5, 1, -3, -7\}$

Exercise 23.4 ▼

1. $a = 5, b = 9, c = 5$ **2.** $p = 13, q = -5, r = 1$

3. $a = 7, b = -8, c = 3$ **4.** $r = 9, s = -7, t = 2$

5. $x = 0, y = -2, z = -4$ **6.** $a = 0, b = 2, c = 3$

7. $p = 5; q = 1; r = 3; s = -3$ **8.** $a = 9; b = -5; c = 3; d = 1$

9. $(2, 9), (0, 1), (1, 5), (-1, -3)$ **10.** $(3, 1), (-3, -11), (4, 3), (-1, -7)$

Exercise 23.5 ▼

1. (a) (i) 13 (ii) 11 (b) $\{-2, 1, 4, 7, 10\}$ (c) $a = 13; b = 1; c = 1$

2. (a) $\{(-1, -5), (0, -3), (1, -1), (2, 1), (3, 3)\}$ (b) $p = 7; q = -2; r = 4$

  (c) (i) 13 (ii) −2 (iii) 11; $-7 < 18$

3. (a) Domain = $\{-2, -1, 0, 1, 2\}$, Range = $\{-13, -8, -3, 2, 7\}$

  (b) Domain = $\{-2, -1, 0, 1, 2, 3, 4, 5\}$, Range = $\{-2, 0, 4, 10\}$

  (c) $\{(-2, -11), (-1, -8), (0, -5), (1, -2), (2, 1), (3, 4)\}$; Range = $\{-11, -8, -5, -2, 1, 4\}$

  (d) $a = 7; b = -7; c = 4; d = -1$.

1. **(i)** $(-1, -4); -4$ **(ii)** $-3, 1$ **(iii)** $-4, 2$ **(iv)** -1.75 **(v)** $-3.4, 1.4$
   (vi) $x = -1$ **(vii)** 54
2. **(i)** $-1, 4$ **(ii)** -2.25 **(iii)** $0, 3$ **(iv)** $-1.4, 4.4$ **(v)** -6.25
3. **(i)** $1, 2$ **(ii)** 1 **(iii)** $-0.8, 3.8$ **(iv)** $0, 3$
4. **(i)** $1, 5$ **(ii)** -3.75 **(iii)** $(3, -4)$ **(iv)** 54 **(v)** $1.3, 4.7$
5. **(i)** $-1, 2$ **(ii)** $-2, 3$ **(iii)** $0, 1$
6. **(i)** $(-1, -9); -9$ **(ii)** $-4, 2$ **(iii)** $-3, 1$ **(iv)** $x = -1$ **(v)** 128
7. **(i)** $-3, 2$ **(ii)** $-2, 1$ **(iii)** $-3.7, 2.7$ **(iv)** -6.25
8. **(i)** $-1, 5$ **(ii)** $(2, -9)$ **(iii)** $1, 3$ **(iv)** $x = 2$
9. **(i)** $(1, -4)$ **(ii)** $-1, 3$ **(iii)** $-2, 4$ **(iv)** 128 **(v)** 8.25
10. **(i)** $1, 3$ **(ii)** $(2, -2); -2$ **(iii)** 4.25 **(iv)** $0.6, 3.4$
11. **(i)** $-2, 1$ **(ii)** -1.25 **(iv)** $-2.6, 1.6$
12. **(i)** $1, 4$ **(ii)** $2, 3$ **(iii)** 1.75 **(iv)** -2.25
13. **(i)** $-4, 1$ **(ii)** $-4.4, 1.4$ **(iii)** -5.8 **(iv)** -6.25
15. **(i)** $-1, 1.5$ **(ii)** -3.1 **(iii)** $-1.5, 2$
16. **(i)** 5.3 **(ii)** $-2, 0.5$ **(iii)** $-1.5, 0$ **(iv)** -3.1
17. **(i)** $-1, 3$ **(ii)** $(1, 4); 4$ **(iii)** $x = 1$ **(iv)** $0, 2$ **(v)** -2.25 **(vi)** 27
18. **(i)** $(-1, 4); 4$ **(ii)** $-3, 1$ **(iii)** -3.3 **(iv)** 8
19. **(i)** $-1, 4$ **(ii)** $1, 2$ **(iii)** -3.4 **(iv)** 6.25
20. **(i)** $-2, 4$ **(ii)** $(1, 9); 9$ **(iii)** $x = 1$ **(iv)** $-1, 3$
21. **(i)** 6.25 **(ii)** $0, 5$ **(iii)** $1, 4$
22. **(i)** $-1, 2.5$ **(ii)** 6.1 **(iii)** $-0.3, 1.8$

1. **(i)** $13:15, 15:45$ **(ii)** 68 km/h **(iii)** $14:30$
2. **(i)** 0.5 secs and 5.5 secs **(ii)** 3 secs
3. **(i)** $-1°$ **(ii)** $03:00$ **(iii)** $23:20$ and $06:40$
4. **(i)** $16:15$ **(ii)** October and January
5. **(i)** 1.25 **(ii)** 1.8 **(iii)** 0 secs **(iv)** 3 secs
6. **(i)** $12°C$ **(ii)** $2\frac{1}{4}°C$ **(iii)** 2 hours **(iv)** 4 hours **(v)** $-4°C$
7. **(i)** 6.25 m **(ii)** 2.5 secs **(iii)** 5 secs **(iv)** 2 secs and 3 secs

1. **(iii)** $x = 2, y = 1$ 2. **(iii)** $x = 1, y = 4$ 3. **(iii)** $(2, 2)$ **(iv)** $x = 2, y = 2$

1. 5   **2.** 13   **3.** 8   **4.** 7   **5.** 20   **6.** 40

7. 34   **8.** 12   **9.** 11   **10.** 16   **11.** 5   **12.** 2

13. 4   **14.** 3   **15.** 2   **16.** 14   **17.** $\sqrt{13}$ **18.** $\sqrt{41}$

19. $\sqrt{24}$ **20.** $\sqrt{11}$ **21.** 2   **22.** 3   **23.** 5   **24.** 4

25. 15 m   **26.** 29 cm   **27.** yes, because $12.5^2 = 12^2 + 3.5^2$ **28.** 5 cm

29. (i) 12   (ii) 6   (iii) 7.81   **30.** 7.5 cm   **31.** (i) 5   (ii) 12

1. (i) 30 cm   (ii) 40 cm^2 **2.** (i) 32 cm   (ii) 30 cm^2 **3.** (i) 24 cm   (ii) 28 cm^2

4. (i) 64 cm   (ii) 160 cm^2 **5.** (i) 40 cm   (ii) 84 cm^2 **6.** (i) 26 cm   (ii) 35 cm^2

7. (i) 50 cm   (ii) 120 cm^2 **8.** (i) 34 cm   (ii) 60 cm^2

9. 8 cm   **10.** 5 cm   **11.** 6 cm   **12.** 5.5 cm

13. (i) 24 cm^2 (ii) 8 cm   **14.** (i) 60 cm^2 (ii) 15 cm   **15.** (i) 72 cm^2 (ii) 12 cm

16. (i) 120 cm^2 (ii) 10 cm   **17.** (i) 4 cm   (ii) 40 cm^2 **18.** (i) 12 cm   (ii) 96 cm^2

19. (i) 15 cm   (ii) 180 cm^2 **20.** (i) 2 cm   (ii) 12 cm^2 **21.** $x = 12$

1. (i) 45   (ii) 50   (iii) 40   (iv) 105   (v) 115   (vi) 76   (vii) 90   (viii) 70

2. 20   **3.** 20°   **4.** 70°   **5.** $x = 54$; $y = 68$ **6.** 10:30 or 22:30

7. △str **8.** △wkx **9.** [sr]   **10.** (i) △srt (ii) (a) $\frac{1}{3}$ (b) $\frac{3}{2}$

11. 24 cm^2 **12.** 8 cm^2 **13.** 38 cm^2

14. (i) 5   (ii) 15   (iii) 7   (iv) 1.5   **15.** 3 cm   **16.** $|ab| = 5 = |ad|$

17. 4   **18.** 3   **19.** $\sqrt{50}$ cm

20. (i) 3 cm   (ii) 4 cm   (iii) 40 cm^2 (iv) 8 cm

21. (ii) △acp (iv) 24   (vi) 5   **22.** (ii) [yt]   (iv) 113°

23. (i) △scr (iv) 12   **24.** (v) 6 cm   **25.** (i) △nkc (iv) 51

26. (i) [ac]   (ii) 6 cm   (iii) 12 cm^2 **27.** (i) 60°   (ii) 120°   (v) $r'p'$

28. (ii) △cda (iv) 10   **29.** (i) 45°   (iii) △dco (iv) 7   (v) $\frac{7}{22}$

30. (i) △yca (ii) 30°   (iv) 14   (v) $\frac{1}{3}$ **31.** (iii) 24

1. (i) $\dfrac{3}{5}$ (ii) $\dfrac{4}{5}$ (iii) $\dfrac{3}{4}$ **2.** (i) $\dfrac{20}{29}$ (ii) $\dfrac{21}{29}$ (iii) $\dfrac{20}{21}$

3. (i) $\dfrac{8}{17}$ (ii) $\dfrac{15}{17}$ (iii) $\dfrac{8}{15}$

4. (i) $\dfrac{7}{25}$ (ii) $\dfrac{24}{25}$ (iii) $\dfrac{7}{24}$ (iv) $\dfrac{24}{25}$ (v) $\dfrac{7}{25}$ (vi) $\dfrac{24}{7}$

5. (i) $\dfrac{9}{41}$ (ii) $\dfrac{40}{41}$ (iii) $\dfrac{9}{40}$ (iv) $\dfrac{40}{41}$ (v) $\dfrac{9}{41}$ (vi) $\dfrac{40}{9}$

6. (i) $\dfrac{1}{2}$ (ii) $\dfrac{\sqrt{3}}{2}$ (iii) $\dfrac{1}{\sqrt{3}}$ (iv) $\dfrac{\sqrt{3}}{2}$ (v) $\dfrac{1}{2}$ (vi) $\dfrac{\sqrt{3}}{1} = \sqrt{3}$

7. 9   **8.** 3   **9.** 8   **10.** 15   **11.** 8   (i) $\dfrac{3}{5}$ (ii) $\dfrac{4}{5}$ (iii) $\dfrac{3}{4}$

12. 1   (i) $\dfrac{1}{\sqrt{5}}$ (ii) $\dfrac{2}{\sqrt{5}}$ (iii) $\dfrac{1}{2}$ **13.** $\sqrt{2}$ (i) $\dfrac{1}{\sqrt{2}}$ (ii) $\dfrac{1}{\sqrt{2}}$ (iii) 1

14. 20   (i) $\dfrac{20}{29}$ (ii) $\dfrac{21}{29}$ (iii) $\dfrac{20}{21}$ **15.** 3   (i) $\dfrac{\sqrt{7}}{4}$ (ii) $\dfrac{3}{4}$ (iii) $\dfrac{\sqrt{7}}{3}$

16. $\sqrt{13}$ (i) $\dfrac{3}{\sqrt{13}}$ (ii) $\dfrac{2}{\sqrt{13}}$ (iii) $\dfrac{3}{2}$

1. 0.6691   **2.** 0.3090   **3.** 0.8391   **4.** 0.9903   **5.** 0.9848   **6.** 2.1445

7. 0.9816   **8.** 1.6643   **9.** 0.9976   **10.** 0.2309   **11.** 0.3746   **12.** 0.9962

13. 13.2704   **14.** 19.1261   **15.** 5.3961   **16.** 2.7280   **17.** 1   **18.** $\dfrac{1}{2}$

19. $\dfrac{1}{2}$ **20.** 0

1. 24°   **2.** 76°   **3.** 51°   **4.** 33°   **5.** 13°   **6.** 17°

7. 63°   **8.** 33°   **9.** 48°   **10.** 14°   **11.** 61°   **12.** 22°

13. 20°   **14.** 71°   **15.** 56°   **16.** 73°   **17.** 29°   **18.** 39°

19. 49°   **20.** 36°   **21.** 35°   **22.** 60°   **23.** 90°   **24.** 60°

25. 30°   **26.** 30°   **27.** 45°

1. 37°   **2.** 39°   **3.** 26°   **4.** 47°   **5.** 44°   **6.** 21°
7. 15°   **8.** 39°   **9.** 60°   **10.** 11°   **11.** 48°   **12.** 25°
13. 46°   **14.** 56°   **15.** 39°   **16. (i)** 34°   **(ii)** 56°

17. (i) 44° **(ii)** 46°   **18. (i)** $\dfrac{3}{4}$ **(ii) (a)** 49° **(b)** 41°

19. (i) 37° **(ii)** 37° **(iii)** 37°   **20. (i)** 44° **(ii)** 48° **(iii)** 51°

1. 4.23   **2.** 10.30   **3.** 3.23   **4.** 6.47   **5.** 24.15   **6.** 6.37
7. 37.61   **8.** 34.64   **9.** 9.27   **10.** 11.35   **11.** 11.92   **12.** 18.54
13. 21.45   **14.** 1.49   **15.** 10.94   **16.** 19.51   **17.** 43.00   **18.** 18.12
19. 5.17   **20. (i)** 18.65 **(ii)** 27.35   **21. (i)** 10 **(ii)** 8.39

1. 76.78   **2.** 11.03   **3.** 11.73   **4.** 56.63   **5.** 42.22   **6.** 111.62
7. 136.87   **8.** 41.52   **9.** 80.74   **10.** 32.59   **11.** 17.10   **12.** 7.25

1. 7.8 m   **2.** 71°   **3.** 42.4   **4. (i)** 40 m **(ii)** 51 m
5. (i) 15.6 m **(ii)** 67°   **6.** 117 cm
7. (i) 1.5 m **(ii)** 2.9 m **(iii)** 53° **(iv)** 46°   **8.** 2,071 m; 7,727 m
9. 31°   **10. (i)** 7.5 m **(ii)** 5.6 m **(iii)** 20° **(iv)** 63°

1. (a) (i) $\dfrac{3}{5}$ **(ii)** $\dfrac{4}{3}$ **(iii)** $\dfrac{3}{5}$ **(b)** 0.28; 74°   **(c)** 50.96 m

2. (a) 58°   **(b)** 4.2 m   **(c) (i)** 35 m **(ii)** 19°

3. (a) 67°   **(b) (i)** 39° **(ii)** 4.9 **(c) (i)** 80 m/s **(ii)** 618 m

4. (a) 12° **(b) (i)** 6.55 cm **(ii)** 4.59 cm   **(c) (i)** 56° **(ii)** 50 m

5. (a) (i) 5 **(ii)** $\dfrac{3}{5}, \dfrac{4}{5}, \dfrac{3}{4}$ **(iii)** 37°   **(b) (i)** 15 m **(ii)** $\dfrac{12}{5}$ **(iii)** 67° **(iv)** 23°
(c) (i) 25 m **(ii)** 10 m
6. (a) (i) 30° **(ii)** $\frac{1}{2}$ **(b) (i)** 48° **(ii)** 42° **(c) (i)** 21 **(ii)** 29 **(iii)** 46°
7. (a) 39° **(b)** $\frac{1}{2}$; 7   **(c)** $x = 48$; 58 m   **(d)** 492 m

1. 3   **2.** 4   **3.** 6   **4.** 12   **5.** 5   **6.** 7

7. 3   **8.** 9   **9.** 10   **10.** 11   **11.** 6   **12.** 2

13. (i) $(4x + 8)$ cm   (ii) $4x + 8 = 32$ (iii) $x = 6$

14. (i) $(x + 10)$ cm   (iii) $(4x + 20)$ cm   (iv) $4x + 20 = 56$ (v) $x = 9$

15. (i) $2x$ cm   (iii) $6x = 42$ (iv) $x = 7$ (v) 98 cm^2

16. (i) $(x + 2)$ years   (ii) $2x + 2 = 38$ (iii) $x = 18$ (iv) 20 years

17. (i) $(x + 6)$ years   (ii) $(x + 2)$ years; $(x + 8)$ years   (iii) $x + 8 = 2(x + 2)$ (iv) $x = 4$

18. (i) $4x$ years   (ii) $(x + 4)$ years; $(4x + 4)$ years   (iii) $4x + 4 = 3(x + 4)$ (iv) $x = 8$

19. (a)(i) $(x + 40)$ c   (ii) $4x$ c   (iii) $(3x + 120)$ c

     (b) $7x + 120 = 330$ (c) $x = 30$ (d) 70 c

20. (i) $13x - 1 = 64$ (ii) $x = 5$ (iii) 24 cm

21. (i) $(2x + 18)$ litres; $(2x + 6)$ litres   (ii) $2x + 18 = 2(2x + 6)$ (iii) $x = 3$

22. (i) $3x + 3 = 33$ (ii) $x = 10$ (iii) 10, 11, 12

23. (i) $\dfrac{x}{2} + \dfrac{x}{5} = 70$ (ii) $x = 100$ (iii) €20

1. 9; 5   **2.** 14 : 6   **3.** 5; 4   **4.** 8; 3   **5.** 7; 4   **6.** 4; 1   **7.** 1; 5

8. 6; 2   **9.** (a) (i) $2x + y = 70$ (ii) $x + y = 50$ (b) $x = 20, y = 30$

     (c) (i) 20 cents   (ii) 30 cents

10. (a) (i) 250c   (ii) 170c   (b) (i) $5x + 2y = 250$ (ii) $3x + 2y = 170$ (c) $x = 40; y = 25$

     (d) (i) 40c   (ii) 25c

11. (a) (i) 350c   (ii) 160c   (b) (i) $5x + 4y = 350$ (ii) $2x + 2y = 160$ (c) $x = 30; y = 50$

     (d) (i) 30c   (ii) 50c

12. (a) (i) $7x + 3y = 82$ (ii) $2x + y = 24$ (b) $x = 10; y = 4$

     (c) (i) €10   (ii) €4   (d) €124

13. (a) (i) 530c   (ii) 410c   (b) (i) $8x + 2y = 530$ (ii) $6x + 2y = 410$

     (c) (i) 60c   (ii) 25c

14. (a) $x + y = 20$ (b) $8x + 5y = 118$ (c) $x = 6; y = 14$

     (d) 6 teachers' tickets at €8 each and 14 pupils' tickets at €5 each.

15. (a) $x + y = 50$ (b) $15x + 10y = 600$ or $3x + 2y = 120$ (c) $x = 20; y = 30$

     (d) 20 seats at €15 each and 30 seats at €10 each.

16. (a) $x + y = 80$ (b) $x - y = 20$ (c) $x = 50, y = 30$ (d) 50

17. (i) $x = 6; y = 2$ (ii) $x = 2; y = 1$ (iii) $x = 5; y = 3$

18. $x = 20; y = 30$

1. −4; 3   **2.** −5; 6   **3. (i)** $x^2 + 2x$ **(ii)** $x^2 + 2x = 15$ **(iii)** $x = 3$
4. (i) $x^2 + 5x$ **(ii)** $x^2 + 5x = 36$ **(iii)** $x = 4$
5. (ii) $x^2 + 4x$ **(iii)** $x^2 + 4x = 21$ **(iv)** $x = 3$
6. (i) €$(x^2 + 3x)$ **(ii)** $x^2 + 3x = 38$ **(iii)** $x = 4$
7. (i) €$(x^2 − 2x)$ **(ii)** $x^2 − 2x = 35$ **(iii)** $x = 7$
8. (i) $x + 2$ **(ii)** $x^2 + 2x$ **(iii)** $x^2 + 2x = 8$ **(iv)** $x = 2$; 2 and 4
9. (i) $x − 3$ **(ii)** $x^2 − 3x$ **(iii)** $x^2 − 3x = 18$ **(iv)** $x = 6$; 3 and 6
10. (i) x^2 **(ii)** $4x$ **(ii)** $x^2 + 4x = 12$ (iv) $x = 2$
11. (i) €$(x^2 + 2x)$ **(ii)** $x^2 + 2x = 24$ **(iii)** $x = 4$; €6
12. (i) $(x^2 − 3x)$ km   **(ii)** $x^2 − 3x = 10$ **(iii)** $x = 5$

1. (i) $(x + 4)$ years   **(ii)** $2x + 4 = 20$ **(iii)** $x = 8$
2. (i) €$(x + 3)$ **(ii)** $5x + 4(x + 3) = 201$ **(iii)** $x = 21$ **(iv)** €24
3. (i) $2x + 6y = 48$; $6x + 26 = 64$ or $x + 3y = 24$; $3x + y = 32$ **(ii) (a)** €9   **(b)** €5
4. (i) $(x^2 + 4x)$ m^2 **(ii)** $x^2 + 4x = 5$ **(iii)** $x = 1$ **(iv)** 12 m
5. (i) $3x + 6 = 45$ **(ii)** $x = 13$ **(iii)** 13; 15; 17
6. 600c;   **(i)** $3q + 10(q + 8) + 2(2q + 5) = 600$ **(ii)** $q = 30$
7. (i) $x + y = 1500$ **(ii)** $20x + 30y = 38\ 000$ or $2x + 3y = 3800$
    (iii) $x = 700$; $y = 800$ **(iv)** 700 of €20 and 800 of €30
8. (i) €2000   **(ii)** €$(3000 − 15x)$ **(iii)** $(3000 − 15x) − 2000 = 400$ **(iv)** $x = 40$
9. (i) $5x + 6y = 580$ **(ii)** $x − y = 50$ **(iii)** $x = 80$; $y = 30$ **(iv) (a)** €80   **(b)** €30
10. (a) (i) $\dfrac{x}{3}$ **(ii)** $\dfrac{x}{4}$ **(b)** $\dfrac{x}{3} + \dfrac{x}{4} = 21$ **(c)** $x = 36$ **(d) (i)** 36   **(ii)** 12   **(iii)** 9

11. (i) €$\dfrac{x}{5}$ **(ii)** €$\dfrac{x − 3}{4}$ **(iii)** $\dfrac{x}{5} + \dfrac{x − 3}{4} = 15$ **(iv)** 35
12. (i) $7x$ **(ii)** $7x + 5$; $x + 5$ **(iii)** $7x + 5 = 4(x + 5)$ **(iv)** $x = 5$ **(v)** 35 years
13. (i) $9 − x$ **(ii)** $9x − x^2 = 20$ **(iii)** 4 and 5